Organometallic

Chemistry‾‾‾‾‾‾‾‾‾‾

Peter L. Pauson

Freeland Professor of Chemistry
The University of Strathclyde, Glasgow

Edward Arnold (Publishers) Ltd, London

Printed in Northern Ireland at The Universities Press, Belfast

Preface

Relatively few organometallic compounds have found direct practical application. Their value as chemical intermediates on the other hand is vast. Whether as isolable compounds or as transient species they play a part in so many synthetic procedures that their study is a necessary part of the chemist's training.

This volume is intended to provide general information for the advanced undergraduate or the postgraduate student. It is not aimed at the specialist and references are therefore confined largely to more detailed reviews.

The term organometallic includes all those compounds in which a metal atom may be considered as bonded directly to carbon. This definition clearly includes not only the metal carbonyls, but also cyanides, fulminates and related compounds. However in a volume whose emphasis must be on hydrocarbon derivatives, only selected aspects of such compounds can be included. Carbides are omitted.

More difficult than the definition of the organic component is that of 'metal'. Metalloids will be excluded from the present treatment and some metals near that borderline can only receive scant attention. Thus boron, silicon and phosphorus are definitely excluded and arsenic, selenium and tellurium mentioned only where direct comparison with neighbouring elements suggests itself. Published information on organometallic compounds of the rare earths and actinides is so scanty that these too, will be almost completely neglected.

This book could not have been written without drawing heavily on the information contained in many earlier and more comprehensive treatises. I am particularly indebted to G. E. Coates' excellent monograph *Organometallic Compounds* (2nd edition, 1960, Methuen, London). I am grateful to Dr. G. R. Knox for reading the manuscript and making valuable suggestions.

P. L. P.

University of Strathclyde, 1967

Contents

Chapter 1

Some General Features

The methyl group, CH_3—, as the simplest hydrocarbon group which can be linked to a metal atom, has undoubtedly been employed more widely than any other group. It is convenient therefore to take these methyl derivatives as a starting point in considering variations of properties with the nature of the metal. Considered as a methyl radical, this group can donate one electron to a metal in the process of forming a covalent bond; hence a metal M of valency n will form a methyl derivative $M(CH_3)_n$. Alternatively methyl groups will accept an electron from a very electropositive metal to form an ionic derivative $M^{n+}(CH_3^-)_n$. All intermediate degrees of partial ionic character will be met in going from the most electropositive elements, e.g. Cs, which form truly salt-like alkyls, e.g. $Cs^+CH_3^-$, to the almost purely covalent methyls of such metals as Sn, Pb or Bi: $(CH_3)_4Sn$, $(CH_3)_4Pb$, $(CH_3)_3Bi$.

Since the formation of such alkyls in more than one valency state is quite rare, the valency displayed in the metal methyl has sometimes been regarded as the 'characteristic' valency of the metal. Thus the formation of stable tetramethyllead $(CH_3)_4Pb$ may appear more characteristic of a metal in group IV of the periodic table than the divalency of, for example, its halides. On the other hand, this criterion breaks down for the elements of most variable valency—the transition metals. Most of these do not form simple alkyls of sufficient stability to permit their isolation.

STRUCTURES OF METHYL DERIVATIVES

Precise structural information concerning the simplest metal alkyls is remarkably scant, but even the limited data available reveal a wide variation in types. Whereas the metalloids (e.g. B, Si) like the non-metals give methyls which are gases or volatile liquids, many metals give crystalline methyls. Thus only gallium (Me_3Ga, b.p. 56°), tin (Me_4Sn, b.p. 78°), lead (Me_4Pb, b.p. 110°) and bismuth (Me_3Bi, b.p. 110°) form liquid methyls in which the individual molecules may be assumed to be largely unassociated and probably have the expected trigonal or tetrahedral structures. At the other extreme the crystals of caesium or rubidium methyls have not been examined, but may well have simple ionic lattices. Between these extremes the structures are all more complex than the simple empirical formulae suggest. A comparison of the physical properties of the group III methyls is revealing:

TABLE 1

	Me_3B	Me_3Al	Me_3Ga	Me_3In	Me_3Tl
m.p. (°C)	−153	15	−16	89·5	38.5
b.p. (°C)	−20	126	56	136	76/85 mm

Trimethylaluminium is known to be dimeric even in the vapour phase. Linkage occurs through two methyl bridges, each forming 3-centre bonds with the two metal atoms. In this so-called 'electron deficient' molecule the available orbitals of the aluminium atoms are thus completely utilized, although an electron count allows each metal atom a share in only six electrons.

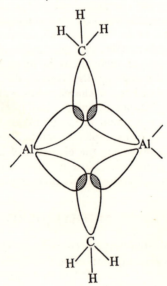

Thus at first sight surprising 'bond angles' (Al—C—Al $\simeq 70°$; C—Al—C $\simeq 110°$) are also adequately explained by this interpretation of the structure: it is the orbitals which will maintain approximately normal tetrahedral angles about both carbon and aluminium and these do not lie along the lines joining atomic centres. Similar bridges are involved in the methyls of beryllium and magnesium, but here involve all the alkyl groups and lead to long polymer chains, the metal atoms having tetrahedral symmetry.

M = Be or Mg

1-2

Although ionic character must be increasing, methyllithium still forms discrete molecular units in the crystal. These units are tetrameric and from x-ray powder studies are thought to consist of tetrahedra of lithium atoms (Li—Li = $2·56$ Å) with methyl groups above the centre of each face of the tetrahedron (Li—C = $2·28$ Å). Each methyl must therefore be thought of as forming a 4-centre bond with three metal atoms.

The physical data quoted above show that in going from trimethylaluminium to the gallium analogue the cohesion via three-centre bonds breaks down, so that trimethylgallium must be regarded as monomeric in all physical states. But a new form of bridging appears in the next member of the series, trimethylindium. Although monomeric in the vapour, this substance is a tetramer in solution and in the crystalline state. X-ray single crystal data have revealed an arrangement consisting of 4 indium atoms in a square with the trigonal Me_3In units lying nearly in planes normal to the In_4 plane.

The tetrameric unit can only be held together by the methyl groups which lie in the direct lines between indium atoms and the $3·1$ Å Me—In distances imply significant if weak covalent bonding. Thus the carbon atoms become 5-coordinate and it is believed that partial trigonal hybridization at these carbons leads to the utilization of a nearly pure p-orbital of carbon for the main C—In bond, leaving a minor lobe protruding towards the more remote indium atom. Significantly the ethyl analogue, Et_3In, where such an arrangement is sterically improbable, is a liquid and probably monomeric. Trimethylthallium is also monomeric in solution;

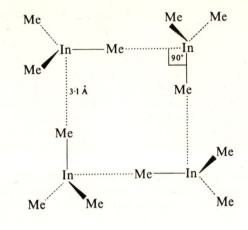

I-3

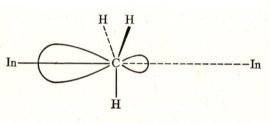

I-4

its crystal structure remains to be determined. Dialkylthallium halides are ionic R—Tl$^{\pm}$—R X^{-} with the linear cation having the same structure as the isoelectronic dialkyls of mercury R—Hg—R.

SOME BONDING CONSIDERATIONS

At the beginning of the chapter the variations of methyl metal bonds in terms of ionic character were considered. Less extreme but still important variations occur for a given metal with change of the attached hydrocarbon group. Changes in bond character might be expected to be reflected best in bond strength. Thermochemical data are, however, quite scarce for organometallic compounds and even thermal stabilities have rarely been reported with sufficient precision to allow comparisons. The impression that stability generally increases in the order

$$Et—M < Me—M < Ph—M < CF_3—M$$

may well prove valid for most or even all metals. Higher primary alkyls are generally not very different from ethyls, but secondary and tertiary alkyls are less stable. In part these differences are attributable to steric factors, e.g. those which prevent association and hence stabilization of the molecules by secondary bonding forces.

The greater stability of aryls compared to alkyls is possibly restricted to those metals which have d-orbitals—either filled and capable of back-donating electrons into the antibonding (π^*) orbitals of the aromatic nucleus or, in the case of the transition metals, empty and hence able to overlap and accept electrons from the π-orbitals. In covalently bound perfluoroalkyls the fluorines will exert an electron-withdrawing effect and lead to greater polarity of the metal-carbon bond. Metals with lone pairs of electrons in suitable orbitals may also form partial double bonds by a hyperconjugative mechanism: $M\overset{+}{=}CF_2\ F^-$. In the more ionic complexes the stability of the perfluoroalkyl anion, e.g. CF_3^-, relative to alkyl anions (CH_3^-) is the chief stabilizing feature.

In both the aryl and perfluoroalkyl complexes referred to above, back-donation will increase the bond-multiplicity and strengthen what would otherwise be a normal covalent bond of rather moderate strength. However, the back-donation will itself be limited here by the charge separation it produces. The corollary to this is provided by the situation when a coordinate bond is formed between a neutral electron donor and a metal. Here negative charge is built up on the electropositive metal and back-donation can disperse this charge. Such back-donation is possible when the ligand has available orbitals, either by virtue of expanding its 'normal' valence shell (e.g. P^{III}) or because it possesses a suitable multiple-bond system. In the multiply-bonded carbon ligands $C\equiv O$ and $C\equiv NR$ it is not only possible, but essential for the formation of stable complexes.

These two ligands are closely analogous in their bonding properties. For $C\equiv O$ we may consider that the free molecule has two π-orbitals as well as a σ-orbital bonding the two atoms and a lone pair of electrons in a p-orbital on carbon. Donation of the latter to a neutral metal atom results in the situation shown (1-5; only one π-orbital is shown, the other is at right angles to the plane of the paper), a σ-bond having been formed from a p-orbital of the CO group by overlap with a vacant orbital of the metal. If M is a transition metal (and only these have been found to give stable compounds of this type) a filled d-orbital of the metal can now overlap with the vacant π^* (antibonding)-orbital of the carbonyl

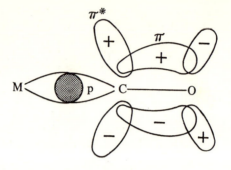

1-5

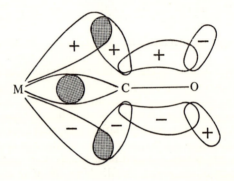

1-6

group as shown (1-6). In valence-bond terminology we can consider the structures $^-M\!-\!C\!\equiv\!O^+$ and $M\!=\!C\!=\!O$ as the main canonical forms contributing to the resonance hybrid.

Although accumulation of negative charge on the metal would be avoided if we combine $C\!\equiv\!O$ with M^+, the accumulation of positive charge on the ligand is still too unfavourable to permit formation of a strong bond without back-donation; i.e. carbon monoxide is too weakly basic: it will not react with acids to form $H\!-\!C\!\equiv\!O^+$ and hence should not be expected to react with M^+ to give $M\!-\!C\!\equiv\!O^+$. Back-donation is adequate in some positive ions, e.g. $Mn(CO)_6^+$ is stable, but more filled orbitals become available for back-donation as we reduce the oxidation number of the metal so that carbonyls are favoured in the zero (e.g. $Ni(CO)_4$) or negative (e.g. $Fe(CO)_4^{2-}$) oxidation states of the metal.

The chief difference between carbon monoxide and isocyanides as ligands arises from the lower electronegativity of nitrogen compared to oxygen (i.e. the greater basicity of CNR compared to

CO). Thus rather higher oxidation states are favoured[$Cr^0 (CNR)_6$ but $Fe^{II}(CNR)_6{}^{2+}$] with correspondingly weaker back-donation.

The cyanide ion $(C{\equiv}N)^-$ is isoelectronic with carbon monoxide, and in at least the majority of its compounds bonds to metals through carbon. Being a negative ion it will, however, form a strong simple covalent bond $M—C{\equiv}N$ with M^+, i.e. with metallic ions quite generally. 'Back-donation' cannot here become a significant factor except in the anionic complexes $[M(CN)_n]^{n-m}$ where m is the oxidation number of the metal. Here, e.g. in the ferricyanide ion $[Fe(CN)_6]^{3-}$, it becomes important to restrict accumulation of negative charge on the metal and to distribute this charge onto the more electronegative nitrogen atoms $[M—C{\equiv}N \leftrightarrow M{=}C{=}N^-]$. The degree of back-donation must again become greater the lower the oxidation number of the metal and it is such back-donation which makes possible the existence of, for example $[Ni(CN)_4]^{4-}$ containing Ni^0 and directly comparable with $Ni(CNR)_4$ and $Ni(CO)_4$.

Very similar considerations apply to the bonding of olefins to metals. But whereas the carbon of CO uses its lone pair to provide the primary (dative) σ-bond, in the case of the olefin the π-electrons themselves are involved. They are thus shared between at least three atoms and the bond would be weak indeed without the back-donation from transition metal d to the π^*-orbital of the ligand as depicted (1-7). In contrast to the carbonyls, etc., where the metal lies in the nodal plane of the π-electrons, bonding in the olefin complexes is at right angles to the nodal plane. Where it is necessary

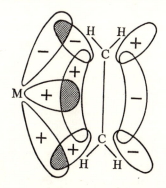

1-7

to distinguish these two situations, the former is referred to as a π-bond, but the latter as a μ-bond. However, since use of π-orbitals is important in both situations, both can be correctly referred to as 'π-complexes' without specifying the precise bond-type.

It must be made clear that the formulation of olefin complexes as π-complexes involving μ-bonding is the best presently available representation. Inter alia, it allows us to rationalize the restriction of such complexes to those metals which have filled d-orbitals. The alternative view that two simple σ-bonds from the metal to the

two carbons of the olefin   M are involved fails to account for

the stability of such olefin complexes relative to, say, dialkyls of the

type M . It also does not lead to correct prediction of the

bond angles observed in some simple olefin π-complexes. Nevertheless we should recognize that the true nature of the bonding may be intermediate between these extreme representations.

Similar arguments apply to diene-metal complexes, e.g. the diene-iron tricarbonyls. There has been much written about the relative merits of formulating these either with two μ-bonds from

1-8

an essentially delocalized 4π-electron system or with one such bond from a central carbon–carbon double bond and two sigma bonds from the two terminal carbon atoms. The experimental evidence is best accommodated by an intermediate state of affairs which may be closer to one or other of these extremes depending on the nature of substituents on the diene system. Thus the arrangement of substituents around the terminal carbon atoms is found to be intermediate between the planar geometry expected for an sp^2 carbon and the tetrahedral sp^3, but to vary between these limits in different complexes. Likewise, the three carbon–carbon bonds are either found to be equal in length or the central bond is slightly shorter. In the related triene complexes of group VI metals the bond alternation of the parent hydrocarbon is preserved, but with the central double bond shorter than the other two.

1-9

A similar question arises with allylic type ligands. The structure

$$
\underset{\textbf{A}}{
\begin{array}{c}
CH_2 \\
HC \qquad M \\
CH_2
\end{array}}
\qquad
\underset{\textbf{B}}{
\begin{array}{c}
CH_2 \\
HC \qquad M \\
CH_2
\end{array}}
$$

1-10

originally proposed for these (1-10, A) differs so little in geometry from its counterpart (1-10, B) that a symmetric hybrid structure might well be expected to be the stable form. Nuclear spin resonance spectroscopy showed that the methylene groups in such allyl–metal complexes are indeed equivalent. Hence the preferred formulation

$$
\begin{array}{c}
CH_2 \\
HC \\
CH_2 \\
M
\end{array}
$$

1-11

is one in which the allyl radical is regarded as a 3-π-electron donor ligand (1-11). However, although symmetrical allylic groups have been demonstrated to be involved in many compounds, less symmetrical bonding may be preferred in some cases where unsymmetrically substituted ligands are involved. Thus present evidence does not justify a preference for the π-allyl formulation of the acrylyl cobalt complex which can be written as having either of the structures (1-12):

$$
\begin{array}{c}
CH_2 \\
HC \!-\!\!-\! Co(CO)_2PPh_3 \\
C \\
\parallel \\
O
\end{array}
\qquad
\begin{array}{c}
CH_2 \\
HC \qquad Co(CO)_2PPh_3 \\
C \\
\parallel \\
O
\end{array}
$$

1-12

There is a related complex of comparable stability which must be written as (1-13)

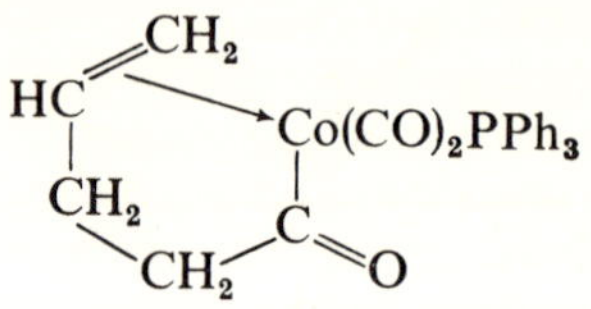

$$HC \overset{CH_2}{\underset{CH_2}{\bigg|}} \underset{CH_2}{\overset{}{\diagdown}} C \overset{}{\underset{C}{\diagup}} \rightarrow Co(CO)_2PPh_3$$

1-13

and may therefore be cited in support of the second formulation.

Asymmetrical bonding of an allyl group may occur whenever the molecule as a whole lacks symmetry. It has been demonstrated crystallographically in (methallyl)-triphenylphosphinechloropalladium (1-14).

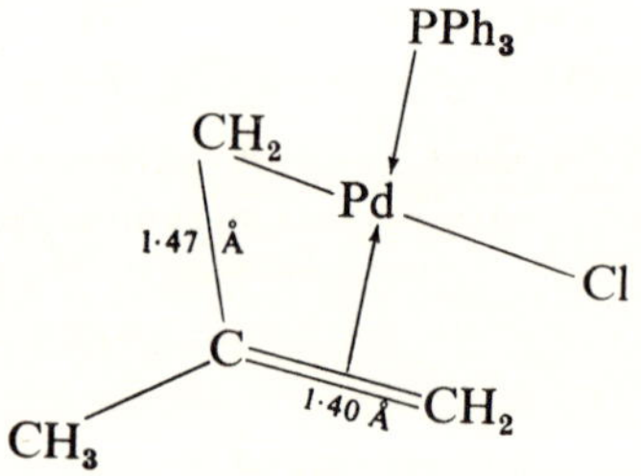

$$\underset{CH_3}{\overset{CH_2}{\bigg\backslash}} \overset{PPh_3}{\underset{1\cdot47\,\text{Å}}{\diagup}} Pd \underset{1\cdot40\,\text{Å}}{\overset{}{\diagdown}} CH_2 \longrightarrow Cl$$

1-14

CLASSIFICATION

In classifying hydrocarbon complexes it is convenient to use the number of electrons formally available from the neutral hydrocarbon or hydrocarbon radical. Such a system is independent of any hypothesis concerning the mode of bonding and hence includes the σ-bonded alkyls along with the π-complexes. Thus with increasing numbers of available electrons we have:

1-electron donors: alkyls, e.g. CH_3—M

2-electron donors: olefin complexes

3-electron donors: allyl complexes

4-electron donors: conjugated diene complexes including cyclobutadiene complexes

5-electron donors: dienyl complexes including cyclopentadienyl complexes

6-electron donors: triene and arene complexes

7-electron donors: trienyl complexes including cycloheptatrienyl complexes

Clearly such classification is independent of the method of formation. It also disregards the apparent relationship of, for example, the cyclopentadienylmetal complexes, like ferrocene, $(C_5H_5)_2Fe$, to the stable aromatic cyclopentadienide ion, $C_5H_5^-$. This may be justified by drawing attention to the very stable complexes obtainable even from the unstable cyclobutadienes. Clearly Hückels' rule restricting aromaticity among monocyclic hydrocarbons to those with $(4n + 2)$ π-electrons has no bearing on the stability of their metal complexes nor even on the aromaticity of the ring when present in such a complex. Therefore we would be equally justified in regarding $[C_5H_5Fe(CO)_3]^+$ as derived from the non-Hückel, unknown, $C_5H_5^+$ ion and hence analogous to $C_4H_4Fe(CO)_3$, as in considering $[C_5H_5Fe(CO)_2]^-$ as formed from the aromatic $C_5H_5^-$ ion. For the quite formal classification here adopted, both these complexes are considered as derived from the C_5H_5 radical, regarded, like all other 5-carbon ligands, as a 5-electron donor; in $[C_5H_5Fe(CO)_3]^+$ it is treated as linked to Fe^+ and in $[C_5H_5Fe(CO)_2]^-$ to Fe^-, but it is not intended to imply that these represent the actual oxidation states of the metal.

According to the above considerations it is also rather arbitrary whether we regard dienyl groups as occupying two or three co-ordination sites. The latter view is adopted in this volume as it leads to coordination numbers similar to those found in many other complexes of the metal. Thus for the cyclopentadienyls:

I-15

We take   6   6   5   4   as
the formal coordination numbers.

By analogy, allyl groups are considered to occupy two coordination positions.

CLEAVAGE OF METAL—CARBON BONDS

Heterolytic cleavage, $M—R \rightarrow M^+ + R^-$ is the basis of most reactions of metal alkyls and is discussed fully in Chapter 3. Here some consideration is given to the homolytic cleavage M—R → M + R·. The occurrence of this reaction on heating metal alkyls was first demonstrated elegantly and clearly by Paneth and Hofeditz in 1929. Their demonstration of the formation of alkyl radicals by this method has served as the model for much later work on these radicals. Alkyls of mercury have been particularly favoured for this purpose and undoubtedly constitute one of the best sources of radicals. Some attention has been given to such reactions as a means of producing pure metals and for vapour plating. In the case of the transition metals, the carbonyls may be used for both purposes. The decomposition $M(CO)_n \to M + nCO$ is used commercially to obtain pure, finely divided iron and has been employed as a means of refining nickel since the discovery by Mond (1888) of this first metal carbonyl. His process is now, however, largely superseded by electrolytic methods.

With the more electropositive metals, notably Mg and Al, an alternative mode of decomposition becomes important:

$$
\begin{array}{ccc}
\text{M—CH}_2 & & \text{M} \quad \text{CH}_2 \\
| & \to & | \; + \; \| \\
\text{H—C—H} & & \text{H} \quad \text{CHR} \\
| & & \\
\text{R} & &
\end{array}
$$

1-16

It leads to olefins as shown and even with the methyl derivatives gives metal hydrides rather than the free metal:

e.g. $$Me_2Mg \to MgH_2 + \frac{2}{n}(CH_2)_n$$

The ready reversibility of the olefin + hydride formation in the case of Be and Al is illustrated by the racemization of $M(CH_2CHMeEt)_3$ (M = Be or Al) at 100° by such dissociation:

$$M(CH_2CHMeEt)_n \rightleftharpoons CH_2{=}CMeEt + (EtMeCHCH_2)_2MH$$

The more stable boron analogue racemizes only slowly under these conditions, while the magnesium derivative requires higher temperature before decomposition sets in. With lithium analogous dissociation occurs, but not the reverse reaction.

THERMOCHEMICAL DATA

Although a wide variety of heats of formation of simple metal alkyls and those of some carbonyls and other complexes have been determined, the most complete data are available for mercury compounds.

Most important from the point of view of decomposition of the compounds is the first or rate-determining step and hence for a dialkyl R_2M the energy necessary to break one metal-carbon bond

$$R—M—R \rightarrow R\cdot + \cdot M—R$$

This can only be determined with reasonable accuracy from kinetic data, as thermochemical data normally yield only the overall energy for the process $R_2M \rightarrow 2R\cdot + M$. Thus kinetic data for the decomposition of dimethylmercury give the bond dissociation

TABLE 2 MEAN BOND DISSOCIATION ENERGIES

| Alkyl | Ph | Energy for R = | |
		Me	Et
ZnR_2	—	$42\cdot0 \pm 1\cdot5$	$34\cdot6 \pm 2\cdot2$
HgR_2	$32\cdot4 \pm 2\cdot1$	$29\cdot2 \pm 1\cdot1$	$24\cdot2 \pm 2\cdot1$
AlR_3	—	$66\cdot0 \pm 1\cdot2$	$57\cdot8 \pm 2\cdot6$
SnR_4	$61\cdot4 \pm 2.1$	$52\cdot1 \pm 1\cdot1$	$46\cdot2 \pm 2\cdot1$
PbR_4	—	$36\cdot5 \pm 1$	$30\cdot8 \pm 2$

energy $Me_2Hg \rightarrow MeHg + Me$ as $51\cdot5 \pm 2$ kcal/mole. From its heat of formation a thermochemical value of $58\cdot4 \pm 2$ kcal/mole is derived for the cleavage of both mercury–carbon bonds. The energy for the second step $MeHg\cdot \rightarrow Me\cdot + Hg$ is thus only of the order of the difference, say 7 kcal/mole. Although in most other cases the energy difference between the successive steps is probably less marked, it is clear that only limited conclusions concerning stabilities can be drawn from the 'bond energies' derived as average bond dissociation energies from thermochemical data. A selection of such mean bond dissociation energies is given in Table 2 and must serve for comparing the different elements until more direct measurements of bond dissociation energies become available.

Another difficulty in interpreting such thermochemical bond energies is that they measure the heat for the process $R_nM \rightarrow nR + M$ with reference to the metal in the ground state, not in the valence state required to form the compound R_nM. Thus the widely different energies estimated to be required to promote the metals Cr, Fe and Ni to the 'valence state' (i.e. electronic configuration) necessary for forming their respective carbonyls (169, 153 and 43 kcal/g atom respectively) have been cited to explain the apparent paradox between the mean dissociation energies, and the observed thermal stabilities. The energies decrease in the series $Ni(CO)_4$ ($35 \cdot 2 \pm 0 \cdot 5$), $Cr(CO)_6$ ($29 \cdot 5 \pm 0 \cdot 3$), $Fe(CO)_5$ ($28 \cdot 0 \pm 0 \cdot 5$), but when corrected for the aforementioned promotion energies these values yield 'intrinsic' metal-carbon bond energies of $45 \cdot 7$, $57 \cdot 7$ and $58 \cdot 6$ kcal/mole respectively, in accord with the observed increase in stability in this series, $Ni < Cr < Fe$. However, in the case of nickel carbonyl the first dissociation $Ni(CO)_4 \rightarrow Ni(CO)_3 + CO$ has been studied kinetically and shown to require only 13 kcal/mole, i.e. much less than the mean bond energy. Until comparable values are available for Fe and Cr the different factors contributing to thermal stability in this series cannot be adequately assessed.

Chapter 2

Methods of Formation

So often do the methods of formation involve transformations of compounds of one metal (usually alkali or alkali earth) into those of another, that any chapter concerned primarily with their preparation will inevitably throw much light also on the reactive behaviour of organometallic compounds. The classification of these methods employed here is not primarily mechanistic, but intended chiefly to aid reference back and comparison between different methods. Thus attention is focussed on the overall process: e.g. $CH_3I + 2Na \rightarrow CH_3Na + NaI$ would be classified as a substitution of metal for halogen; a mechanistic interpretation, viz.

$$CH_3I + Na \rightarrow CH_3\cdot + NaI,$$

$CH_3\cdot + Na \rightarrow CH_3Na$ might have led to its classification as an additive process (so far as the product-forming step is concerned).

A. FORMATION BY ADDITION REACTIONS

1 Radicals + Metals

The general reaction $R\cdot + M \rightarrow R{-}M$ as a means of forming a metal–carbon bond is the exact reversal of the pyrolytic decomposition discussed in Chapter 1. It is more practically useful as a means of detecting free radicals than as a method of preparation. In the original work of Paneth and Hofeditz, already referred to, methyl radicals were generated by pyrolysis of tetramethyllead and were allowed to react both with lead and other metals (Zn, Sb) to form (or reform) the corresponding methyl. It is known that similar reactions are possible with a wide range of metals although the exact limits have never been defined. Conceivably it could find application to the preparation of miscellaneous otherwise inaccessible compounds. It is certainly not restricted to gas phase work, but as a means of detecting radicals has been used, for example to demonstrate the formation of phenyl radicals in the decomposition of benzenediazo-acetate; in carbon tetrachloride attack on mercury gives PhHgCl, while using other metals (Zn, Fe, Cu, etc.) in aqueous medium leads to soluble salts, probably via unstable organometallic derivatives.

That the same reaction occurs with stable radicals if the metal is sufficiently electropositive is well-known in the case of triphenyl-methyl:

$$Ph_3C\cdot + Na \rightarrow Ph_3C^-Na^+$$

The reversibility of the reaction in this case is established by the observed formation of sodium amalgam when a solution of the sodium salt is shaken with mercury.

2 Carbonyls, etc.

Nickel and iron, and, somewhat less readily, cobalt, combine directly with carbon monoxide:

e.g. $Ni + 4CO \rightarrow Ni(CO)_4$

Isonitrile or other similar complexes with carbon containing ligands have not been obtained by such a direct process. Only certain phosphorus and arsenic compounds are known to react similarly with nickel metal to give Ni(0) complexes directly.

3 Olefin and benzene complexes

(a) Covalent-π-complexes

Silver ions appear unique among the metallic ions in adding directly to numerous olefins or to aromatic rings, to form isolable complexes. Bonding is believed to involve principally the donation of π-electrons to the Ag⁺ ion. The solubility of such salts as silver nitrate in many aromatic and unsaturated solvents is attributed to such complex formation, but crystalline products are best obtained from more ionic salts, e.g. $AgClO_4$. A simple additive process can also convert allyl bromide to π-allylpalladium bromide dimer

$$Pd + CH_2{=}CH{-}CH_2Br \rightarrow \tfrac{1}{2}\left[HC \begin{matrix} CH_2 \\ \\ CH_2 \end{matrix} Pd \begin{matrix} Br \end{matrix} \right]_2$$

2-1

(b) Covalent-σ-complexes

Mercury salts, like those of silver, readily precipitate as olefin adducts. However, there is much evidence that the addition

products have the metal bonded to one particular carbon atom
e.g.

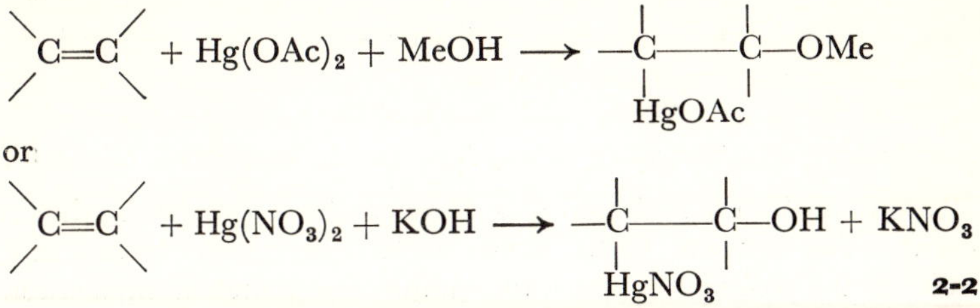

$$\diagdown C = C \diagup + Hg(OAc)_2 + MeOH \longrightarrow -\overset{|}{\underset{|}{C}}\underset{HgOAc}{\overset{}{\text{------}}}\overset{|}{\underset{|}{C}}-OMe$$

or

$$\diagdown C = C \diagup + Hg(NO_3)_2 + KOH \longrightarrow -\overset{|}{\underset{|}{C}}\underset{HgNO_3}{\overset{}{\text{------}}}\overset{|}{\underset{|}{C}}-OH + KNO_3 \qquad \textbf{2-2}$$

The adducts resemble those of silver in the ease with which the olefin may be regenerated (e.g. by acid, H_2S or KCN),

e.g. $NO_3HgCH_2-CH_2OH + 4KCN \rightarrow$
$$C_2H_4 + K_2Hg(CN)_4 + KNO_3 + KOH.$$

Both the silver and mercury derivatives may therefore be used for purification as well as characterization. The reversible formation of the silver salt complexes has also been utilized in the form of silver salt containing stationary phases for vapour phase chromatography of hydrocarbons, especially for aromatic hydrocarbons. The mercury adducts may be intermediate in the mercury catalyzed hydration of acetylene to acetaldehyde and related reactions.

(c) *Ionic complexes*

The direct addition of sodium and other alkali metals is an important route to a restricted range of organometallic compounds. Most olefins do not react. But those highly substituted with aromatic rings add two atoms of sodium or potassium [for many purposes conveniently as the liquid alloy (1:3) of both metals]. Illustrative examples are:

(i) $Ph_2C = CPh_2 + 2Na \rightarrow Ph_2\overset{\overset{\displaystyle Na}{|}}{C}-\overset{\overset{\displaystyle Na}{|}}{C}Ph_2$

(ii)   [cyclopentadienylidene]$=C\diagup^{Ph}_{\diagdown Ph} + 2Na \rightarrow$ [cyclopentadienyl]$^{\ominus}Na^+ - \overset{\overset{\displaystyle Na}{|}}{C}\diagup^{Ph}_{\diagdown Ph}$

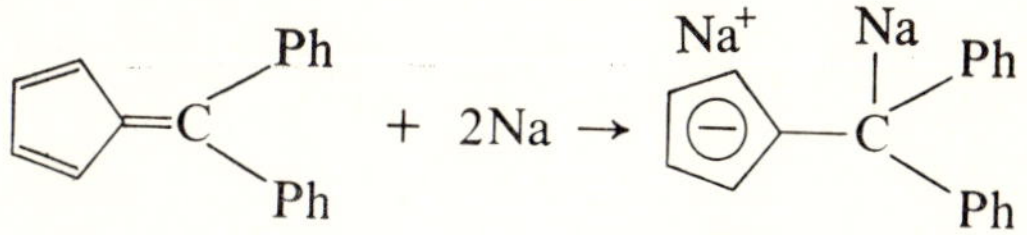

(iii)
$$PhCH = CH-CH = CHPh + 2Na \rightarrow Ph\overset{\overset{\displaystyle Na}{|}}{C}H-CH = CH-\overset{\overset{\displaystyle Na}{|}}{C}HPh$$

$\textbf{2-3}$

(iv)   2-3

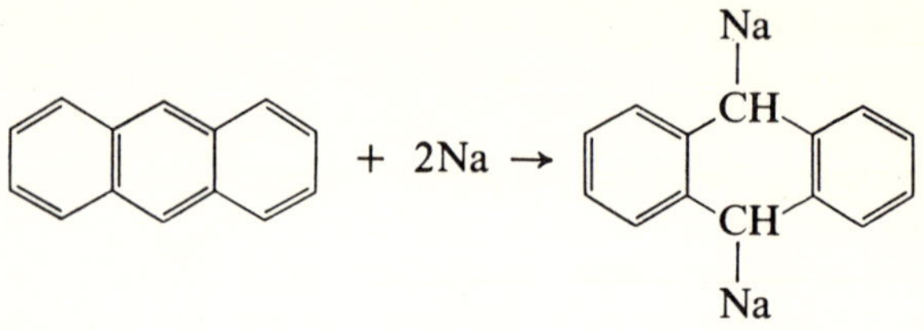

We may justify the inclusion of anthracene here as behaving like a diene. The covalent C–Na bonds written are purely formal and indicate the positions at which the sodium compounds formed react, e.g. (2-3, v) with water to give the corresponding hydrocarbons. In

(v)   2-3

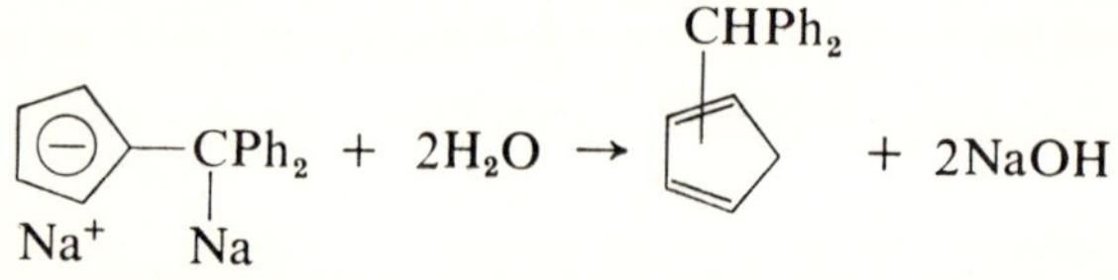

this particular example, benzhydrylcyclopentadiene is presumably formed as an equilibrium mixture of the three possible isomers. Its overall formation from the fulvene constitutes a selective method of reduction.

With less highly substituted olefins and with certain acetylenes two atoms of sodium may add to two molecules of hydrocarbon as illustrated by the following examples:

(i)

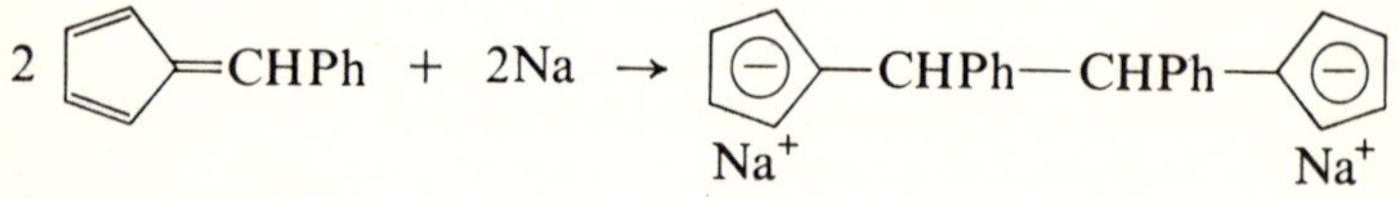

(ii)

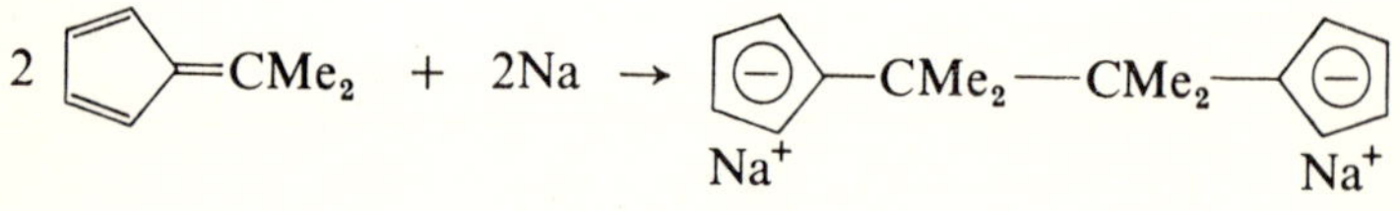

(iii) $2Ph_2C=CH_2 + 2Na \rightarrow Ph_2C-CH_2-CH_2-CPh_2$

with Na below each CPh_2

(iv) $2PhC\equiv CPh + 2Na \longrightarrow PhC=CPh-CPh=CPh$

with Na below

2-4

Some caution is required in interpreting the results of further transformations of these sodium adducts. Thus hydrolysis of the product from reaction (iii) leads to 1,1,4,4-tetraphenylbutane, demonstrating the structure of the adduct. But its reaction with metallic mercury gives back 1,1-diphenylethylene and might thus have led to the deduction that a monomeric adduct is formed.

The mechanism of such additions has not been clarified. Thus simple stepwise addition via radicals might have been expected to proceed thus:

$$Ph_2C{=}CH_2 + Na \longrightarrow NaCH_2{-}\dot{C}Ph_2$$

$$\xrightarrow{Ph_2C=CH_2} NaCH_2CPh_2{-}CH_2{-}\dot{C}Ph_2$$

$$\xrightarrow{Na} NaCH_2CPh_2CH_2CPh_2Na$$

giving a different isomer from the observed product. To rationalize the experimental observations we may perhaps postulate a π-complex,

$$[Ph_2C{=}CH_2],$$
$$\downarrow$$
$$Na$$

sufficiently stable to survive until it dimerizes. It can then do so in the direction giving the most stable dimer.

Where the initial adduct is less stable, as with the sodium adduct of butadiene, polymerization may result. The lithium catalyzed polymerization of isoprene is the basis of a commercially important process for the manufacture of synthetic rubber.

$$Na + CH_2{=}CH{-}CH{=}CH_2 \longrightarrow$$

$$NaCH_2{-}CH{=}CH{-}CH_2{\cdot} \xrightarrow{CH_2=CH-CH=CH_2}$$

$$NaCH_2{-}CH{=}CH{-}CH_2{-}CH_2{-}CH{=}CH{-}CH_2{\cdot}$$

$$NaCH_2{-}\dot{C}H{-}CH{=}CH_2 \xrightarrow{CH_2=CH-CH=CH_2}$$

$$Na{-}CH_2{-}CH{-}CH_2{-}CH{=}CH{-}CH_2{\cdot}$$

etc.

$$\underset{CH{=}CH_2}{|} \qquad \textbf{2-5}$$

In special cases the radical first formed in reactions of the above type may itself be a stable product. It is of course better formulated as a radical anion, associated with the alkali metal cation (sodium is used for illustration solely because it has been investigated much more than the other alkali metals). Thus with naphthalene we get

That a monomeric product, i.e. a radical, is formed has been clearly demonstrated inter alia by examination of its electron spin resonance spectrum. This also shows that the free electron is not localized, but is part of the delocalized π-electron system distributed over the whole aromatic nucleus. Such salts are stabilized by those solvents which best solvate the cation (without, of course, reacting with the radical anion), e.g. by tetrahydrofuran. The sodium salt conveniently prepared in this medium acts as a powerful electron transfer agent, interacting with any more electronegative aromatic hydrocarbon to give the corresponding anion. Depending on the solvent and temperature it may disproportionate according to

$$2[\text{hydrocarbon}]^- \rightarrow \text{hydrocarbon} + [\text{hydrocarbon}]^{2-}$$

The resultant di-anion is diamagnetic and a strong base reacting with proton sources to give the protonated anion [hydrocarbon + H]$^-$ and further to the dihydro-derivative [hydrocarbon + H$_2$].

4   Addition of metal hydrides to unsaturated hydrocarbons

We may write the general reaction $\overset{\diagdown}{}C{=}C\overset{\diagup}{} + M^+H^- \rightarrow$ H—C—C—M, viz. H—C—C—M$^+$. Use of the alkali metal hydrides has received little attention, probably because of their insolubility. The reaction is important with aluminium hydrides where it occurs readily as $R_2AlH + CH_2{=}CH{-}R' \rightarrow R_2AlCH_2CH_2R'$. Since in the specific case $Et_2AlH + CH_2 = CH_2 \rightarrow Et_3Al$ can be followed by $2Et_3Al + Al + 1\frac{1}{2}H_2 \rightarrow 3Et_2AlH$ the overall process represents a net synthesis of triethylaluminium from aluminium metal, hydrogen and ethylene and hence by far the cheapest route to this industrially important catalyst and intermediate.

Addition of lithium aluminium hydride requires elevated

temperatures except with the most reactive olefins. Thus

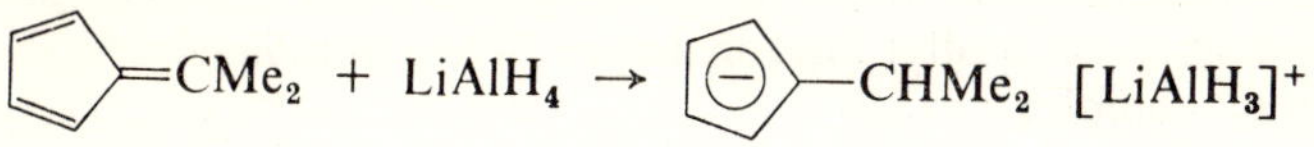

$$\text{2-6}$$

is favoured by the stability of the anion formed. The nature of the cation in this product is not clear; the above formulation is based solely on the fact that only one hydrogen atom is utilized per mole of $LiAlH_4$.

In general both this hydride and aluminium hydride itself add only to terminal ethylenes. For example, propylene adds stepwise to give finally $Li[Al(CH_2CH_2CH_3)_4]$. Selective hydrogenation of terminal olefins

e.g.

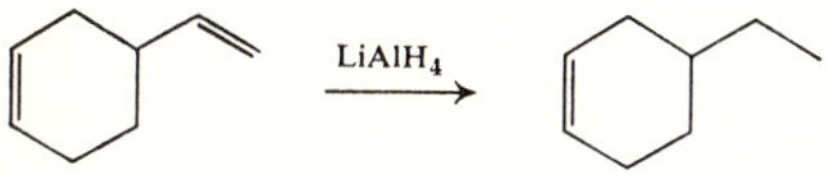

becomes possible in the presence of non-terminal double bonds.

Both germanes and stannanes add to reactive double or triple bonds,

e.g.

$$Ph_3SnH + CH_2{=}CHCN \longrightarrow Ph_3SnCH_2CH_2CN$$
$$Ph_3SnH + HC{\equiv}CPh \longrightarrow Ph_3SnCH{=}CHPh$$

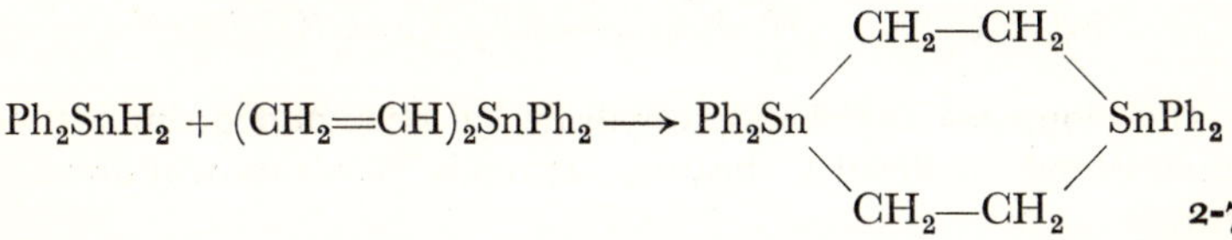

$$Ph_2SnH_2 + (CH_2{=}CH)_2SnPh_2 \longrightarrow Ph_2Sn\begin{array}{c} CH_2{-}CH_2 \\ \diagup \qquad \diagdown \\ \diagdown \qquad \diagup \\ CH_2{-}CH_2 \end{array}SnPh_2 \qquad \text{2-7}$$

Metal carbonyl hydrides, especially the cobalt derivative, $HCo(CO)_4$, add to olefins and this is regarded as a key step in the hydroformylation reaction, discussed more fully in Chapter 6. Thus $HCo(CO)_4 + CH_2{=}CH_2 \rightarrow CH_3CH_2Co(CO)_4$ is thought to proceed by a dissociative mechanism:

$$HCo(CO)_4 \rightleftharpoons CO + HCo(CO)_3$$
$$HCo(CO)_3 + CH_2{=}CH_2 \rightleftharpoons H{-}Co(CO)_3 \rightleftharpoons HCH_2CH_2Co(CO)_3$$
$$\underset{CH_2{\overset{|}{=}}CH_2}{\uparrow} \qquad \underset{-co \,\|\, co}{\uparrow}$$
$$CH_3CH_2Co(CO)_4$$

$$\text{2-8}$$

With conjugated dienes, both $HCo(CO)_4$ and the isoelectronic $HFe(CO)_3NO$ have been shown to give π-allyl type complexes, presumably via σ-allyl intermediates. Thus butadiene affords the π-crotyl complex:

e.g.

$$HFe(CO)_3NO + CH_2{=}CH{-}CH{=}CH_2 \rightarrow$$

$$[CH_3CH{=}CH{-}CH_2Fe(CO)_3NO]$$

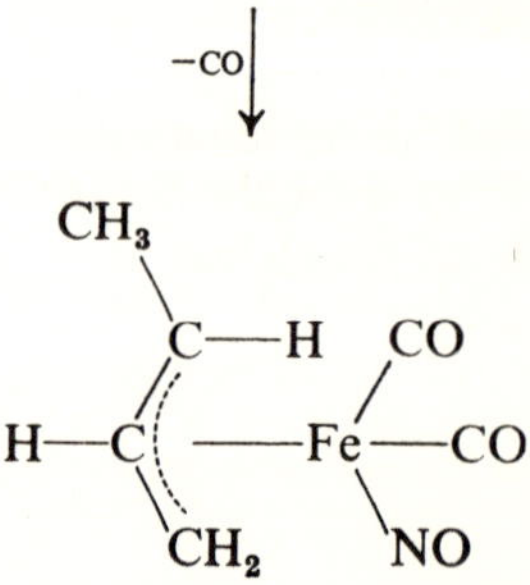

$$-CO \downarrow$$

2-9

With the carbonyl hydrides of Mn and Re similar additions have only been achieved using highly halogenated olefins or acetylenes,

e.g. $Cl_2C{=}CF_2 + HMn(CO)_5 \rightarrow CHCl_2CF_2Mn(CO)_5$

$CF_3C{\equiv}CCF_3 + HRe(CO)_5 \rightarrow CF_3CH{=}C(CF_3)Re(CO)_5$

Dicyclopentadienylrhenium hydride has been added similarly to unsaturated molecules bearing strongly electron-withdrawing groups,

e.g.

$(C_5H_5)_2ReH + HC{\equiv}CCO_2Me \rightarrow (C_5H_5)_2ReCH{=}CHCO_2Me$

5   Addition of metal alkyls to unsaturated hydrocarbons

This is the basis of the Ziegler polyethylene process in which triethylaluminium adds to ethylene:

$$Et_3Al + CH_2{=}CH_2 \rightarrow Et_2AlCH_2CH_2Et$$

The reaction can clearly proceed indefinitely. It is discussed more fully in Chapter 6. Before studying this system, Ziegler and his coworkers had demonstrated the ability of alkyllithiums to undergo such additions. The ease of addition increases in the series primary < secondary < tertiary alkyls and only the two latter add ethylene at ordinary pressure:

e.g. $\quad Pr^iLi + CH_2{=}CH_2 \xrightarrow{\;0^\circ\;} Pr^iCH_2CH_2Li$

The reaction stops here since the product is a primary alkyllithium which will only add further to ethylene (giving polymer) at high pressure.

However, olefins which are activated by conjugation are much more reactive. Thus reaction of butyllithium with butadiene does not stop after the first step:

$BuLi + CH_2{=}CH{-}CH{=}CH_2$

$\longrightarrow BuCH_2CH{=}CH{-}CH_2Li + BuCH_2{-}\underset{\underset{Li}{|}}{CH}{-}CH{=}CH_2$

Further addition of butadiene leads to oligomers and polymers. Simple additions readily occur with poly-aryl olefins and with fulvenes:

e.g. $\quad Ph_2C{=}CH_2 + BuLi \longrightarrow Ph_2\underset{\underset{Li}{|}}{C}{-}CH_2Bu \xrightarrow{\;CO_2\;} Ph_2\underset{\underset{CO_2H}{|}}{C}{-}CH_2Bu$

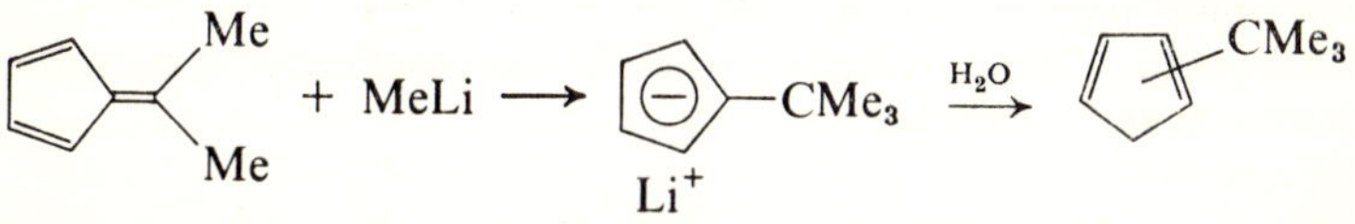

2-10

The above equations illustrate the use of carbonation or hydrolysis to indicate the nature of the organometallic product first formed.

Organosilyl and germyl–lithium derivatives likewise add to these more reactive olefins:

e.g. $\quad Ph_3GeLi + CH_2{=}CPh_2 \longrightarrow Ph_3GeCH_2CPh_2Li$

$\qquad\qquad\qquad\qquad\qquad\qquad \big\downarrow {\scriptstyle H_2O}$

$\qquad\qquad\qquad Ph_3GeCH_2CHPh_2$

2-11

Azulenes behave like fulvenes in such additions:

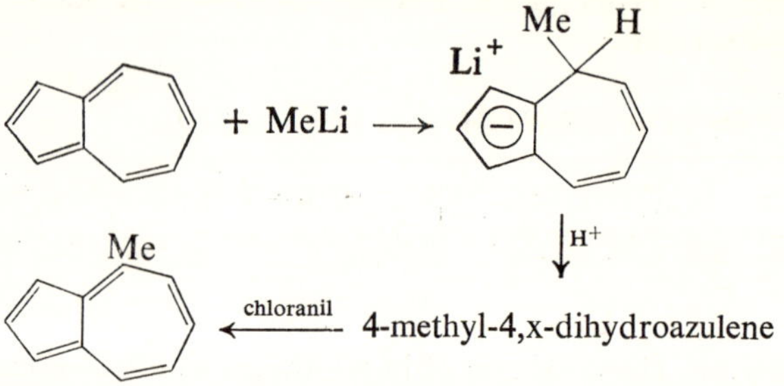

$\xleftarrow{\text{chloranil}}$ 4-methyl-4,x-dihydroazulene

2-12

Addition also occurs readily with certain heterocycles, e.g. pyridine derivatives:

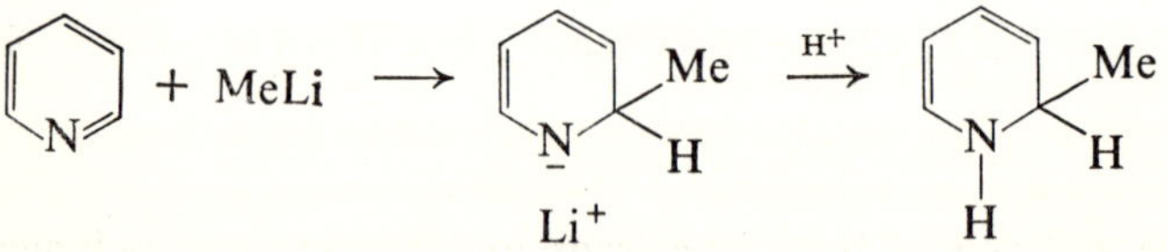

2-13

Perfluoroethylene has been shown to add to the covalent alkyl: pentacarbonylmethylmanganese:

$$\text{MeMn(CO)}_5 + \text{CF}_2\!\!=\!\!\text{CF}_2 \xrightarrow{100°} \text{MeCF}_2\text{CF}_2\text{Mn(CO)}_5$$

Closely related to additions of the type discussed above are those of bi-metallic compounds. These, like the preceding example, have only been reported with perfluoro-olefins and under U.V. irradiation. They probably proceed homolytically with initial metal—metal bond cleavage.

e.g.

$$\text{Me}_3\text{Sn—SnMe}_3 + \text{CF}_2\!\!=\!\!\text{CFCF}_3 \xrightarrow{h\nu} \text{Me}_3\text{SnCF}_2\text{CF(CF}_3)\text{SnMe}_3$$

$$\text{Me}_3\text{Sn—Mn(CO)}_5 + \text{CF}_2\!\!=\!\!\text{CF}_2 \xrightarrow{h\nu} \text{Me}_3\text{Sn—CF}_2\text{CF}_2\text{—Mn(CO)}_5$$

B. FORMATION BY SUBSTITUTION REACTIONS

These reactions can be further subdivided according to whether they follow the general patterns:

(i) $RX + M \rightarrow RM + X$

(ii) $RX + 2M \rightarrow RM + MX$

(iii) $RX + MY \rightarrow RM + XY$

(iv) $A + MY \rightarrow AM + Y$

In the following account methods (1)–(2) proceed according to (i), (3)–(4) according to (ii), (5)–(10) according to (iii), and (11)–(12) according to (iv).

1   Hydrocarbons + metals

Very few hydrocarbons possess sufficiently acidic hydrogen atoms to react even with the most electropositive metals. The best known examples are, of course, the terminal acetylenes:

$$RC{\equiv}CH + Na \rightarrow RC{\equiv}C^-Na^+ + \tfrac{1}{2}H_2$$

Not only the alkali metals, but also the alkali earths and aluminium can be induced to react directly with acetylenes. The acidity of these acetylenes is generally attributed to the greatly increased electronegativity of sp hybridized carbon compared to sp^3 or sp^2 hybridized states of this element.

The other factor which allows a hydrocarbon to become acidic is the resonance stabilization of the corresponding anion. Thus Ph_3CH reacts directly with alkali metals in liquid ammonia to give $Ph_3C^-M^+$. Perhaps the best known example of this type is cyclopentadiene, C_5H_6. Its reaction with potassium giving $C_5H_5^-K^+$ occurs in benzene solution, as discovered by Thiele in 1900. Direct reaction with sodium was only demonstrated more than 50 years later and requires solvation by such polar media as 1,2-dimethoxyethane, tetrahydrofuran or dimethyl formamide. At high temperature it reacts with magnesium to give dicyclopentadienylmagnesium and even with iron to give ferrocene. Eu and Yb react in liquid ammonia according to $M + 3C_5H_6 \rightarrow M(C_5H_5)_2 + C_5H_8$.

2   Organometallic compounds + more electropositive metals

In general the reaction $RM + M' \rightarrow RM' + M$ is expected to proceed in a forward direction if M' is higher in the electrochemical series than M. Its preparative value is very limited, but it is probably the best source of alkali and alkali-earth metal alkyls and aryls of high purity. For this purpose the readily available, easily purifiable and stable mercury derivatives are commonly chosen as starting materials:

e.g. $Bu_2Hg + 2Na \rightarrow Hg + 2BuNa$

$$Ph_2Hg + Be \rightarrow Hg + Ph_2Be$$

The method succeeds for, e.g., the preparation of benzylsodium, $PhCH_2Na$, which cannot be obtained from benzyl chloride due to the ease of Wurtz reaction in such cases. Its value is also evident for the preparation of, for example, dialkylmagnesium according to $R_2Hg + Mg \rightarrow Hg + R_2Mg$ thus avoiding the complexity of the Grignard method in giving an equilibrium mixture of the dialkylmagnesium and alkylmagnesium halide.

The success of the reaction depends on quite wide separation of the metals in the electrochemical series. Thus even the cadmium and mercury alkyls co-exist as an equilibrium mixture:

$$R_2Hg + Cd \rightleftharpoons R_2Cd + Hg$$

3   Halocarbons + metals

This is probably the most important and most widely used of all the methods. From Frankland's original preparation of the zinc alkyls in 1849:

$$EtI + Zn \rightarrow EtZnI$$

$$2EtZnI \rightarrow Et_2Zn + ZnI_2$$

through the pioneering work of Grignard, on the magnesium compounds around 1900:

e.g. $MeI + Mg \xrightarrow{\text{Ether}} MeMgI$

and then of Ziegler around 1930 on the organolithium compounds:

e.g. $PhBr + 2Li \rightarrow PhLi + LiBr$

this type of process has served as the cornerstone of organometallic chemistry. Many of the following methods rely on further transformations of products obtained in this fashion into other organometallic compounds either of the same, or of a different metal.

The simple zinc alkyls are spontaneously inflammable gases or volatile liquids. For the preparation of organic compounds they have been almost completely supplanted by the more reactive, yet more easily handled Grignard reagents. The reaction of α-haloesters, e.g. ethyl bromoacetate with zinc, is, however, employed in the widely used Reformatski reaction. The organometallic reagent is here generated in the presence of the carbonyl compound with which it then reacts. Thus isolation is avoided and the lower reactivity of the zinc reagent compared to the magnesium analogue reduces the side reaction with the ester group of the reagent itself:

$$Zn + BrCH_2CO_2Et \longrightarrow BrZnCH_2CO_2Et \xrightarrow{>C=O} \underset{OZnBr}{\overset{|}{-C}} - CH_2CO_2Et$$

The reaction of zinc with allylic and especially propargylic halides is sometimes used similarly:

$$Zn + BrCH_2C\equiv CH$$

$$\longrightarrow BrZnCH_2C\equiv CH \xrightarrow{>C=O} \underset{CH_2C\equiv CH}{\overset{OZnBr}{C}}$$

A more recent revival of interest in zinc arose from the widespread researches on carbenes. The reaction of diiodomethane with zinc (as Cu—Zn) provides one of the best sources of methylene for addition to double bonds, though genuinely free methylene is apparently not involved and reactivity of the ICH_2ZnI reagent thus differs from other sources of methylene.

$$CH_2I_2 + Zn + ICH_2ZnI \rightarrow ZnI_2 + \text{`}CH_2\text{'}$$

The extremely common use of Grignard reagents has led to many detailed investigations of their preparation. Grignard's original method, employing diethyl ether as solvent, remains the preferred method in the vast majority of cases. The halides increase in reactivity in the order $Cl < Br < I$; hence the bromides and iodides are usually preferred. Fluorides cannot be used and vinylic or aromatic chlorides also fail to react in ether. Chlorobenzene, however, reacts smoothly with magnesium at its boiling point or in tetrahydrofuran solution. The latter solvent is equally valuable for the preparation of vinylmagnesium halides, e.g.:

$$CH_2=CHCl + Mg \xrightarrow{\text{tetrahydrofuran}} CH_2=CHMgCl$$

Its effectiveness undoubtedly results from its better donor properties compared to ether leading to a stronger complex of the product with the solvent.

Although Tschelizeff showed in 1904 that tertiary amines can replace ethers as donor solvents, they have found little subsequent use and other ethers have been employed only sporadically. Dioxan precipitates magnesium halide derivatives from ethereal solution

2

(leaving R₂Mg) and has therefore figured in studies of the constitution of Grignard reagents, but appears unsuitable for their preparation.

Reactivity of the halocarbon is of course markedly dependent on the nature of the hydrocarbon fragment as well as on the halogen atom and difficulty is frequently encountered in initiating the formation of Grignard reagents. Occasionally high-boiling ethers have been used to overcome such difficulty but more frequently success is achieved by alloying the magnesium metal (with copper) or activating it with such 'catalysts' as iodine or carbon tetrachloride. In extreme cases the 'entrainment method' has been employed, whereby the unreactive halide and a more reactive one (e.g. ethyl bromide) are allowed to react simultaneously. In most of the recorded cases the need for this technique could probably be avoided by substitution of tetrahydrofuran for ether.

For the more reactive halides, especially allylic or benzylic halides, care is needed to avoid the competing Wurtz-type reaction, which leads to destruction of the organomagnesium reagent:

$$RMgX + RX \rightarrow R\text{---}R + MgX_2$$

Low reaction temperatures usually suffice to minimize this, but high dilution techniques have sometimes been used, most effectively by percolating the ethereal alkyl halide through a column of magnesium and recycling the solvent, so that a concentrated solution can be formed at the foot of the column.

Low temperatures are also essential in the formation of perfluoro-alkylmagnesium halides

$$CF_3CF_2I + Mg \rightarrow CF_3CF_2MgI$$

because higher temperatures lead to elimination of fluoride and formation of olefin:

$$F\text{---}CF_2\text{---}CF_2\text{---}MgI \rightarrow CF_2{=}CF_2 + F^- + \overset{+}{Mg}I$$

Organolithium compounds are usually best prepared from chlorides, due to the increased tendency to lose part of the product by a Wurtz reaction if bromides or iodides are employed. No complex formation with a donor solvent is necessary here and hydrocarbon solvents are to be preferred. This is partly because the ethers appear to favour Wurtz reactions, but chiefly to avoid loss due to reaction with the ether itself. This takes the form of a metalation:

e.g. $CH_3CH_2OCH_2CH_3 + BuLi \rightarrow CH_3CHLiOCH_2CH_3 + C_4H_{10}$

followed by elimination

$$CH_3 \cdot CHLi \cdot OCH_2CH_3 \rightarrow CH_2{=}CH_2 + LiOCH_2CH_3$$

presumably by a mechanism of the type:

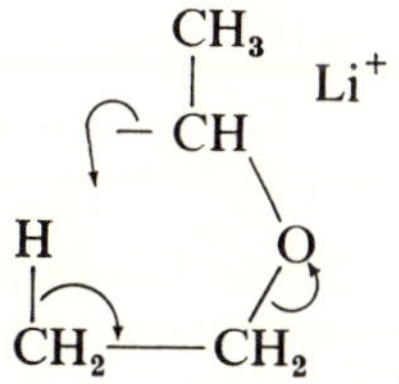

The tendency to react with the ether increases sharply in the order $Ph < Me < Et < Bu^n < Bu^t$. Thus both methyl- and phenyl-lithium may conveniently be prepared in ether and the latter even in tetrahydrofuran. Vinyllithium and its derivatives are likewise stable in such solvents and substituted vinyl bromides react smoothly with lithium metal in boiling ether provided pure reagents are employed. The unsubstituted vinyllithium is best made by the sequence:

$$CH_2{=}CHCl + Mg \rightarrow CH_2{=}CHMgCl \xrightarrow{SnCl_4} (CH_2{=}CH)_4Sn$$
$$\xrightarrow{4PhLi} Ph_4Sn + 4CH_2{=}CHLi$$

Preparation of derivatives of the alkyls of Na, K, Rb and Cs meets increasing difficulty from the competing Wurtz reactions. By slow addition of the halide to an excess of very finely divided metal at low temperature this can be minimized and most of the simple alkyls are accessible in this way. Fine dispersions of sodium are suitable or a high surface area of metal may be provided by using the liquid (1:3) sodium potassium alloy with efficient stirring. The relatively stable aryls are readily obtained in this way:

$$C_6H_5Cl + 2Na \xrightarrow{pentane} C_6H_5Na + NaCl$$

The other metals which can react directly with alkyl and aryl halides comprise calcium, strontium and barium. Information about their organometallic derivatives is remarkably scanty, but they seem to form mixtures of RMX and R_2M like magnesium, and to be roughly comparable to RLi in reactivity. Beryllium reacts only on heating with the simpler alkyl halides,

e.g. $CH_3I + Be \xrightarrow{90°} CH_3BeI$

Aluminium reacts to give the sesquihalides:

e.g. $2Al + 3EtCl \rightarrow Et_2AlCl \cdot EtAlCl_2$

and the reactions of the magnesium alloy:

e.g. $AlMg_3 + 6EtCl \rightarrow Et_6Al_2 + 3MgCl_2$

may be assumed to involve further reaction of these sesquihalides with simultaneously formed organomagnesium derivatives.

e.g. $Et_3Al_2Cl_3 + 3EtMgCl \rightarrow Et_6Al_2 + 3MgCl_2$

Reaction of EtCl with very finely divided lead according to $2EtCl + Pb \rightarrow Et_2PbCl_2$ may possibly be involved in the commercial tetraethyllead process from sodium–lead alloys, but alternative mechanisms can be written. On the above basis it would be combined with the steps:

$EtCl + 2Na—Pb \rightarrow EtNa + NaCl + 2Pb$ and

$Et_2PbCl_2 + 2EtNa \rightarrow Et_4Pb + 2NaCl$ to give the overall reaction

$4EtCl + 4NaPb \rightarrow Et_4Pb + 4NaCl + 3Pb$

Thallium has been reported to react with methyl iodide, probably via monovalent MeTl:

$2Tl + 2MeI \rightarrow TlI + [TlMe] + MeI \rightarrow Me_2TlI$

4   Ethers + metals

The reaction $ROR' + 2M \rightarrow RM + MOR'$ owes its preparative value to the fact that it occurs most readily and smoothly in those cases where the corresponding halides RX are most prone to give only Wurtz reaction products. Thus benzyl and benzylhydryl methyl ethers react smoothly as do related α-alkoxyaromatic or allylic ethers

e.g. $PhCH_2OMe + 2Li \xrightarrow{THF} PhCH_2Li + LiOMe$

gives up to 80 % yields of a lithium compound not accessible from $PhCH_2Cl$;

$PhCMe_2OMe + Na—K \xrightarrow{pentane} PhCMe_2Na + KOMe$

provides a convenient route to a base stronger than triphenyl-methylsodium;

$$C_5H_5FeC_5H_4CH_2OMe + 2Li \rightarrow C_5H_5FeC_5H_4CH_2Li + LiOMe$$

exemplifies extension of the reaction to a non-benzenoid analogue of a benzylic system.

In liquid ammonia the cleavage of ethers with sodium occurs readily even with diaryl ethers, $ArOAr + Na \xrightarrow{NH_3} ArNa + ArONa$, but this has acquired only degradative, not preparative importance.

5 Metalation

$$RH + MY \rightleftharpoons RM + HY$$

In its commonest form this reaction may be considered to be that of an acid with a salt and unless the equilibrium is displaced by other factors (e.g. precipitation) with the salt of a weaker acid (i.e. relatively speaking, a base).

This classification therefore includes the formation of, for example, the sodium salts from all the 'active methylene compounds'—malonic, cyanoacetic and β-keto esters, β-diketones, nitroalkanes, dimethyl sulphoxide and the like. These will not be discussed here as the negative charge cannot be considered to be primarily on carbon, but is delocalized and chiefly on oxygen or other hetero-atoms. Moreover, their preparation and reactions are adequately covered in most general texts on organic chemistry. Nevertheless we should remember that in most of their reactions they behave as carbanion salts, i.e. they react in a manner entirely comparable to, for example, the lithium alkyls.

Equally 'active' methylene groups occur in such acidic hydro-carbons as cyclopentadiene and its derivatives including indene and fluorene. We have already seen that these and the acetylenes react (method (1) above) with the alkali metals, and both groups react readily with many different bases—indeed with alkoxides and any bases comparable to or stronger than these.

Thus the equilibrium

$$\text{⬠} + RONa \rightarrow C_5H_5Na + ROH$$

lies largely to the right with R = Et and completely so with R = Bu^t. Sodium hydride is not only a strong enough base so that reaction with most active hydrogen compounds would go to completion, but the evolution of hydrogen ensures this completion and further serves to remove the only other product, leaving the pure sodium salt in the solvent used:

e.g. $RC\equiv CH + NaH \rightarrow RC\equiv CNa + H_2$

For acetylenes, the most widely used base is sodium amide in liquid ammonia

$$RC\equiv CH + NaNH_2 \xrightarrow{NH_3} RC\equiv CNa + NH_3$$

We may note here that whereas alkylfulvenes add both sodium metal and alkyllithium [2-3, 2-4 and 2-10] they are metalated by sodium amide:

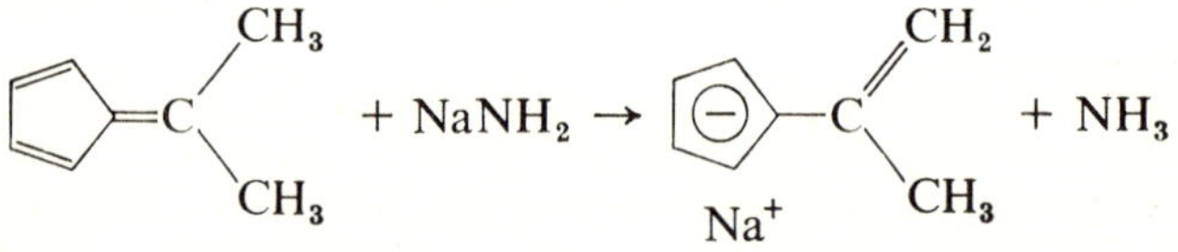

2-14

Lithium and magnesium salts are most conveniently made using alkyllithium or Grignard reagents respectively

e.g.

$$RC\equiv CH + EtMgBr \rightarrow C_2H_6{\uparrow} + RC\equiv CMgBr$$

2-15

These reagents however interact not only with these typically 'acidic' hydrocarbons but with many others, which are acids only relative to the alkanes. Grignard reagents are relatively inefficient in this respect. Organolithium compounds have therefore been used very frequently and sodium compounds occasionally to effect metalation reactions. Most aromatic systems are acidic relative to alkyllithium. Metalation of benzene itself is of no preparative value, but that of substituted benzenes frequently is, especially in view of the strong tendency to substitute *ortho* to ether oxygen, CF_3, etc:

e.g.

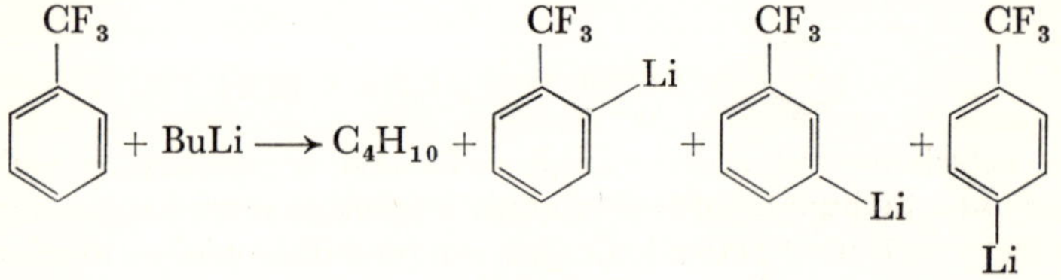

40%   8%   0·5%

2-16

1,3-Dimethoxybenzene gives as much as 55% of the 2-lithio derivative (A) on treatment with phenyllithium and anisole gives at least 68% of the *ortho*-lithio derivative as judged by the isolation

A B C

D E

2-17

of the carbinol (B) after treatment with benzophenone. The use of phenyllithium here shows that anisole is more acidic than benzene. In such ways we can set up series of hydrocarbons of increasing acidity or of decreasing basicity of their conjugate bases, e.g. $Bu^nLi > MeLi > PhLi > o\text{-}MeOC_6H_4Li$.

In contrast to anisole, thioanisole appears to metalate in the side-chain to give C, albeit in poor yield. The side-chain metalation of α- and γ-alkyl-pyridines and similar systems may be regarded as special cases of methylene activation by $C{=}N$. Thus α-picoline with methyllithium gives D. Thiophene is readily metalated by butyllithium and furan by either phenyllithium or phenylsodium. Both substitute in the 2-position (E; X = S or O). Ferrocene gives mixtures of mono- and 1,1'-dimetalated products, butyllithium in ether giving chiefly the former, but predominant dilithiation is achieved when this reagent is complexed with an equivalent amount of tetramethylethylenediamine. Both phenyl- and amylsodium give predominantly the disubstituted compound.

Closely related to these metalations is the action of organolithium compounds on ammonium, phosphonium or sulphonium salts. Phenyllithium is most commonly used and here again the phenyl anion abstracts a proton from a more acidic CH group, but as the starting material is a cation, a zwitterion or neutral product results, not a lithium derivative:

Examples occur in the preparation of the phosphinylides used in the Wittig reaction:

e.g. $Ph_3PCH_3{}^+I^- + PhLi \longrightarrow C_6H_6 + LiI + Ph_3\overset{+}{P}—\overset{-}{C}H_3$

$$\updownarrow$$

$$Ph_3P{=}CH_2$$

and as intermediate steps in the Stevens and Sommelet rearrangements of quaternary ammonium salts:

e.g. $(PhCH_2)_2\overset{+}{N}Me_2 \xrightarrow{PhLi} PhCH_2\overset{+}{N}Me_2—\overset{-}{C}HPh$

$$\longrightarrow Me_2N—CHPhCH_2Ph$$

or $PhCH_2\overset{+}{N}Me_3 \xrightarrow{PhLi} PhCH_2\overset{+}{N}Me_2\overset{-}{C}H_2$

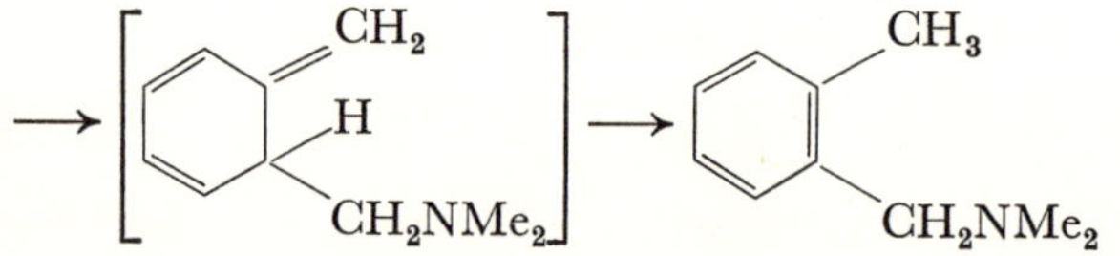

                                                                2-18

Neutral products also result from some metalations by elimination of metal hydride, especially when the resultant product becomes aromatic.   For example, 1,4-dihydro-naphthalene reacts with phenyllithium in refluxing ether to give naphthalene and lithium hydride.   But by working with butyllithium at $-15°$ decomposition of the intermediate metalation product is avoided and carbonation then yields 2-carboxy-1,2-dihydronaphthalene.   Formation of the 2-substituted product with the double bond in conjugation with the benzene ring is in accord with the formulation shown for the intermediate allylic anion

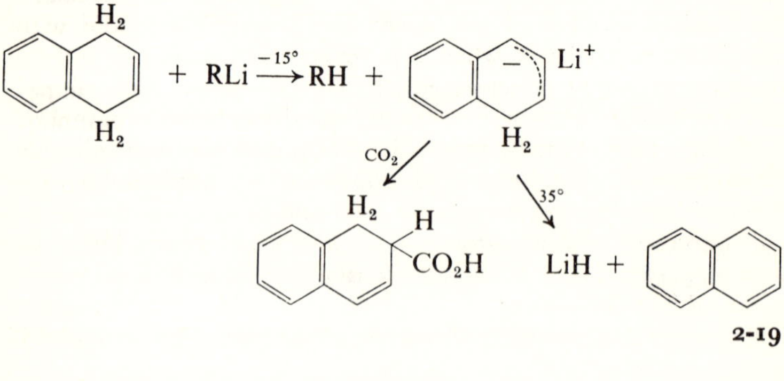

                                                                2-19

The term metalation should be restricted to the metal-hydrogen exchange reactions and should not be extended to include:

6   Metal–halogen exchange reactions

$$RX + MY \rightarrow RM + XY.$$

The value of these rests in their possibility in many cases where direct reaction of the alkali metal with the halide does not succeed. This is perhaps best illustrated by the halogenated phenols and benzoic acids. With lithium metal these afford only the corresponding lithium salts, but both types react with a second equivalent of butyllithium as in the examples:

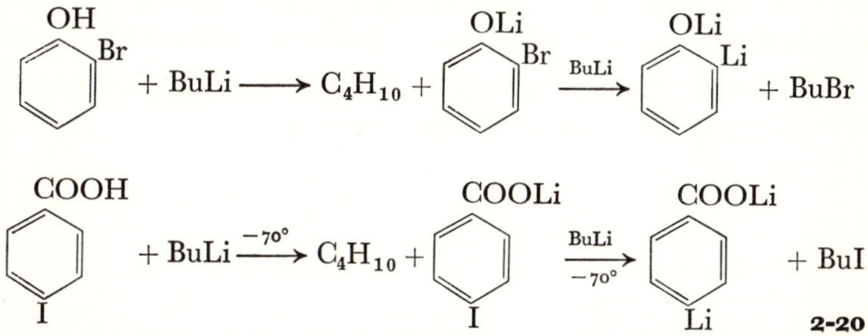

2-20

In the latter case low temperature is essential, otherwise the carboxylate group —CO_2Li reacts further with butyllithium to give —$CBu(OLi)_2$ and hence on hydrolysis of the reaction product —COBu.

Metal-halogen exchange is useful for the preparation of such compounds as o-lithioanisole using butyl- or phenyllithium:

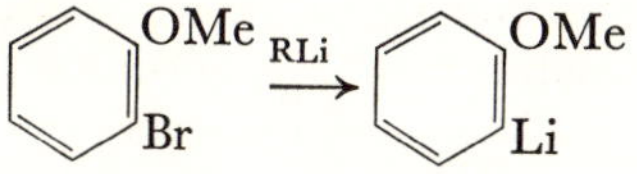

2-21

thus ensuring exclusive o-orientation and giving better yields than metalation. The latter reaction, however, may compete, as with p-bromoanisole:

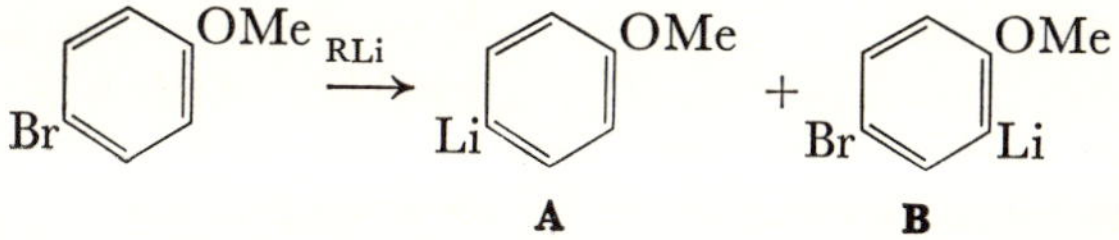

A   B   2-22

Here the choice of metalating agent becomes important as it is found that butyllithium acts primarily by metal–halogen exchange giving p-methoxyphenyllithium (A) whereas phenyllithium causes far more metalation to give the o-lithio derivative (B). In general iodo- and bromo-compound readily undergo metal–halogen exchange, chloro-compounds are less effective and fluoro-aromatics do not exchange. Thus o-bromofluorobenzene is an excellent reagent for the preparation of the transient species 'benzyne', reacting by way of bromine-lithium exchange followed by elimination of lithium fluoride:

$$\text{(ring: F, Br)} + \text{PhLi} \longrightarrow \text{(ring: F, Li)} \longrightarrow \text{LiF} + \text{(benzyne ring)} \qquad \text{2-23}$$

The same reactive intermediate is formed, somewhat less efficiently by the *ortho*-metalation of fluorobenzene itself:

$$\text{(ring: F)} + \text{PhLi} \longrightarrow C_6H_6 + \text{(ring: F, Li)} \longrightarrow \text{(benzyne ring)} \qquad \text{2-24}$$

7   Mercuration and related covalent metalations

Purely formally the mercuration of benzene, e.g. $C_6H_5\cdot H$ + $AcOHgOAc \rightarrow C_6H_5HgOAc + HOAc$, belongs with the metalation reactions $RH + MY \rightarrow RM + HY$ discussed under (5) above. Mechanistically it is, however, distinct, involving electrophilic attack by $AcOHg^+$ or similar cations whereas the alkyllithium metalations must be assumed to involve proton abstraction by the strong base Y^- as the rate controlling step. Hence this type of metalation depends on the electrophilicity of M^+, not on the base strength of Y^-. Nevertheless the same relative order of reactivity of the aromatic substrates RH is to be expected, that for alkyllithium metalations running parallel with the ease of electrophilic substitution as may be judged from the examples already quoted.

Although probably any species XHg^+ is effective, mercuric acetate has been used in most cases. Benzene and toluene mercurate smoothly with this reagent in boiling ethanol to give the corresponding mercuriacetate $RC_6H_4Hg(OAc)$ where R = H or CH_3. Under similar conditions thiophene and furan give the di- and tetra-substituted compounds A and B respectively.

A 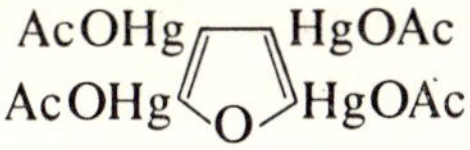   B

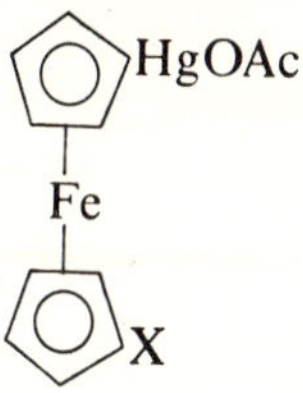

C 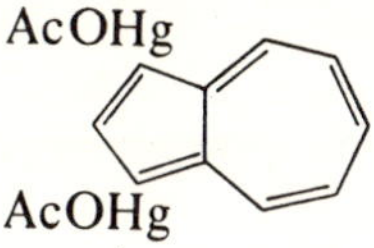   D   2-25

Ferrocene reacts at room temperature to give a mixture of mono- and di-mercurated products (C) (X = H or HgOAc). Azulene reacts even more readily and only the 1,3-disubstituted product (D) has been isolated. It is frequently convenient to convert such products to the mercurichlorides by simple exchange with potassium chloride before isolation.

The surprising relative ease of mercuration of nitrobenzene and other deactivated aromatic systems together with the observed *ortho*-orientation in such cases have been explained by an alternative free radical mechanism of the type:

$$Hg(OAc)_2 \rightleftharpoons AcOHg\cdot + AcO\cdot$$

$$AcOHg + C_6H_5\!\!-\!\!NO_2 \longrightarrow$$

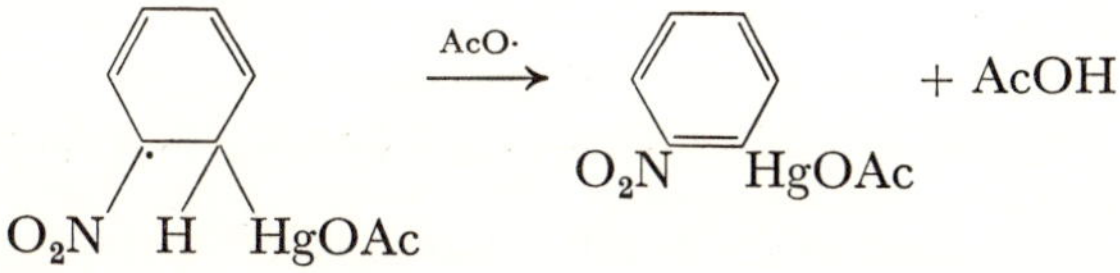

2-26

Competition between the ionic and radical mechanism may lead to somewhat unusual orientation in more reactive systems. This is circumvented by the addition of a small quantity of perchloric acid, believed to react with the acetate thus:

$$HClO_4 + Hg(OAc)_2 \rightarrow HOAc + AcOHg^+ClO_4^-$$

The resulting solutions are much more reactive, e.g. leading to relatively rapid reaction with toluene at room temperature, as well as more 'normal' orientation.

Thallic and auric salts have been shown to metalate benzene and thiophene similarly,

e.g.

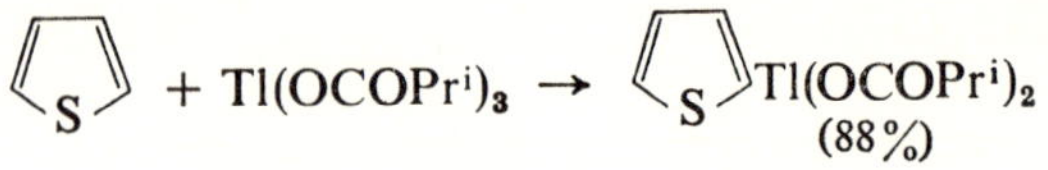

$$\langle_S\rangle + Tl(OCOPr^i)_3 \rightarrow \langle_S\rangle Tl(OCOPr^i)_2$$
$$(88\%)$$

$$C_6H_6 + AuCl_3 \rightarrow C_6H_5AuCl_2$$

2-27

The latter product readily decomposes to gold(I) chloride and chlorobenzene.

8   Miscellaneous replacements of non-metallic groups

Apart from the replacements of hydrogen and halogens (5–7 above) certain other groups may be replaced directly by metals. Mercury as mercuric chloride displaces boronic acid $[B(OH)_2]$, and sulphinic acid (SO_2H) groups from aromatic substances. The former reaction has been applied in the ferrocene series as well as to benzenoid systems and the sulphinic acid method proved useful to obtain the tricarbonylcyclopentadienylmanganese derivative:

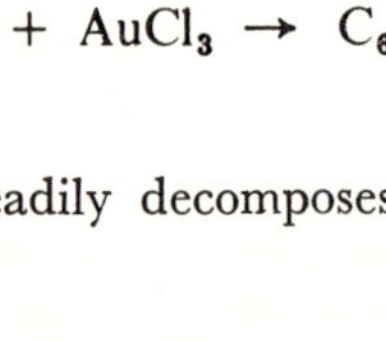

$$
\begin{array}{c}
\bigcirc\hspace{-1.5em}\bigcirc\!-HgCl \\
| \\
Mn \\
OC^{\diagup}\, |\, ^{\diagdown}CO \\
CO
\end{array}
$$

2-28

Alkaline solutions of iodoxybenzene react with mercuric oxide thus:

$$C_6H_5IO_2 + HgO \rightarrow C_6H_5\text{—}HgIO_3$$

Metallic bismuth or mercury reduce aryliodonium salts to the corresponding metal compounds

e.g. $$Ph_2I^+ Cl^- + Bi \rightarrow Ph_3Bi$$

$$p\text{-MeOC}_6H_4\overset{+}{I}Ph\ Cl^- + Hg \rightarrow PhHgCl + p\text{-MeOC}_6H_4I$$

The second example shows that in a mixed salt the more nucleophilic of two aryl groups becomes attached to the metal.

Of much wider applicability are the displacements of diazonium groups by metal halides. Reminiscent of the Bart reaction for the preparation of arylarsonic acids, they were discovered and intensively studied by Nesmeyanov. His method consists of preparing the appropriate complex salt and then reducing with a suitable metal (e.g. Zn, Sn, Cu),

e.g.
$$2Ar\overset{+}{N_2}\overset{-}{Cl} + SnCl_4 \longrightarrow (ArN_2{}^+)_2(SnCl_6{}^{2-})$$
$$\downarrow Zn$$
$$Ar_2SnCl_2 + 2N_2 + 2ZnCl_2$$

It is applicable to mercury, thallium, tin, lead, antimony and bismuth. The fact that decomposition of the diazonium fluoroborate in the presence of finely divided metal can give the same product in suitable cases is consistent with a free radical mechanism, but the influence of substituents has been interpreted as demonstrating a heterolytic mechanism for the Nesmeyanov reaction.

The replacement of chloride from benzyl chloride by chromium(II) ions may be thought of as involving a disproportionation. In aqueous solution the reaction has been formulated as

$$PhCH_2Cl + 2Cr^{2+} + 10H_2O \rightarrow$$
$$PhCH_2Cr(H_2O)_5{}^{2+} + CrCl(H_2O)_5{}^{2+}$$

The stability of the resultant benzylchromium complex in water as an aquo-complex is without parallel among transition metal derivatives. The aquo-complex itself has not been isolated, but its behaviour leaves no doubt that a species containing a benzyl-chromium bond is present in solution and a similar red-brown crystalline benzylchromium pyridine complex has been obtained both from benzylmagnesium chloride, and by the analogous reaction of dipyridochromous chloride:

$$Cr(C_5H_5N)_2Cl_2 + PhCH_2Cl \xrightarrow[0°]{C_5H_5N} PhCH_2Cr(C_5H_5N)_3Cl_2$$

9 Reactions of organometallic compounds with metal salts

$RX + MY \rightarrow RM + XY$, where X is a metal or metal-containing group, is the counterpart to method (2) in that replacement of metal X by metal M will occur if M is lower in the electrochemical series than X. Thus whereas we have seen that, for example, sodium metal will replace mercury according to

$$R_2Hg + 2Na \rightarrow 2RNa + Hg$$

we would expect—and indeed find—the reverse displacement with mercuric chloride:

$$2RNa + HgCl_2 \rightarrow R_2Hg + 2NaCl$$

This is probably the most important method of preparing all those organometallic compounds which cannot be obtained directly from the metal and hydrocarbon or halocarbon. Examples are therefore very numerous. They include the use of alkyls of many different metals; e.g. for preparing alkylplatinum halides the mercury alkyls are convenient:

$$3HgMe_2 + PtCl_4 \rightarrow 3MeHgCl + Me_3PtCl$$

But in general the most conveniently accessible starting materials are the Grignard reagents and these or the organolithium compounds have been most widely used. They have been treated with the appropriate metal chloride except where solubility or other special considerations make the use of other salts preferable.

The alkyls and aryls of cadmium, mercury, beryllium and aluminium among others are all best prepared in this way, as outlined in the equations:

$$2RMgX + CdCl_2 \rightarrow R_2Cd + MgX_2 + MgCl_2$$

$$RMgCl + HgCl_2 \rightarrow MgCl_2 + RHgCl \xrightarrow{RMgCl} R_2Hg$$

$$BeCl_2 \cdot 2Et_2O + 2RMgCl \rightarrow R_2Be$$

$$AlCl_3 \cdot Et_2O + 3RMgCl \rightarrow R_3Al \cdot Et_2O$$

Only two chlorine atoms are replaced in thallium(III) chloride by Grignard reagents, but all three by alkyllithium

e.g. $$2MeMgCl + TlCl_3 \rightarrow Me_2TlCl + 2MgCl_2$$

$$3MeLi + TlCl_3 \rightarrow Me_3Tl + 3LiCl$$

Since methylthallium reacts with methyl iodide to give dimethyl-thallium iodide, the same product also results starting from thallium(I) salts in the presence of methyl iodide:

$$2MeLi + MeI + TlI \rightarrow [MeTl] \rightarrow [Me_2TlI] \rightarrow Me_3Tl$$

The group 4 metals, Ge, Sn and Pb tend to give complex mixtures of RMX_3, R_2MX_2, R_3MX and R_4M and a large excess of Grignard reagent is required to reach the fully substituted compounds R_4M. In the case of germanium and tin the tetrahalides, e.g. $GeCl_4$ and $SnCl_4$, can serve as convenient starting materials, but since lead only gives dihalides the reactions become even more complex. The presumptive intermediates from $RMgX + PbX_2$, i.e. the dialkyls of lead R_2Pb, are too unstable to be isolated (some unstable diaryls have been obtained). They disproportionate giving initially the hexa-alkyldileads:

e.g.
$$2MeMgBr + PbBr_2 \rightarrow 2MgBr_2 + [Me_2Pb]$$
$$3[Me_2Pb] \rightarrow Me_3Pb{-}PbMe_3 + Pb$$

The latter on warming disproportionate further to tetraalkyllead and lead metal, so that at higher temperature the net reaction becomes:

$$4MeMgBr + 2PbBr_2 \rightarrow Me_4Pb + Pb + 4MgBr_2$$

With methyllithium in the presence of methyl iodide, however, all the lead is converted to the tetramethyl, probably by a mechanism similar to that outlined for thallium, above, i.e. addition of MeI to $Me_2Pb \rightarrow Me_3PbI$ which can then react further.

In the case of antimony and bismuth, both tri- and pentavalent derivative are accessible by such sequences as

e.g.
$$BiCl_3 + 3PhMgCl \rightarrow 3MgCl_2 + Ph_3Bi$$

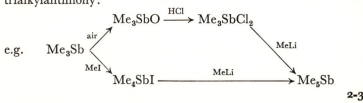

$$Ph_5Bi \xleftarrow[75°]{2PhLi} Ph_3BiCl_2$$

2-29

In the case of antimony alternative routes to the pentavalent state are available from the addition of oxygen or alkyl halides to trialkylantimony:

e.g.

$$Me_3SbO \xrightarrow{HCl} Me_3SbCl_2$$

$$Me_3Sb$$ (air / MeI)

$$Me_4SbI \xrightarrow{MeLi} Me_5Sb$$

(MeLi)

2-30

The formation of intermediate alkylmetal halides is useful when mixed alkyls (or aryls) are desired, e.g. isolation of Ph_2SnCl_2 from PhLi and $SnCl_4$ will permit its further transformation according to:

$$Ph_2SnCl_2 + 2RLi \rightarrow Ph_2SnR_2 + 2LiCl$$

where R = e.g. Me or Bu.

It must be assumed that rare earth metals can give alkyls by similar processes although these appear to be unstable and recorded examples are restricted to the cyclopentadienyls $(C_5H_5)_nMCl_{3-n}$

and $(C_5H_5)_2M$ (M = Eu or Yb) all of which may be regarded as having strongly polar σ-bonds between the metal atom and the ring. Transition metals on the other hand were long believed not to give simple alkyls as many early attempts to form them by the above type of reaction led only to free metal and hydrocarbon,

e.g. $2RMgX + CoX_2 \rightarrow R\text{—}R + 2MgX_2 + Co$

The view that metal alkyls if formed as intermediates must be very unstable has received some support from later work in which simple alkyls and chloroalkyls of titanium, niobium and tantalum have been isolated and alkyls and aryls of vanadium, chromium, manganese and nickel shown to exist at least in solution, but in each case only at very low temperatures. It does not necessarily follow that the dimeric hydrocarbons, R—R, must always arise via metal alkyls as intermediates, although they can clearly do so in suitable cases:

$$R_2M \rightarrow R_2 + M$$

The formation of free radicals from Grignard reagents and cobalt, iron or chromium salts has frequently been interpreted without assuming such intermediates.

The presence of other ligands can greatly stabilize the alkyls or aryls of transition metals. Thus solvent-free triphenylchromium cannot be isolated (see Chapter 5 for its behaviour) but the tris-tetrahydrofuranate, $Ph_3Cr(OC_4H_3)_3$, is relatively stable. Phosphines and similar ligands can stabilize the aryls of the iron, cobalt and nickel groups giving complexes like $(Et_3P)_2NiPh_2, (Et_3P)_2PdMe_2$, and

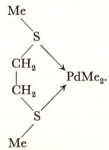

Especially favourable situations arise with highly sterically hindered groups which prevent hydrolytic cleavage of such products as

$(Et_2PPh)_2Fe(C_6Cl_5)_2$; $(Et_2PPh)_2Co(C_6H_3Me_3\text{-}1,3,5)_2$;

$(Et_3P)_2Rh(\alpha\text{-}C_{10}H_7)Br$.

Ligands which are more strongly π-bonding than phosphines give particularly stable alkyls and aryls. Thus

$$XMn(CO)_5 + RMgX \rightarrow RMn(CO)_5 + MgX_2$$

Better routes to these carbonyl complexes are discussed below. More relevant here are the examples:

$$C_5H_5Cr(NO)_2Cl + MeMgI \rightarrow C_5H_5Cr(NO)_2Me$$
$$(C_5H_5)_2TiCl_2 + 2MeLi \rightarrow (C_5H_5)_2TiMe_2$$
$$(C_5H_5)_2VCl + PhLi \rightarrow (C_5H_5)_2VPh$$

The reducing action of the organometallic reagent is illustrated by the fact that the same product is obtained in the last case if the starting material is the dichloride $(C_5H_5)_2VCl_2$.

π-Complexes themselves are frequently best made by the same method. This applies both to the allyl- and the cyclopentadienyl complexes. In the former case Grignard reagents have been most used,

e.g. $$C_3H_7MgBr + NiBr_2 \rightarrow (C_3H_7)_2Ni$$

but in the cyclopentadienyl series sodium salts are usually preferred although not only Grignard reagents and organolithium compounds, but also cyclopentadienides of many other metals have been employed:

$$2C_5H_5Na + MX_2 \rightarrow (C_5H_5)_2M + 2NaX$$

is a general reaction which has been applied to $TiCl_2$, VCl_2, $CrCl_2$, Mn^{2+}, Fe^{2+}, Co^{2+}, Ni^{2+} and many non-transition metal salts. When the metal is introduced in a higher oxidation state it may give derivatives at that level

e.g. $$2C_5H_5Na + TiCl_4 \rightarrow (C_5H_5)_2TiCl_2$$
$$2C_5H_5Na + IrCl_3 \rightarrow [(C_5H_5)_2Ir]^+Cl^-$$

or may suffer reduction, as in the original preparation of ferrocene from cyclopentadienylmagnesium bromide and ferric chloride.

In the case of titanium it has been shown that the reaction may be stopped at the intermediate stage:

$$C_5H_5Na + TiCl_4 \rightarrow C_5H_5TiCl_3$$

or pushed further to give a tris-cyclopentadienyltitanium $(C_5H_5)_3Ti$ of low stability and uncertain structure.

Outside the transition series the products are usually σ-bonded or ionic cyclopentadienides. Thus Sn, Pb and Hg derivatives probably belong to the former type and the Tl^I and rare earth compounds, $(C_5H_5)_3M$, to the latter. But in a number of cases interesting and unexpected structures result. For example, $(C_5H_5)_2Be$

has been shown by electron diffraction to have an unsymmetrical structure with the metal atom closer to one of the two rings, in

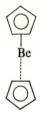

2-31

contrast to the symmetrical (ionic) structure of the magnesium analogue. A significant covalent contribution to the bonding of *one* ring to beryllium must therefore be assumed.

Substituted cyclopentadienes including indenes have been employed in many similar reactions with ferrous chloride to give substituted ferrocenes, and in a few illustrative cases with cobalt, nickel and other transition metal halides.

The use of chlorodicarbonylcyclopentadienyliron in the reaction

$$C_5H_5Fe(CO)_2Cl + C_5H_5Na \rightarrow C_5H_5Fe(CO)_2C_5H_5$$
$$\rightarrow 2CO + C_{10}H_{10}Fe$$

has been shown to give an isolable intermediate with one π- and one σ-bonded cyclopentadienyl group. The latter becomes π-bonded by elimination of two moles of carbon monoxide on warming. The sequence can be utilized to prepare unsymmetrically substituted ferrocenes and an analogous sequence has been employed to prepare the heterocyclic analogue, azaferrocene:

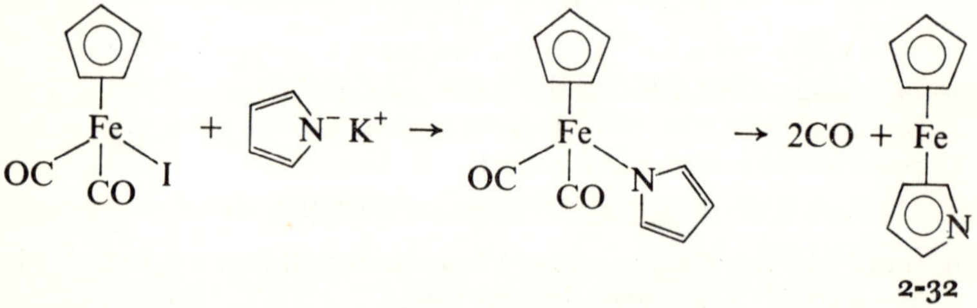

2-32

10   Reaction of bimetallic compounds with halides

$RX + MY \rightarrow RM + XY$ where Y is a second metal or metal containing group.

This method has important applications to group IV metals and to metal carbonyl or other anionic transition metal complexes. In the former case it is used chiefly to introduce a fourth organic group into a trialkyl- or aryl metal derivative. The intermediate Pb, Sn or Ge—lithium or sodium (or potassium) derivatives—may be obtained by one of the processes illustrated by the following equations:

(i) $\qquad PbCl_2 + 3PhLi \rightarrow Ph_3PbLi + 2LiCl$

(ii) $\qquad Bu_3SnCl + 2Na \rightarrow Bu_3SnNa + NaCl$

(iii) $\quad Et_3Ge\text{–}GeEt_3 + 2K \rightarrow 2Et_3GeK$

(iv) $\quad (PhCH_2)_4Ge + 2Li \rightarrow (PhCH_2)_3GeLi + PhCH_2Li$

The first of these methods is applicable to lead or tin, the others to all three metals.

In each case the product will react smoothly with alkyl or aryl-alkyl halides

e.g. $\qquad Ph_3PbNa + PhCH_2Cl \rightarrow Ph_3PbCH_2Ph$

If different alkyl groups are present reaction (iv) may be selective enough to allow successive replacement of one type preferentially

e.g.

$$(PhCH_2)_3GeLi + MeI \longrightarrow (PhCH_2)_3GeMe \xrightarrow{\text{Li}} (PhCH_2)_2GeMeLi$$
$$\downarrow \text{MeI}$$
$$(PhCH_2)_2GeMe_2$$

Analogous reactions with covalent metal halides may be used to obtain bi-metallic compounds, with two atoms of the same or of different metals.

e.g. $\qquad Ph_3GeNa + BrSnMe_3 \rightarrow Ph_3Ge\text{–}SnMe_3$

In the metal carbonyl series the reactions of the alkali-metal derivatives with both alkyl and acyl halides have been employed:

e.g. $\qquad MeI + NaMn(CO)_5 \rightarrow MeMn(CO)_5$

$\qquad MeCOCl + NaRe(CO)_5 \rightarrow MeCORe(CO)_5$

The ready interconvertibility of the alkyl and acyl derivatives (see Chapter 6) leads sometimes to isolation of the unexpected product

e.g. $\qquad C_2F_5COCl + Na_2Fe(CO)_4 \rightarrow (C_2F_5)_2Fe(CO)_4$

$\qquad EtBr + NaFe(CO)_3NO \rightarrow EtCOFe(CO)_3NO$

Hydrocarbon metal carbonyl anions react similarly

e.g. $\quad C_5H_5Mo(CO)_3Na + ClCH_2\text{—}CH{=}CH_2 \rightarrow$

$\qquad\qquad\qquad\qquad C_5H_5Mo(CO)_3CH_2\text{—}CH{=}CH_2$

$\quad 2C_5H_5Fe(CO)_2Na + ClCOCH_2CH_2CH_2COCl \rightarrow$

$\qquad\qquad C_5H_5Fe(CO)_2\text{—}COCH_2CH_2CH_2CO\text{—}Fe(CO)_2C_5H_5$

Although aromatic halides are generally unreactive in such processes, perfluorobenzene derivatives undergo nucleophilic substitution by the anions $C_5H_5Fe(CO)_2^-$ and $Re(CO)_5^-$

e.g. $C_6F_5CF_3 + C_5H_5Fe(CO)_2Na \rightarrow$

$$NaF + p\text{-}CF_3C_6F_4Fe(CO)_2(C_5H_5)$$

Perhalo-olefins behave similarly with various carbonyl-anions

e.g. $CF_2{=}CF_2 + Re(CO)_5^- \rightarrow CF_2{=}CF\text{---}Re(CO)_5$

Examples of related reactions with other transition metal complexes are almost confined to cobalt, of special interest from a biological point of view because of the organometallic grouping (∗) in the coenzyme form of Vitamin B_{12} (A).

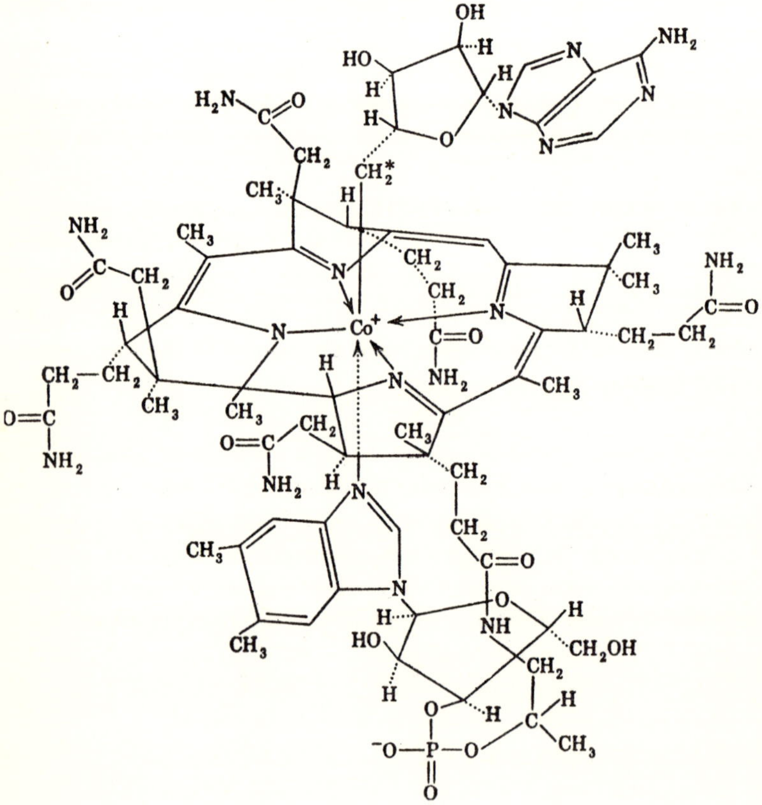

A

2-33

The introduction of different organic groupings at this site (∗) in the vitamin has been studied and similar methods applied to simpler model systems, e.g. the aetioporphyrin complex (B: Y = pyridine) and the dimethylglyoxime complex (C: Y = pyridine).

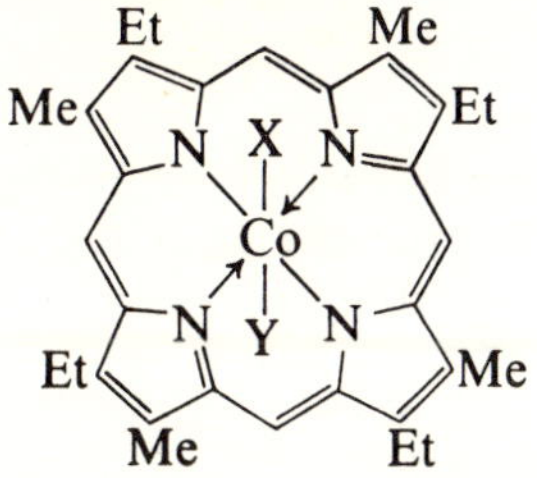

B 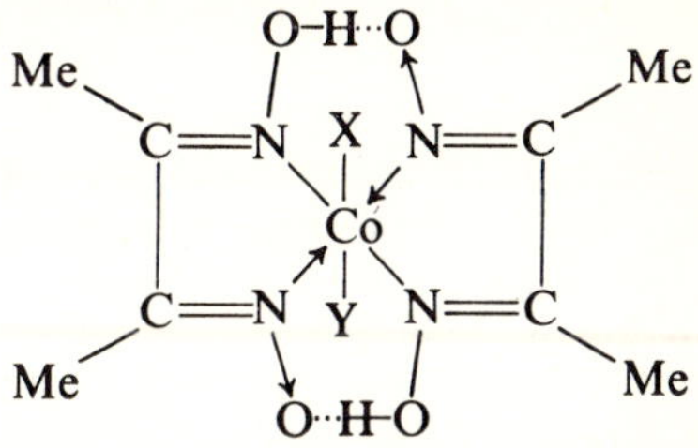   C

2-33

Thus X = Br will react with MeMgBr to give X = Me or the reduced forms (e.g. the anion of the hydride, X = H) react with methyl iodide giving the same product. An even simpler system undergoing alkylation reactions of apparently similar type is the pentacyanocobalt(II) ion

e.g. $[Co(CN)_5]^{3-} + CH_2{=}CHCH_2Br \rightarrow$
$$[CH_2{=}CH_2CH_2{-}Co(CN)_5]^{2-} + I^-$$

This behaviour must be contrasted with that of the hexacyanocobaltate and ferrocyanide ions which have no free position for coordination and hence alkylate on nitrogen (see p. 103).

11   Simple ligand exchange

$$A + MY \rightarrow AM + Y$$

(a) Exchange of one neutral ligand for another

The exchange of a variety of neutral ligands for others has been demonstrated. It includes examples of the displacement of phosphorus and other hetero-atoms by carbon, as well as numerous examples of the displacement of one carbon ligand by another. Thus isonitriles replace carbon monoxide according to such schemes as

(i) $Ni(CO)_4 + 4PhNC \rightarrow Ni(CNPh)_4 + 4CO$

(ii) $Cr(CO)_6 + 3PhNC \rightarrow Cr(CO)_3(CNPh)_3 + 3CO$

(iii) $Fe(CO)_5 + 2MeNC \rightarrow Fe(CO)_3(CNMe)_2 + 2CO$

(iv) $IMn(CO)_5 + 4PhNC \rightarrow IMn(CO)(CNPh)_4 + 4CO$

Displacement of hydrocarbon ligands is illustrated by:

(v) $C_7H_8Mo(CO)_3 + 3ArNC \rightarrow Mo(CO)_3(CNAr)_3 + C_7H_8$

(C_7H_8 = cycloheptatriene) and of a phosphine by:

(vi) $C_5H_5Fe(CO)(PPh_3)I + PhNC \rightarrow$

$$C_5H_5Fe(CO)(CNPh)I + PPh_3$$

The extent of displacement varies with the metal, the type of ligand (e.g. ethyl isocyanide only displaces three CO groups from nickel carbonyl; contrast (i)), the nature of the solvent and of any ligands not suffering replacement. Thus equation (iv) refers to the reaction in boiling tetrahydrofuran; under the same conditions all five carbonyls are replaceable from bromopentacarbonyl-manganese, $BrMn(CO)_5$, but in ethanol solution reaction stops at the $BrMn(CO)_3(CNPh)_2$ stage.

In this class belong further the numerous preparations of hydrocarbon metal carbonyls by direct displacement of carbon monoxide. Some like

$$Fe(CO)_5 + \overset{\displaystyle CHCO_2Et}{\underset{\displaystyle CHCO_2Et}{\|}} \longrightarrow Fe(CO)_4 \leftarrow \overset{\displaystyle CHCO_2Et}{\underset{\displaystyle CHCO_2Et}{\|}} + CO$$

or $$C_5H_5Mn(CO)_3 + \overset{\displaystyle CH_2}{\underset{\displaystyle CH_2}{\|}} \longrightarrow C_5H_5Mn(CO)_2 \leftarrow \overset{\displaystyle CH_2}{\underset{\displaystyle CH_2}{\|}}$$

or $$C_5H_5V(CO)_4 + \overset{CH \quad\quad CH_2}{\underset{CH_2 \quad CH}{\diagup \diagdown \diagup}} \longrightarrow C_5H_5V(CO)_2C_4H_6$$

2-34

require considerable energy and have been achieved by irradiation probably involving a unimolecular cleavage, e.g. $Fe(CO)_5 \xrightarrow{h\nu} Fe(CO)_4 + CO$ as the rate controlling step. Others are achieved thermally under not too drastic conditions:

e.g. (i) $Fe(CO)_5 + CH_2{=}CH{-}CH{=}CH_2 \xrightarrow{135°}$

$$C_4H_6Fe(CO)_3 + 2CO$$

(ii) $Fe_2(CO)_9 + PhCH{=}CHCO_2H \xrightarrow[\text{benzene}]{40-45°}$

$$(PhCH{=}CHCO_2H)Fe(CO)_4 + Fe(CO)_5$$

(iii) $Cr(CO)_6 + C_6H_5CH_3 \xrightarrow[\text{excess toluene}]{\text{reflux in}} (CH_3C_6H_5)Cr(CO)_3 + 3CO$

(iv) $Co_2(CO)_8 + PhC{\equiv}CH \xrightarrow[\text{pentane}]{\text{room temp.}} Co_2(CO)_6(PhC_2H) + 2CO$

The reactions of olefins and acetylenes with cobalt hydrocarbonyl, $HCo(CO)_4$ and with nickel carbonyl occur without heating and must have very low activation energies. They are important steps in catalytic reactions and hence are discussed more fully in Chapter 6.

In principle all such reactions may be reversible and in several cases such reversal has been clearly demonstrated,

e.g. $(C_3H_5)_2Ni + 4CO \rightarrow Ni(CO)_4 + C_6H_{10}$

In cases like (iii) above the reverse reaction has been developed into a practical synthesis of chromium hexacarbonyl, starting from dibenzenechromium or related diarenechromiums.

$$(C_6H_6)_2Cr + CO \xrightarrow[-C_6H_6]{} C_6H_6Cr(CO)_3 \xrightarrow[-C_6H_6]{} Cr(CO)_6$$

A variety of displacements of one hydrocarbon ligand by another have been demonstrated or even used as preparative methods.

Thus $C_6H_6Cr(CO)_3 + C_6H_5CO_2Me \rightarrow$

$$(C_6H_5CO_2Me)Cr(CO)_3 + C_6H_6$$

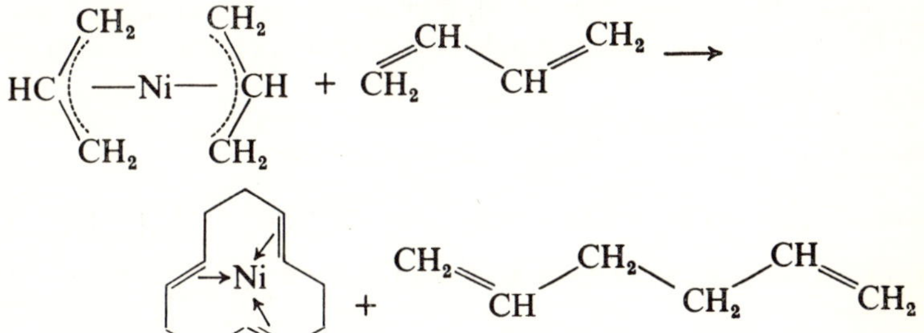

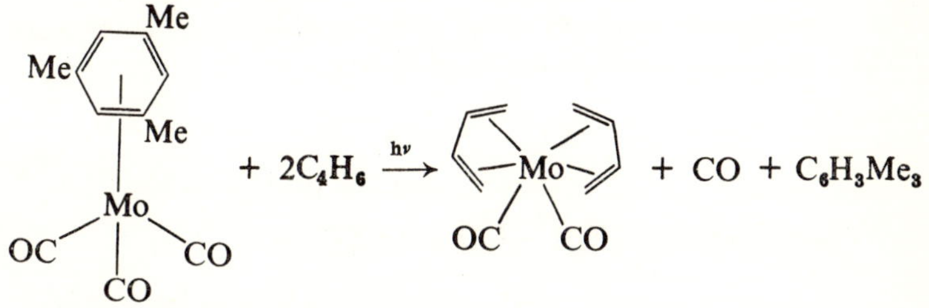

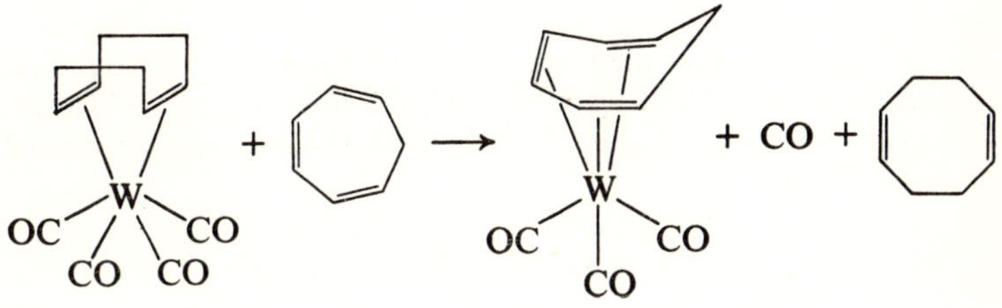

2-35

(b) Exchange of neutral ligands for anionic ligands

Halocarbonyls, isocyanide and olefin complexes, especially the platinum derivatives, may be formed by displacing anionic groups from a complex anion as exemplified by

$$K_2[PtCl_4] + CO \longrightarrow K[PtCOCl_3] + KCl$$
$$\downarrow CO$$
$$Pt(CO)_2Cl_2 + KCl$$

$$K_2[PtBr_4] + 2RNC \longrightarrow Pt(CNR)_2Br_2 + 2KCl$$

$$K_2[PtCl_4] + CH_2{=}CH_2 \longrightarrow K[Pt(C_2H_4)Cl_3] + KCl$$

2-36

When the starting material is a neutral halide, a 'catalyst', e.g. an aluminium halide, capable of complexing with the halide ion and thus assisting its removal, may be required. This is the case in the reactions of halocarbonyls with carbon monoxide or olefins:

e.g.

$$Re(CO)_5Br + CO + AlBr_3 \rightarrow [Re(CO)_6]^+AlBr_4^-$$

$$Mn(CO)_5Br + CH_2{=}CH_2 + AlBr_3 \rightarrow [Mn(CO)_5(C_2H_4)]^+AlBr_4^-$$

$$Co(CO)_2(PPh_3)_2Cl + CO + AlCl_3 \rightarrow [Co(CO)_3(PPh_3)_2]^+AlCl_4^-$$

Alternatively, complex ions like perchlorate or tetraphenylborate will promote such reactions either alone or with silver ions to assist further by precipitation of the halide ion:

e.g. $C_5H_5Fe(CO)_2Cl + CO + NaBPh_4 \rightarrow$

$$NaCl + [C_5H_5Fe(CO)_3]BPh_4$$

$$C_5H_5Co(CO)(C_2F_5)I + CO + AgClO_4 \rightarrow$$

$$AgI + [C_5H_5Co(CO)_2(C_2F_5)]^+ClO_4^-$$

The incoming ligand may occupy more than one coordination position, with or without expulsion of additional (neutral) ligands. Thus, the cations $(ArH)_2Fe^{2+}$ form by both the methods illustrated for mesitylene:

$$2C_6H_3Me_3 + FeCl_2 + 2AlCl_3 \rightarrow [(C_6H_3Me_3)_2Fe](AlCl_4)_2$$

$$2C_6H_3Me_3 + Fe(CO)_4X_2 + 2AlX_3 \rightarrow [(C_6H_3Me_3)_2Fe](AlX_4)_2 + 4CO$$

and similarly two examples with cobalt compounds:

$$2C_6Me_6 + CoCl_2 + 2AlCl_3 \rightarrow [(C_6Me_6)_2Co](AlCl_4)_2$$

$$C_6H_5Me + Ph_4C_4Co(CO)_2Br + AlBr_3 \rightarrow$$
$$[Ph_4C_4CoC_6H_5Me][AlBr_4]$$

Even a cyclopentadienide ion from ferrocene can act as the leaving group in

$$(C_5H_5)_2Fe + ArH \xrightarrow{\text{AlCl}_3} [C_5H_5FeArH]^+$$

(c) Exchange of one anionic ligand for another

Most such exchanges are in effect covered by method (B), (9) above, but the simple preparation of metal cyanides, fulminates and acetylides from halides or other simple salts belong in this category, as well as the displacement of one such group by another.

e.g.   (i) $Pr_3PbOH + NaCNO \rightarrow Pr_3PbCNO + NaOH$

(ii) $K_2[Pt(SCN)_4] + 4KC\equiv CR \xrightarrow{\text{NH}_3}$
$$K_2[Pt(C\equiv CR)_4] + 4KSCN$$

(iii) $K_2[Ni(CN)_4] + 4KC\equiv CR \xrightarrow{\text{NH}_3} K_2[Ni(C\equiv CR)_4] + 4KCN$

The completion of each of these reactions depends on the insolubility of one of the products, e.g. of KSCN in liquid ammonia in case (ii).

(d) Displacement of neutral ligands by anionic ligands

These differ little from the preceding examples in such reactions as

$$[Cr(NH_3)_6](NO_3)_3 + 6KC\equiv CH \rightarrow$$
$$K_3[Cr(C\equiv CH)_6] + 6NH_3 + 3KNO_3$$

$$[Co(NH_3)_4](SCN)_2 + 6NaC\equiv CMe \rightarrow$$
$$Na_4[Co(C\equiv CMe)_6] + 4NH_3 + 2NaSCN$$

$$[Fe(CN)_5OH_2]^{3-} + CN^- \rightarrow [Fe(CN)_6]^{4-} + H_2O$$

Displacement may also be from neutral or cationic complexes as exemplified by

$$Cr(CO)_3(NH_3) + 3KC\equiv CR \rightarrow K_3[Cr(CO)_3(C\equiv CR)_3]$$
and

$$[Fe(C_{12}H_8N_2)_3]^{2+} + 2KCN \rightarrow Fe(C_{12}H_8N_2)_2(CN)_2 + 2K^+ + C_{12}H_8N_2$$

where $C_{12}H_8N_2 = $ o-phenanthroline.

12   Reactions according to AB + MY → AMB + Y

This variation of the previous method involves a reactant which adds in two positions as it displaces the ligand Y.

Thus $C_2F_5I + Fe(CO)_5 \rightarrow C_2F_5\text{---}Fe(CO)_4\text{---}I + CO$

$CH_2\text{=}CH\text{---}CH_2Cl + Fe(CO)_5 \longrightarrow$

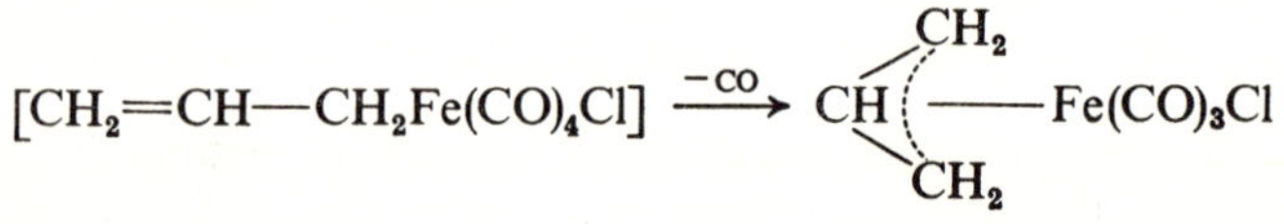

$$[CH_2\text{=}CH\text{---}CH_2Fe(CO)_4Cl] \xrightarrow{-CO} CH\underset{CH_2}{\overset{CH_2}{\diagdown}}\text{---}Fe(CO)_3Cl$$

A   B

2-37

Only perfluorinated or allylic halides have been shown to react with iron carbonyl in the above manner. In the second case the only isolated product is the tricarbonyl (B). The intermediate formation of the tetracarbonyl (A) is assumed and included to show the similarity of the two reactions. A third carbonyl group is extruded in the example (2-38) and all four in the reaction of nickel carbonyl

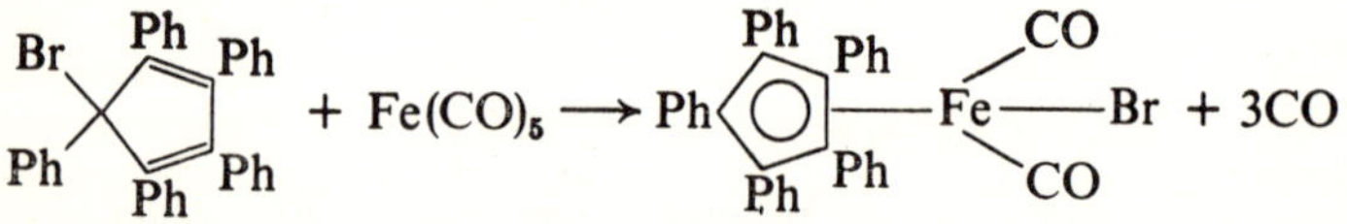

$$\text{(structure)} + Fe(CO)_5 \longrightarrow \text{Ph}\underset{Ph}{\overset{Ph}{\diagdown}}\text{---}Fe\underset{CO}{\overset{CO}{\diagup}}\text{---}Br + 3CO$$

2-38

with allyl bromide:

$$C_3H_5Br + Ni(CO)_4 \rightarrow [C_3H_5NiBr]_2 + 4CO$$

C.   MISCELLANEOUS METHODS

1   Reactions of diazoalkanes with metal hydrides and halides

These should be compared with the Nesmeyanov reactions described in section (B).(8) above. Like method (B),(10) they have been applied chiefly to metals of group IV and to metal carbonyls, but the reaction with halides is probably capable of wider extension.

The following examples illustrate the processes involved.

(a) $CH_2N_2 + HMn(CO)_5 \rightarrow CH_3Mn(CO)_5 + N_2$

$N_2CH(COOEt) + HSnBu_3 \rightarrow EtOCOCH_2SnBu_3 + N_2$

(b) $RCHN_2 + SnCl_4 \xrightarrow{-N_2} RCHClSnCl_3 \dashrightarrow (RCHCl)_4Sn$

$CH_2N_2 + HgCl_2 \xrightarrow{-N_2} ClCH_2HgCl \longrightarrow (ClCH_2)_2Hg$

$CH_2N_2 + C_5H_5Cr(NO)_2Cl \longrightarrow C_5H_5Cr(NO)_2CH_2Cl$

2   The addition of M—OR to C=C

The reaction

$$R_3SnOMe + CH_2\!\!=\!\!\underset{\underset{OCOCH_3}{|}}{C}\!\!-\!\!CH_3 \longrightarrow$$

$$R_3SnCH_2COCH_3 + CH_3COOMe$$

is an apparently isolated example of a method that may well be capable of extension to give functional derivatives of other metals.

3   Electrolytic reduction using metal cathodes

This is likewise an apparently general route for organometallic synthesis which deserves much fuller exploitation. Known examples include (a) formation of $Sn(CH_2CH_2CN)_4$ when an aqueous alkaline (NaOH) solution of acrylonitrile is electrolyzed with a tin cathode, (b) formation of $(Me_2CH)_2Hg$ and $(Me_2CH)_4Pb$ when solutions of acetone are electrolyzed with mercury or lead cathodes and (c) production of tetraethyllead by electrolysis of triethyl-aluminium-sodium fluoride melts with lead cathodes according to $3Pb + 2(Et_3Al)_2 \cdot NaF \rightarrow 4Al + 3PbEt_4 + 2NaF$. The reaction produces very pure aluminium.

4   Reductive methods for forming metal carbonyls and isonitrile and hydrocarbon complexes

The majority of methods for forming metal carbonyls depend on a selective method of reducing the metal salt to the zero (or lower) oxidation state in the presence of carbon monoxide. In general it is not known whether or to what extent complexing with CO precedes or follows such reduction.

In a large number of cases carbon monoxide is itself a sufficiently good reducing agent. Thus cobalt and nickel sulphides react in alkaline solution according to the equations:

$$2CoS + 11CO + 12OH^- \rightarrow 2Co(CO)_4^- + 3CO_3^{2-} + 2S^{2-} + 6H_2O$$

$$NiS + 5CO + 4OH^- \rightarrow Ni(CO)_4 + CO_3^{2-} + S^{2-} + 2H_2O$$

There is evidence for an initial disproportionation of Ni^{II} to $Ni^0 + Ni^{IV}$ followed by interaction of the latter with CO to give $Ni^{II} + CO_2$ from the behaviour of the dithiobenzoate which yields a stable Ni^{IV} derivative in the presence of sulphide:

$$2Ni\left(\begin{array}{c} S \\ \diagdown \\ S \end{array} C{-}Ph\right)_2 + 4CO + S^{2-} \rightarrow$$
$$Ni(CO)_4 + \tfrac{1}{2}[SNi(S_2CPh)_2]_2 + 2PhCS_2^-$$

A more remarkable case of disproportionation occurs in the formation of the platinum carbonyl fluoride:

$$2PtF_4 + 2CO \rightarrow Pt(CO)_2F_8 + Pt$$

Although sulphides are particularly reactive in the formation of metal carbonyls, oxides and halides can be employed under somewhat more drastic conditions. Thus the oxides and/or halides of Co, Tc, Re, Ru, Os, Ir, Pt and Au have been reported to be suitable.

e.g.
$$Tc_2O_7 + CO \xrightarrow{275°/400 \text{ atm}} Tc_2(CO)_{10}$$

$$2RuCl_3 + 5CO \rightarrow 2Ru(CO)_2Cl_2 + COCl_2$$

$$2IrBr_3 + 5CO \rightarrow 2Ir(CO)_2Br_2 \xrightarrow{3CO} 2Ir(CO)_3Br$$

These examples include the formation of halocarbonyls, involving less drastic reduction. They also illustrate the formation of phosgene and carbonyl bromide when chlorides and bromides are used. The iodides tend to liberate free iodine under comparable conditions. It is usually preferable, however, to add a reducing metal to take up the halogen.

e.g.
$$2CoI_2 + 8CO + Cu \rightarrow [Co(CO)_4]_2 + 4CuI$$

Alternative reducing agents may be used as in the preparation of octacarbonyldicobalt from $CoCO_3$, H_2 and CO. Stronger reducing agents are frequently necessary, e.g. for the group VI metals:

$$WCl_6 + 6CO + 2Al \rightarrow W(CO)_6 + Al_2Cl_6$$

$$CrCl_3 + CO + LiAlH_4 \xrightarrow[\text{Ether}]{65°} Cr(CO)_6 \quad (65\%)$$

$$VCl_3 + CO + Mg + Zn \xrightarrow[\text{pyridine}]{135°}$$

$$V(CO)_6{}^- \xrightarrow{\text{H}+} H_2 + V(CO)_6 \quad (40\%)$$

A more convenient laboratory synthesis of hexacarbonylchromium employs the soluble acetylacetone complex with magnesium metal

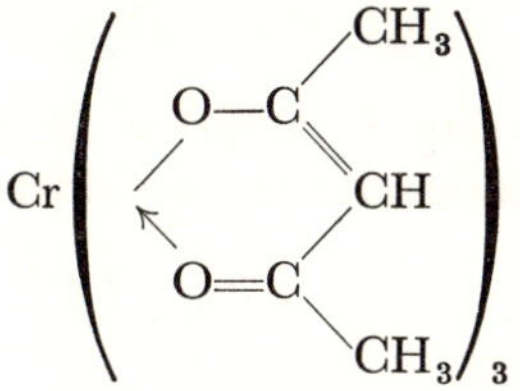

$$Cr\left(\begin{array}{c} O-C \diagup \diagdown \overset{CH_3}{} \\ \diagup \quad \diagdown CH \\ O=C \diagdown \diagup \\ CH_3 \end{array}\right)_3$$

in pyridine and carbon monoxide under pressure. For Mo and W a convenient procedure employs iron carbonyl as both source of carbon monoxide and reducing agent.

e.g. $$WCl_6 + 3Fe(CO)_5 \xrightarrow{100°} W(CO)_6 + 3FeCl_2 + 9CO$$
$$(75\%)$$

Probably the most efficient procedure for V, Nb and Ta employs sodium metal in diglyme (diethylene glycol dimethyl ether, $C_6H_{14}O_3$)

e.g. $$VCl_3 + 4Na + 6CO + 2C_6H_{14}O_3 \xrightarrow{100°}$$
$$3NaCl + [Na(C_6H_{14}O_3)_2]^+[V(CO)_6]^- \quad (80\%)$$

Nb and Ta are used as the pentachlorides. Chromium trichloride reacts like the vanadium chloride to give the sodium diglyme salt $[Na(C_6H_{14}O_3)_2]_2[Cr(CO)_5]$ but for the preparation of the neutral carbonyl the triethylaluminium method would appear most convenient:

$$CrCl_3 + Et_3Al + CO \xrightarrow[\text{ether}]{115°/1000 \text{ psig}} Cr(CO)_6 \quad (92\%)$$

The same method serves for manganese and follows the expression:

$$MnCl_2 + Et_3Al + 5CO \rightarrow$$
$$\tfrac{1}{2}Mn_2(CO)_{10} + EtAlCl_2 + C_2H_4 + C_2H_6$$

This method may be regarded as similar in mechanism to the method by which chromium carbonyl was first obtained (by Job and Cassall in 1926) using chromic chloride and phenylmagnesium bromide in ether at atmospheric pressure. It probably involves intermediate formation of the metal alkyls ($CrPh_3$, $MnEt_2$) and their subsequent reaction with CO.

Another interesting technique, useful for chromium and especially for manganese employs the benzophenone ketyl prepared thus:

$$Na + Ph_2C{=}O \rightarrow Ph_2C{-}ONa$$

$$MnCl_2 + 2Ph_2\dot{C}ONa \rightarrow (Ph_2\dot{C}{-}O)_2Mn$$

This then reacts directly with carbon monoxide under pressure to give decarbonyldimanganese in high yield:

$$2Mn(\dot{O}CPh_2)_2 + 10CO \rightarrow Mn_2(CO)_{10} + 4Ph_2C{=}O$$

The reaction probably proceeds via the salt $Mn^{2+}[Mn(CO)_5^-]_2$.

Isonitrile complexes are prepared by similar reductive techniques. With Cr^{II} disproportionation occurs and has been formulated as

$$Cr(OAc)_2 + 6RNC \rightarrow [Cr(CNR)_6](OAc)_2$$

$$3[Cr(CNR)_6](OAc)_2 \rightarrow Cr(CNR)_6 + 2[Cr(CNR)_6](OAc)_3$$

although neither the Cr^{II} nor the Cr^{III} isonitrile complexes have been isolated.

With MnI_2 and ReI_3, disproportionation is at the expense of the iodide in

$$2MnI_2 + 12RNC \rightarrow [Mn(CNR)_6]^+I^- + [Mn(CNR)_6]^+I_3^-$$

and $$ReI_3 + 6RNC \rightarrow [Re(CNR)_6]^+I_3^-$$

Magnesium metal has served as reductant in the preparation of the Mo and W derivatives.

e.g. $$MoCl_3 + RCN + Mg \rightarrow MgCl_2 + Mo(CNR)_6$$

occurs at 0° in acetic acid-ethanol solution. Hydrazine has also proved useful in a number of cases, e.g. in the conversion of Ni^{II} salts to $Ni(CNR)_4$.

In this category of reactions belongs also the preparation of di-arene chromium cations by Fischer and Hafner's process illustrated for benzene:

$$2C_6H_6 + CrCl_3 + Al + AlCl_3 \rightarrow (C_6H_6)_2Cr^+AlCl_4^-$$

Aluminium (or magnesium) metal functions in this process as reducing agent to convert Cr^{III} to Cr^I.

Many related preparations have been carried out by the same method.

e.g. $$ReCl_5 + ArH + Al + AlCl_3 \rightarrow [Re(ArH)_2]AlCl_4$$

or without reduction (cf. p. 50). To make possible the introduction of olefinic ligands, Fischer has introduced an equally valuable method employing ultraviolet irradiation together with isopropyl-magnesium bromide as reductant. Thus ferric chloride reacts with 1,3-cyclohexadiene in the presence of this Grignard reagent to give the neutral benzenecyclohexadiene-iron:

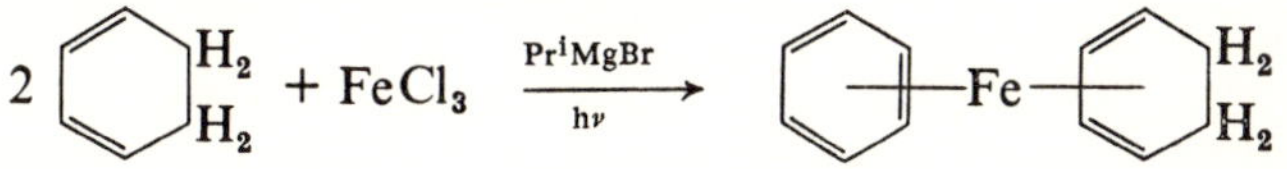

2-39

With mixtures of dienes and trienes similar reactions occur,

e.g.

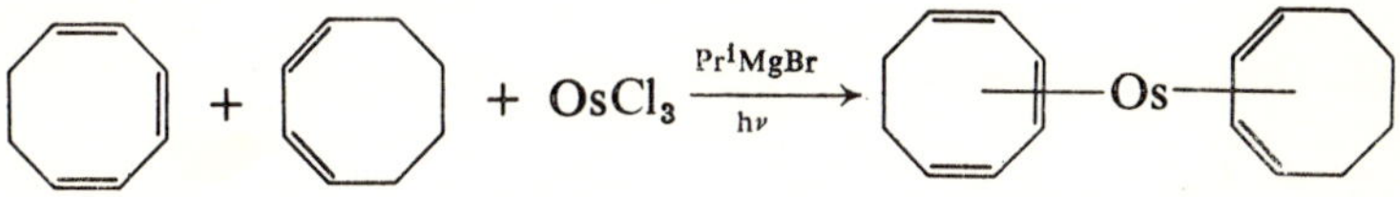

2-40

Cyclopentadienylchromium(III) chloride has been used similarly in

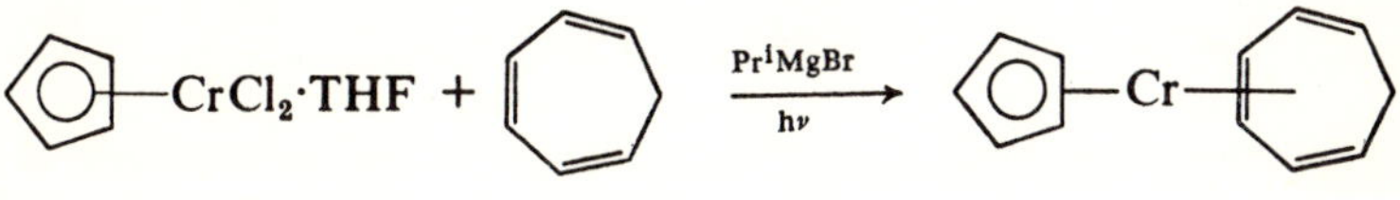

2-41

5   Decarboxylation

$RCO_2M \rightarrow RM + CO_2$ has been described as a method of preparation in only a few isolated instances. R must be a strongly electron-withdrawing group. With arsenic the reaction

$$Me_2AsOCOCF_3 \rightarrow Me_2AsCF_3 + CO_2$$

has been described and the analogous reaction of mercury carboxyl-ates $(RCO_2)_2Hg \rightarrow RCO_2HgR \rightarrow R_2Hg$ is known to occur with $R = CF_3$ or $2,4,6\text{-}(NO_2)_3C_6H_2$.

Several lead carboxylates are known to behave similarly

e.g. $Ph_3PbOCOCH_2CO_2Et \rightarrow Ph_3PbCH_2CO_2Et$

$Ph_3PbOCOC{\equiv}CPh \rightarrow Ph_3PbC{\equiv}CPh$

The efficiency of the reaction is illustrated by the high yield (80 %) obtained in the last example by 7 min heating to 155°.

Chapter 3

Properties and Reactions of the Alkyls and Aryls of Metals

Reactivity of alkyls is highest for those of the most electropositive elements, i.e. it increases with increasing ionic character. Thus we find that, in general, reactivity will increase with increasing atomic weight in a given group of the periodic table, e.g. from Li to Cs: however, clear reversal occurs in the three series Al—Tl, Ni—Pt and Zn—Hg. The latter case is most striking and well illustrated by the transition from the spontaneously inflammable zinc alkyls to the air-stable alkyls of mercury. The cadmium compounds are intermediate in character. Thus they are hydrolyzed rapidly by cold water whereas the mercury alkyls are inert.

COMPLEX FORMATION

Reactivity in solution may be modified considerably by complex formation with the solvent. Thus ethers form not only their well-known complexes with Grignard reagents but also complexes with dialkylmagnesiums (e.g. $Et_2Mg \cdot OEt_2$), with dialkylberyllium [e.g. $Ph_2Be \cdot (OEt_2)_2$], trialkylaluminium [e.g. $Me_3Al \cdot OEt_2$] and many others. In so doing the polymeric structures of the corresponding alkyls are broken down and the compounds thus made soluble, but generally less reactive. If more strongly basic donor solvents are used complex formation is stronger and reactivity lowered more markedly. The widespread modern use of tetrahydrofuran in organometallic chemistry is connected with its greater basicity and better complex-forming properties than ether. Tertiary amines generally lower reactivity more drastically.

Complexing between different organometallic reagents has been demonstrated chiefly with phenyllithium and other lithium and sodium alkyls. Phenyllithium is itself dimeric in strong dietyhl ether solutions, probably forming the ion-pair $Li[LiPh_2]$. From its mixture with PhNa one can isolate crystalline $Na[LiPh_2]$ which is intermediate in reactivity between PhLi and PhNa. Unlike the latter it does not decompose ether at all rapidly. Phenyllithium adds to Ph_2Be, Ph_2Mg, Ph_2Zn and Ph_2Cd giving the corresponding salts $Li[MPh_3]$ which are all less reactive than phenyllithium alone and increase in reactivity with decreasing stability in the series $LiCdPh_3$, $LiMgPh_3$, $LiZnPh_3$, $LiBePh_3$. In contrast to these triphenyl derivatives, methylzinc adds two equivalents of methyllithium in ether solution to give $Li_2[ZnMe_4]\cdot Et_2O$, but the higher alkyls again form $1:1$ adducts. The benzene soluble $Na[ZnEt_3]$ has been prepared by the reaction of sodium metal with an excess of diethylzinc (cf. p. 25): $2Na + 3Et_2Zn \rightarrow Zn + 2Na[ZnEt_3]$.

Similar complexes with group III metals may be exemplified by $Li[AlPh_4]$ which is rapidly hydrolyzed by water in contrast to Na- or $Li[BPh_4]$ which are familiar as reagents for the precipitation of potassium and other large univalent cations from aqueous solution. In Group V, pentaphenylantimony readily affords the hexacoordinate $Li[SbPh_6]$; this also is hydrolyzed by water though only to give back the penta-aryl:

$$Li[SbPh_6] + H_2O \rightarrow SbPh_5 + LiOH + C_6H_6$$

Examples of relatively stable adducts of lithium alkyls to alkyls of the transition metals, chromium and manganese have also been described. Thus $CrCl_3 + 6LiMe \xrightarrow[18°]{ether} Li_3[CrMe_6]$ isolated (45%) as a red crystalline dioxan adduct. Manganous iodide reacts according to: $3RLi + MnI_2 \rightarrow R_3MnLi$ with both alkyl and aryllithiums.

Complexing also occurs between metal alkyls and metal halides. Most studies of such interactions have been devoted to magnesium and to aluminium. In the former case the work has arisen from the long-standing problem as to the precise constitution of Grignard reagents. The suggestion of equilibria of the type

$$2RMgX \rightleftharpoons (RMgX)_2 \rightleftharpoons R_2Mg\cdot MgX \rightleftharpoons R_2Mg + MgX_2$$

was based originally on Schlenk's observation that most of the halide may be precipitated as the dioxan adduct of MgX_2 leaving chiefly R_2Mg in solution. The presence of all the above species is consistent with recent studies of molecular weights, conductivities and infrared spectra of these reagents, and with observations on exchange with radioactive MgX_2.

Similar exchange studies have also demonstrated an equilibrium between Et_2Zn and $ZnCl_2$ believed to involve a dimeric complex.

Trialkyls of aluminium tend to react with aluminium chloride to give the symmetrical dimers $R_2Al_2Cl_4$ and $R_4Al_2Cl_2$ according to the proportions used

e.g.
$$Ph_3Al + Al_2Cl_6 \rightarrow 3PhAlCl_2$$

$$4Et_3Al + Al_2Cl_6 \rightarrow 3Et_4Al_2Cl_2$$

The behaviour of gallium and of bismuth compounds is quite analogous:

e.g.
$$4Me_3Ga + Ga_2Cl_6 \rightarrow 3Me_4Ga_2Cl_2$$

$$Ph_3Bi + BiCl_3 \rightarrow Ph_2BiCl + PhBiCl_2$$

Similar reactions occur between the alkyl of one metal and the halide of another

e.g.
$$Me_4Sn + HgCl_2 \xrightarrow{EtOH} MeHgCl + Me_3SnCl \quad (70\%)$$

The so-called sesquihalides $R_3Al_2X_3$ behave as mixtures of $R_2Al_2Cl_4$ and $R_4Al_2Cl_2$, not as '$R_3Al \cdot AlX_3$'. Both the trialkyls and these mixed alkylaluminium halides form ionic complexes with alkali-metal halides. Fluorides afford both 1:1 and 1:2 complexes, e.g. $K[AlEt_3F]$ and $Na[Al_2Bu_6F]$: chlorides form stable complexes only with the halogen rich species, e.g. $2KCl + R_2Al_2Cl_4 \rightarrow 2K[AlRCl_3]$. Stability of such complexes increases with the size of the cation, i.e. $Cs > K > Na$.

REACTIONS WITH ACTIVE HYDROGEN COMPOUNDS

The general expression $RM + HX \rightarrow RH + MX$ may be taken to represent the behaviour of organometallic compounds with all acidic (active hydrogen) compounds. Apart from stronger acids it represents the reaction with water ($X = OH$), alcohols ($X = OR'$), ammonia ($X = NH_2$), amines ($X = NHR'$ or NR'_2) or amides ($X = NHCOR'$) and even with certain hydrocarbons (see pp. 31–35).

Some differences in reactivity to water have already been referred to. Being subject to minimal steric hindrance, reactions with water would provide the ideal way to compare reactivities of organo-metallic compounds, were they not too fast in most cases to be conveniently measured. Alkyls which are relatively inert to water include those of Ge, Sn, Pb, Sb and Bi apart from a variety of complex alkyls such as the transition metal alkyls described in section (B).(9) and (10) of Chapter 2.

Slow hydrolysis occurs when most of these derivatives are treated with acids, frequently stopping cleanly at an intermediate stage. Thus tetra-alkyls of tin may be smoothly converted with hydrogen halides to tri-alkyltin halides:

$$R_4Sn + HX \rightarrow R_3SnX + RH$$

Tri-alkyls of antimony resist even this degree of hydrolysis and reduce hydrogen chloride on heating in a sealed tube:

$$Me_3Sb + 2HCl \rightarrow Me_3SbCl_2 + H_2$$

Whereas trialkyls of thallium are rapidly hydrolyzed by water, the dialkylthallous hydroxide formed is completely stable, as are the salts $R_2Tl^+X^-$.

Other acids have been used to hydrolyze the more stable alkyls. For example, sulphurous acid (SO_2 in the presence of a little H_2O) converts lead alkyls smoothly to sulphites,

e.g. $$Et_4Pb + H_2SO_3 \rightarrow 2C_2H_6 + Et_2PbSO_3$$

Triphenylbismuth is attacked by mercaptans to give Ph_2BiSR.

Reaction of triphenyltin chloride with carboxylic acids affords the chlorodiphenyltin carboxylates $Ph_2SnCl(OCOR)$ in two stereo-isomeric forms. These appear to have the acyl groups bonded symmetrically and hence are 5-coordinate, probably having the trigonal bipyramidal structures with the two phenyl groups either *cis*- or *trans*-:

3-1

Most other alkyls react rapidly with water and the reaction may reach explosive force with the ionic alkyls.

Reactivity of other active hydrogen compounds relative to water is dependent on their relative acidity. Thus alcohols react more slowly: e.g. triethylindium is hydrolyzed by ethanol only on heating and loses only one ethyl group at $70°$.

$$Et_3In + EtOH \xrightarrow{70°} Et_2InOEt + C_2H_6$$

compare

$$Et_3In + H_2O \xrightarrow[temp.]{room} Et_2In(OH) + C_2H_6$$

$$Et_3In + 3H_2O \xrightarrow{90°} In(OH)_3 + 3C_2H_6$$

Ammonia and amines are less reactive still and although they interact rapidly with the alkali and alkaline earth metal derivatives,

e.g.
$$PhNHMe + EtMgBr \longrightarrow PhNMgBr + C_2H_6$$
$$\underset{Me}{|}$$

they form relatively stable complexes with, for example, gallium and even aluminium. Thus $Me_3Ga{\leftarrow}NH_3$ is a volatile crystalline solid which gives off methane only on heating:

$$Me_3Ga{\leftarrow}NH_3 \xrightarrow[-CH_4]{70°} [Me_2Ga{-}NH_2] \longrightarrow Me_2Ga \overset{NH_2}{\underset{NH_2}{\diamond}} GaMe_2 \qquad \textbf{3-2}$$

and $Me_3Al{\leftarrow}NHMe_2$ behaves similarly.

REACTIONS WITH HALOGENS

These occur more readily than the reactions with the corresponding halogen acids. Thus reaction of tetramethyltin with bromine: $Me_4Sn + Br_2 \rightarrow Me_3SnBr + MeBr$ is fast whereas the formation of the same product by $Me_4Sn + HBr \rightarrow Me_3SnBr + CH_4$ is slow.

The extent of replacement of alkyl by halogen can be adequately controlled with such stable alkyls by the amount of halogen used. Thus one mole of Br_2 (in CCl_4) converts bromodiethylgold, $(Et_2AuBr)_2$ to dibromoethylgold $(EtAuBr_2)_2$ and two moles of bromine convert tetraphenyl-germanium, Ph_4Ge, to the dibromo-diphenyl compound, Ph_2GeBr_2. Bonds between germanium or tin and aryl groups are broken more readily than those with alkyl groups

e.g.
$$Ph_2GeEt_2 + 2Br_2 \rightarrow Et_2GeBr_2 + 2PhBr$$

Trialkyls of antimony are not cleaved, but oxidized to the stable Sb^V derivatives:

e.g. $$Me_3Sb + Cl_2 \rightarrow Me_3SbCl_2$$

In the case of bismuth the triphenyl derivative behaves similarly: $Ph_3Bi + Br_2 \rightarrow Ph_3BiBr_2$, but the methyl derivative is less stable and suffers cleavage: $Me_3Bi + Br_2 \rightarrow Me_2BiBr + MeBr$. Cleavage of the pentaphenyl derivative Ph_5Bi yields first the salt $[Ph_4Bi^+]Br_3^-$, but this is unstable above $-30°$ and affords Ph_3Bi or Ph_3BiBr_2.

The cleavage of α,α'-bipyridyldimethylpalladium by trifluoromethyl iodide:

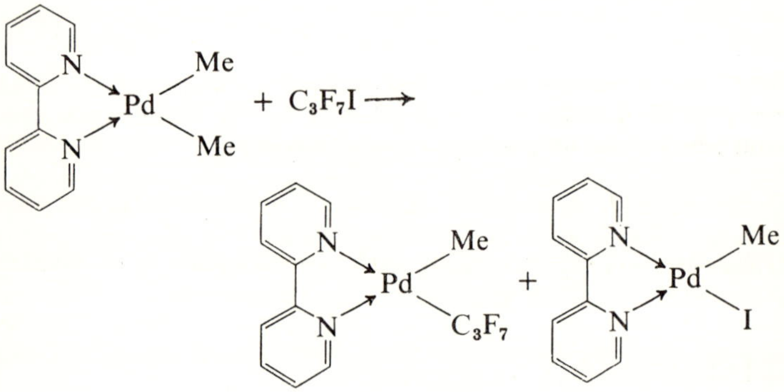

3-3

may be regarded as an example of analogous cleavage by a pseudo-halogen.

REACTIONS WITH ALKYL HALIDES
AND ACID HALIDES

The more reactive alkyls react with alkyl halides according to the well known Wurtz reaction: e.g. $RMgX + R'X \rightarrow RR' + MgX_2$. The reaction is considerably smoother and more rapid when $R'X$ is an allyl- or benzyl-type of halide than with simple alkyl halides.

Acid chlorides react according to a formally similar scheme. For carboxylic acid halides this is treated as a reaction of the carbonyl group (see p. 67).

Reaction with sulphonyl chlorides gives sulphones according to $RSO_2Cl + R'MgX \rightarrow RSO_2R'$ only in poor yields. The reaction is complicated by reduction to the sulphoxides, $RSOR'$, and even sulphides, RSR′, and in most cases by the competing process $RSO_2Cl + R'MgX \rightarrow RSO_2MgX + R'Cl$ which leads to the formation of sulphinic acids. The latter are frequently the main products.

Phosphorus halides (PCl_3, $POCl_3$, etc.) normally react in straightforward fashion with replacement of halogen by alkyl

e.g. $$PCl_3 + EtMgBr \rightarrow Et_3P \quad (70\%)$$

OR and NR_2 groups on phosphorus are replaced similarly,

e.g. $$Et_2NPOCl_2 + 2Bu^nMgBr \rightarrow (n-C_4H_9)_2PO(OH) \quad (82\%)$$

Silicon compounds behave similarly, both the halides and the alkoxides (orthosilicates) reacting smoothly. In the sequence $SiCl_4 + RMgX \dashrightarrow R_4Si$ it has been noted that replacement of the second chlorine atom occurs most readily and that of the fourth chlorine least readily. Reaction of $Si(OR)_4$ is generally more sluggish and readily arrested after replacement of a single OR group.

The more stable covalent alkyls are inert to both alkyl and acyl halides unless they can add these with increase in oxidation number. Thus

$$R_3Sb + MeI \rightarrow [R_3SbMe]I$$

and the alkyls of, for example, Sn^{II}, Pb^{II} and Tl^{I} behave similarly.

REACTIONS WITH OXYGEN

Reactivity towards oxygen runs broadly parallel to other, for example, hydrolytic, reactivity. The general mode of reaction may be represented by the sequence

$$R-M + O_2 \rightarrow R-O-O-M$$

$$R-O-O-M + R-M \rightarrow 2R-O-M$$

but is frequently accompanied by cleavage of the hydrocarbon group as a radical. Thus air oxidation of a benzene solution of triphenylindium gives not only the expected phenol, but also diphenyl. Aryls in general appear to react less smoothly than alkyls. Thus whereas air oxidation of alkyl Grignard reagents is a good source of alcohols,

$$2RMgX + O_2 \rightarrow 2ROMgX \xrightarrow{H_2O} 2ROH + MgX_2 + Mg(OH)_2$$

arylmagnesium halides give only poor yields of phenols by this procedure. The oxidation of trialkyls of aluminium has been studied in detail by Ziegler in connection with his controlled ethylene polymerization, as it provides a commercially attractive source of alcohols of suitable chain length for e.g. detergent manufacture.

The peroxy intermediates may be isolable, as for example in the case of Me_2Cd and Et_2Cd which yield MeCdOOMe and $Cd(OOEt)_2$ respectively.

REACTIONS WITH CARBONYL COMPOUNDS

These reactions account for by far the most common laboratory uses of organometallic reagents. The reactions of Grignard reagents with carbon dioxide, aldehydes and ketones, esters, amides and acid chlorides are familiar to all students of chemistry and need be summarized here only by a few typical equations:

$$RMgX + CO_2 \longrightarrow R\overset{\overset{\textstyle O}{\|}}{C}-OMgX \xrightarrow{HX} RCOOH + MgX_2$$

$$RMgX + R'COR'' \longrightarrow RR'R''COMgX \xrightarrow{HX} RR'R''COH + MgX_2$$

$$RMgX + R'CO_2Et \longrightarrow RR'C\overset{\displaystyle OEt}{\underset{\displaystyle OMgX}{\big\langle}} \xrightarrow{-EtOMgX}$$

$$RR'C{=}O \xrightarrow{RMgX} R_2R'COMgX \xrightarrow{HX} R_2R'COH$$

$$2RMgX + R'CONH_2 \longrightarrow RR'C\overset{\displaystyle OMgX}{\underset{\displaystyle NHMgX}{\big\langle}} \xrightarrow{3HX}$$

$$RR'C{=}O + 2MgX_2 + NH_4X$$

3·4

The last (amide) case contrasts with the ester case in that ketone formation only occurs on hydrolysis so that reaction cannot go beyond this stage. The first product, however, is the rather unreactive R'CONHMgX and reaction is therefore frequently incomplete. The situation is similar to that with free acids which give the magnesium salts $RCOOMgX$ and react no further. The more reactive alkyllithiums however do react with the lithium salts so that the sequence

$$RCOOH + R'Li \rightarrow R'H + RCOOLi \xrightarrow{R'Li} RR'C(OLi)_2 \xrightarrow{H_2O}$$
$$RR'C{=}O + 2LiOH$$

provides generally a better route to ketones than the above amide method. Even better perhaps is the dialkylcadmium method.

$$2RMgX + CdX_2 \rightarrow R_2Cd + MgX_2$$
$$R_2Cd + 2R'COCl \rightarrow 2R'COR + CdCl_2$$

This depends on the rapid reaction of the cadmium compounds with acid chlorides (or anhydrides), but only very slow reaction with ketones. The presence of magnesium halides from the first step is essential as pure (distilled) dialkylcadmiums have little reactivity towards acyl halides.

Organozinc compounds can be used in the same way, but are less selective. More frequent use is made of the ability of alkylzinc reagents to react much faster with keto than with ester groups. This is the basis of the Reformatski reaction:

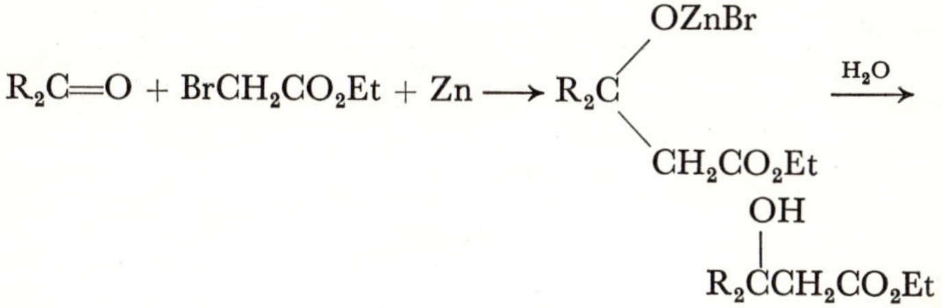

$$R_2C{=}O + BrCH_2CO_2Et + Zn \longrightarrow R_2C \overset{OZnBr}{\underset{CH_2CO_2Et}{<}} \xrightarrow{H_2O}$$

$$\underset{R_2CCH_2CO_2Et}{\overset{OH}{|}}$$

3-5

and its extensions

e.g. $R_2C{=}O + BrCH_2{-}CH{=}CH{-}CO_2Et + Zn \longrightarrow$

$$R_2C \overset{OZnBr}{\underset{CH_2CH=CHCO_2Et}{<}} \xrightarrow{H_2O} R_2C\overset{OH}{\underset{|}{}}CH_2CH{=}CHCO_2Et$$

$$R_2C{=}O + BrCH_2C{\equiv}CH + Zn \longrightarrow R_2\overset{OZnBr}{\underset{|}{C}}{-}CH_2C{\equiv}CH \xrightarrow{H_2O}$$
$$R_2C(OH)CH_2C{\equiv}CH$$

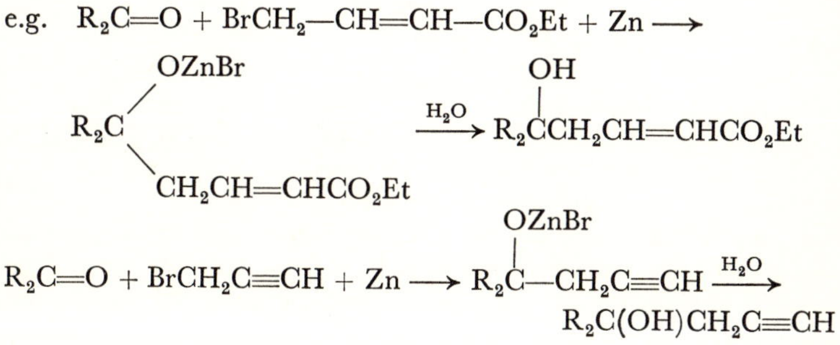

3-6

In all these cases the first stage must be formation of the organozinc bromide, e.g. $BrZnCH_2CO_2Et$, but this has to be carried out in the presence of the carbonyl component (aldehyde or ketone) to minimize reaction with the ester (or $—C\equiv CH$) group.

Various deviations from normal attack by Grignard reagents on carbonyl groups must be noted. Perhaps the commonest, enolization, leads in its simplest form only to incompleteness of reaction. Thus when α-tetralone is treated with methylmagnesium halide, a 57% yield of the expected addition product is accompanied by 17% enolization. The latter may be estimated both from the amount of ketone recovered and from the amount of methane evolved. Such formation of methane from readily enolizable ketones will lead to high or false positive values in active hydrogen determinations by the Zerewitinoff method. As a further consequence of enolization, aldol or Claisen type condensations have frequently been observed.

Steric hindrance to attack on the carbonyl group will enhance the degree of enolization. Thus, whereas simple Grignards add normally to pinacolone, $MeCOCMe_3$, they cause predominant enolization of the more hindered 3,3-diethylpentan-2-one, $MeCOCEt_3$. As a corollary ketones will become end-products in the reaction of Grignard reagents with hindered acid chlorides. Thus, when mesitoyl chloride ($X = CH_3$) or other 2,6-disubstituted benzoyl chlorides are added to excess of methylmagnesium bromide, the acetyl derivatives result:

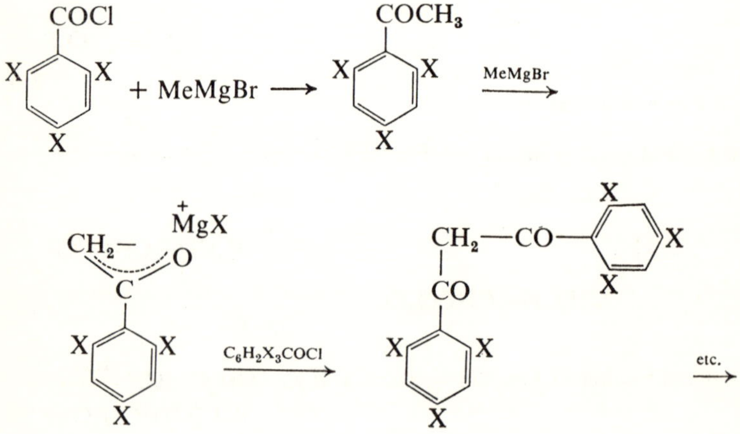

3·7

However, excess acid chloride can now react further by C-acylation of the enolate to give the di- or even triketone as shown. Steric hindrance can also lead to 1,4-addition in such aromatic ketones as mesityl-α-napthyl ketone:

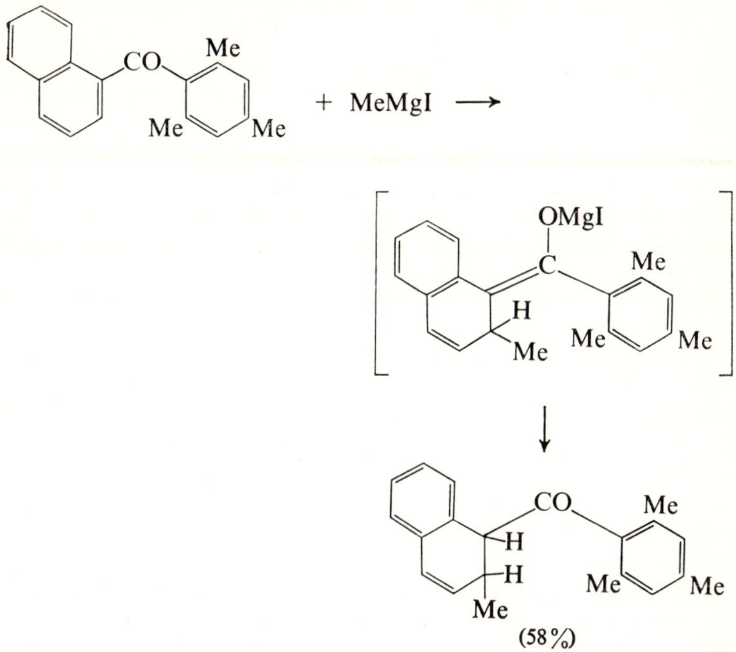

(58%)

3-8

Organolithium and sodium derivatives are much less susceptible to such steric influences than Grignard reagents. Thus isopropyl-lithium (but not the corresponding Grignard reagent) adds normally to di-isopropyl ketone:

$$Pr_2^iC{=}O + Pr^iLi \rightarrow Pr_3^iCOLi$$

But even lithium fails in the tert.-butyl series, where tert.-butyl-sodium still gives a low yield of the expected carbinol with di-tert.-butyl ketone.

Such differences between different metal alkyls have not been widely explored, but another well known example is the behaviour with αβ-unsaturated carbonyl compounds. The lithium alkyls can usually be relied upon to add 1,2-, i.e., to the carbonyl carbon. They must be preferred where this mode of addition is desired since

Grignard reagents are prone to add 1,4. The product ratio in the following example is rather typical:

$$EtCOCH{=}CHMe + EtMgX \rightarrow EtCOCH_2CHMeEt +$$

70%

$$Et_2C(OH)CH{=}CHMe$$

30%

Kharasch and his coworkers have demonstrated the importance of the purity of the magnesium and attributed the effect of certain metal salts to the promotion of free radical reactions. Thus, isophorone (A) reacted under 'ordinary conditions' to nearly equal extent by 1,2- and 1,4 addition:

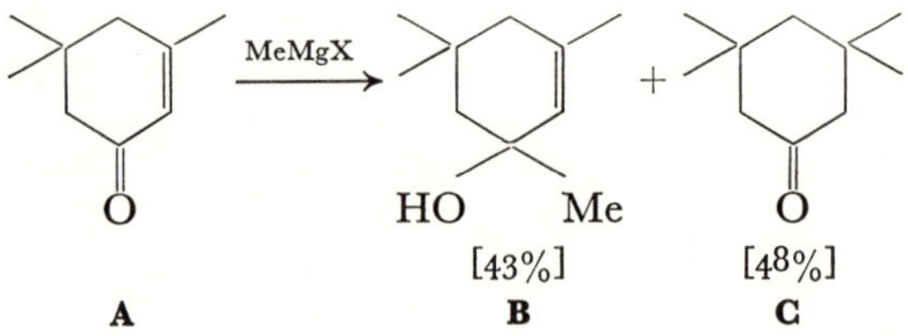

[43%] [48%]

A   B   C   3·9

When highly purified magnesium was used in preparing the Grignard reagent only the carbinol (B) (91 %) was obtained, but addition of 1 mole % of cuprous chloride reduced its yield to 7% and resulted mainly in 1,4-addition to give the ketone (C) (82·5 %). Although the mechanistic difference cannot be regarded as settled, the addition of copper or cobalt chloride is of general utility when the 1,4 adduct from an unsaturated ketone is desired.

Conjugate (1,4) addition is rare with unsaturated aldehydes. It has been observed with some acid chlorides: e.g. cinnamoyl chloride, PhCH=CHCOCl, with phenylmagnesium bromide gives products derived from the intermediate ketene, Ph₂CH—CH=C=O. It becomes predominant with unsaturated esters,

e.g. $Me_2C{=}C(CO_2Et)_2 + MeMgI \rightarrow Me_3CCH(CO_2Et)_2$

Finally reduction must be mentioned as a side reaction which depends chiefly on the structure of the Grignard reagent. e.g. $Ph_2C{=}O + Me_2CH{-}CH_2MgBr \rightarrow Ph_2CHOH + Me_2C{=}CH_2$. It involves the transfer of the β-hydrogen of the Grignard reagent, possibly through a quasi-6-membered ring intermediate of the type:

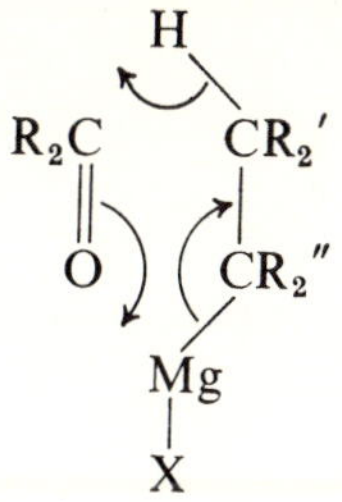

$$
\begin{array}{c}
\text{H} \\
\overset{\curvearrowleft}{\quad}\diagdown \\
R_2C \qquad CR_2{}' \\
\Vert \qquad | \\
O \;)\;(\; CR_2{}'' \\
\diagdown \\
\overset{|}{\underset{|}{Mg}} \\
X
\end{array}
$$

3-10

Thus the most effective reducing agents are Grignards which have a tertiary β-hydrogen. Secondary β-hydrogens (as for example in cyclohexylmagnesium bromide) are effective, but less so. Primary hydrogens, even in tert.-butylmagnesium bromide, Me_3CMgBr, with nine such atoms do not lead to reduction in comparable cases.

REACTIONS WITH MULTIPLY-BONDED NITROGEN COMPOUNDS

Carbon nitrogen triple ($-C\equiv N$) and double $\left(\diagup\overset{\diagdown}{C}=N\right)$ bonds would be expected to behave similarly to carbonyl groups but the imines are much less reactive than ketones and hence more prone to side-reactions of the types discussed above. Thus only aldimines add Grignard reagents smoothly at the imine carbon atom giving secondary amines:

$$RCH{=}NR' + R''MgX \rightarrow RR''CH{-}NR'MgX \xrightarrow{H_2O} RR''CHNHR'$$

Ketimines, if aliphatic, give enamines (equivalent to enolization in the carbonyl case):

e.g. $Me_2C{=}NPh + EtMgBr \rightarrow$

$$CH_2{=}CMe{-}NPhMgBr \xrightarrow{H_2O} CH_2{=}CMe{-}NHPh$$

and the fully aromatic ketimines are unreactive but add 1,4- on heating:

e.g. $Ph_2C{=}NPh + PhMgBr \xrightarrow{70°} Ph{-}CH{-}NHPh$

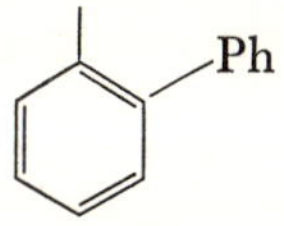

with structure showing benzene ring bearing —Ph substituent below

A special case of addition to C=N is the smooth addition of alkyllithium to pyridine and related bases:

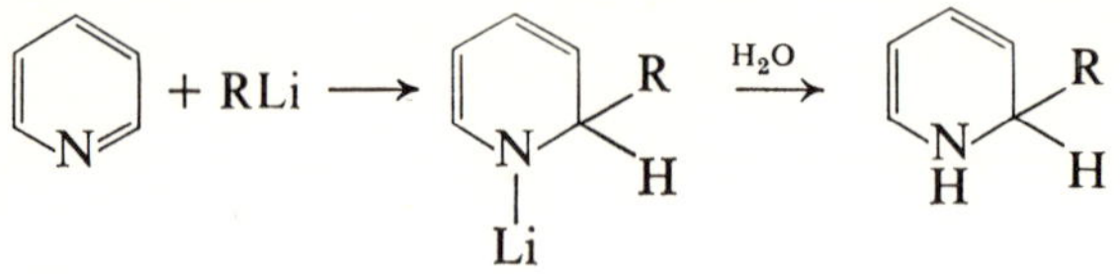

$$\text{3-11}$$

Addition at the α-position (1,2-addition) is the general rule for such heterocycles, but Grignard reagents again appear to have more tendency to cause conjugate (1,4-) additions than alkyllithiums. Thus benzylmagnesium chloride has been reported to add to the γ-(4-) position of both pyridine and 2-methoxylepidine:

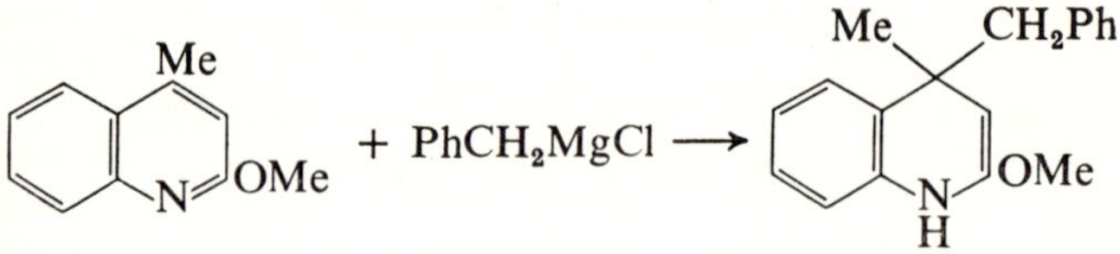

$$\text{3-12}$$

Nitriles in general react smoothly with Grignard reagents to give imines, or (after hydrolysis) the corresponding ketones:

$$RC{\equiv}N + R'MgX \rightarrow RR'C{=}NMgX \xrightarrow{H_2O}$$
$$[RR'C{=}NH] \rightarrow RR'C{=}O$$

The reaction has been used to compare reactivities of different Grignard reagents. Thus relative reactivities towards benzonitrile establish inter alia the order:

$$p\text{-MeC}_6H_4 > Ph > Et > i\text{-Pr} > t\text{-Bu}$$

Only in rare cases have the intermediate iminemagnesium halides been found to add a second mole of Grignard reagent to give an amine as end-product: e.g. with alkoxyacetonitriles:

$$EtOCH_2CN + 2PrMgBr \longrightarrow [EtOCH_2CPr_2N(MgBr)_2]$$
$$\downarrow H_2O$$
$$EtOCH_2CPr_2NH_2 \quad (99\%)$$

On the other hand the intermediate lithio-imines formed when alkyllithiums are used in place of Grignard reagents are sufficiently reactive so that they may add to a second mole of nitrile:

e.g. $PhC{\equiv}N + MeLi \longrightarrow PhMeC{=}NLi \xrightarrow{PhC{\equiv}N}$

$PhMeC{=}N{-}CPh{=}NLi \xrightarrow{PhCN}$

$PhMeC{=}N{-}CPh{=}N{-}CPh{=}NLi \longrightarrow$

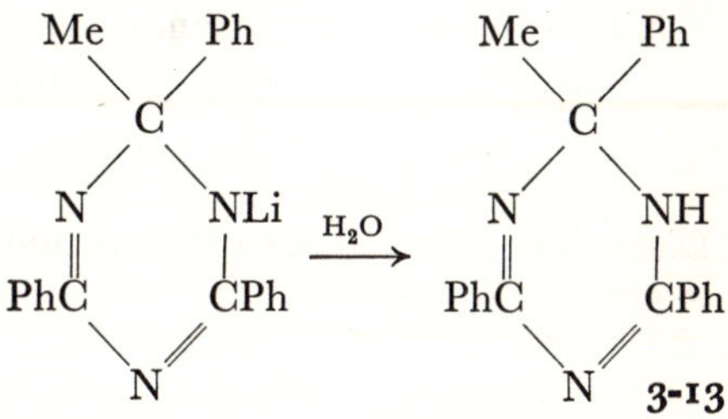

3-13

The final cyclic product rearranges on heating with loss of ammonia to give 2,4,6-triphenylpyrimidine.

Alternatively N—Li compounds can metalate methylene groups adjacent to cyano-groups. This is made use of in the Ziegler modification of the Thorpe reaction in which lithiomethylaniline is used to effect cyclization of a dinitrile, e.g. $NC(CH_2)_nCH_2CN$. The first intermediate is undoubtedly the metalation product $NC(CH_2)_nCHLiCN$ which then undergoes normal alkyllithium to nitrile addition:

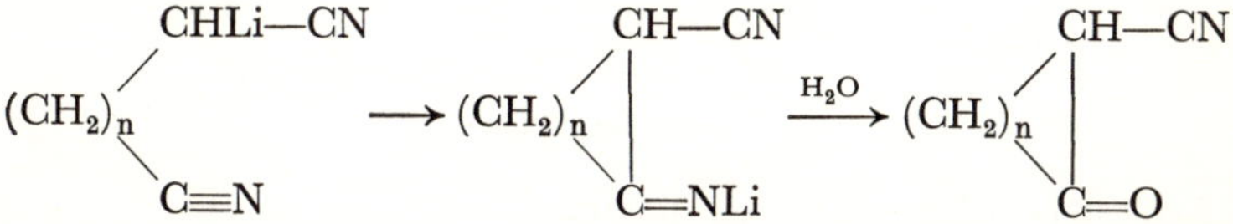

3-14

In cases where removal of CN groups as cyanide ion is facilitated by electron-donating groups, substitution of cyanide by alkyl may compete with the normal addition. Thus α-dialkylamino nitriles react at least in part by the pathway:

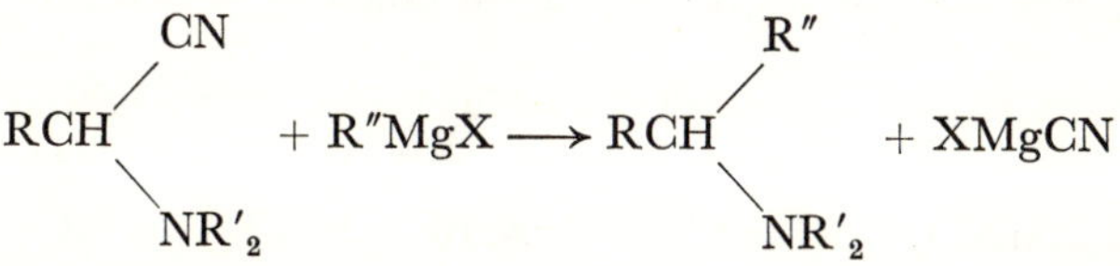

3-15

Related to this is the reaction of Grignard reagents with cyanogen

$$RMgX + NC\text{---}CN \rightarrow RCN + XMgCN$$

Further reaction of the nitrile formed severely limits the synthetic usefulness of this process.

Systems containing N=N and N=O bonds have been studied much less extensively, but the following examples are probably typical.

Nitrous oxide with phenyllithium gives a mixture of products including benzene diazotate and azobenzene:

$$PhLi + N\equiv\overset{+}{N}\text{---}\overset{-}{O} \rightarrow PhN\text{=}N\text{---}OLi + PhN\text{=}NPh$$

Diazonium salts and diazoalkanes add Grignard reagents similarly to give azo compounds or the tautomeric hydrazones:

$$RMgX + \overset{-}{X}\, N\equiv\overset{+}{N}Ar \longrightarrow RN\text{=}NAr + MgX_2$$

$$RMgX + N\equiv\overset{+}{N}\text{---}\overset{-}{C}HR' \longrightarrow \underset{MgX}{\underbrace{RN\text{=}NCHR'}}\text{---}\Big\langle \quad \begin{matrix} RNH\text{---}N\text{=}CHR' \\ \Big\updownarrow H^+ \\ RN\text{=}N\text{---}CH_2R' \end{matrix}$$

$$\textbf{3-16}$$

but methyllithium metalates diazomethane:

$$CH_2N_2 + MeLi \longrightarrow HCN_2Li$$

$$OH^- \diagdown \qquad \diagup H_2O$$

$$HC\equiv\overset{+}{N}\text{---}\overset{-}{N}H \leftrightarrow H\overset{-}{C}\text{=}\overset{+}{N}\text{=}NH$$

isodiazomethane

Azides give diazo-amino compounds

e.g. $PhN_3 + PhCH_2MgCl \rightarrow PhN\text{=}NNHCH_2Ph$

Reactions of nitroso- and nitro-compounds are frequently complicated, addition of Grignard reagent at the nitrogen atom being accompanied or followed by reduction:

$$RN\text{=}O + R'MgX \longrightarrow RR'NOMgX \xrightarrow{H_2O} RR'NOH$$

$$\diagdown RMgX$$

$$RR'NH$$

$$ArNO_2 + RMgX \longrightarrow ArNHR + ROH + R\text{---}R \qquad \textbf{3-17}$$

REACTIONS WITH ETHERS

Of most preparative use is the reaction with epoxides and to a lesser extent oxetanes. With ethylene or trimethylene oxide the product is a primary alcohol:

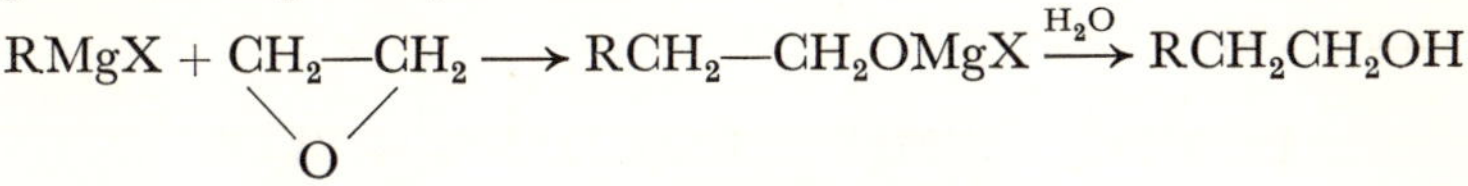

$$RMgX + CH_2\!\!-\!\!CH_2 \longrightarrow RCH_2\!\!-\!\!CH_2OMgX \xrightarrow{H_2O} RCH_2CH_2OH$$
$$\underset{O}{\diagdown\diagup}$$

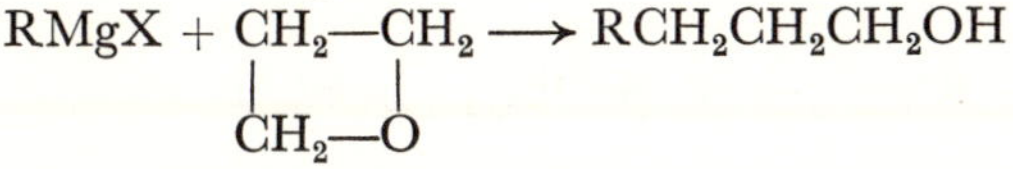

$$RMgX + CH_2\!\!-\!\!CH_2 \longrightarrow RCH_2CH_2CH_2OH$$
$$\;\;\;\;\;\;\;\;\;\;\;\;\;\; | \quad\quad |$$
$$\;\;\;\;\;\;\;\;\;\;\;\;\;\; CH_2\!\!-\!\!O \hspace{6cm} \textbf{3-18}$$

With epoxides of higher olefins the principal direction is that giving the most highly α-substituted alcohols,
e.g.

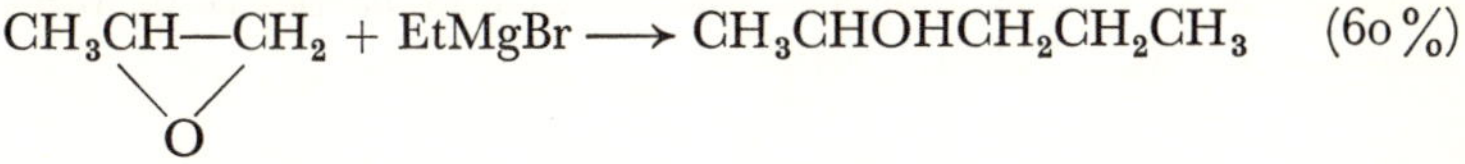

$$CH_3CH\!\!-\!\!CH_2 + EtMgBr \longrightarrow CH_3CHOHCH_2CH_2CH_3 \quad (60\%)$$
$$\underset{O}{\diagdown\diagup}$$

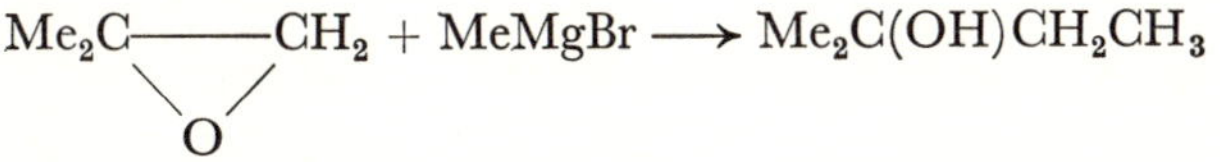

$$Me_2C\!\!-\!\!\!-\!\!\!-\!\!CH_2 + MeMgBr \longrightarrow Me_2C(OH)CH_2CH_3$$
$$\underset{O}{\diagdown\;\;\diagup}$$
$$\hspace{8cm} \textbf{3-19}$$

Reaction may be complicated by ring opening of the epoxide prior to its reaction with the Grignard reagent. This is caused by the Lewis acidity of the magnesium halide present. Thus in the above case:

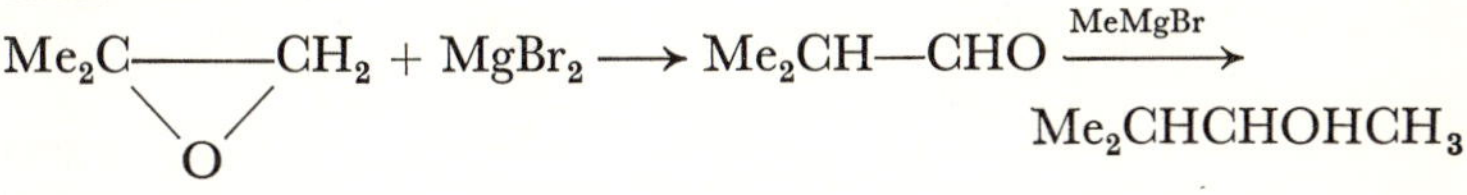

$$Me_2C\!\!-\!\!\!-\!\!\!-\!\!CH_2 + MgBr_2 \longrightarrow Me_2CH\!\!-\!\!CHO \xrightarrow{MeMgBr}$$
$$\underset{O}{\diagdown\;\;\diagup}$$
$$\hspace{7cm} Me_2CHCHOHCH_3$$

The ratio of the two alcohols formed in this system depends on the precise reaction conditions. The use of lithium alkyls while largely avoiding this difficulty may result in metalation as an alternative side reaction. Thus cyclohexene oxide reacts according to the scheme:

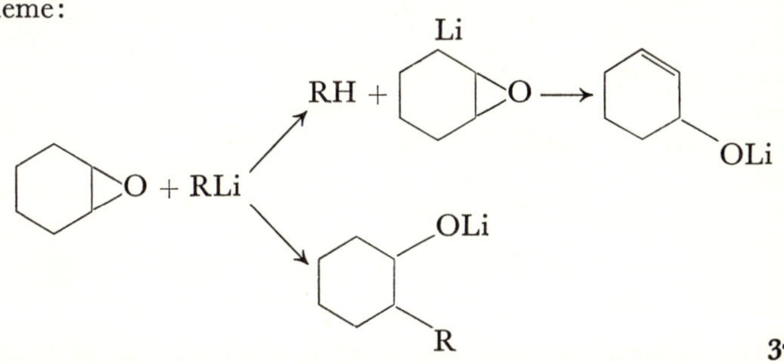

$$\hspace{11cm} \textbf{3-20}$$

This side-reaction is analogous to the cleavage of simple ethers discussed in connection with the preparation of organolithium reagents (see Chapter 1, Section B.3).

The much greater reactivity of *ortho* esters than of ketals makes possible their use for the preparation of ketones and especially aldehydes:

$$RC(OEt)_3 + R'MgX \rightarrow RC(OEt)_2R' \xrightarrow{H^+} RCOR'$$

$$HC(OEt)_3 + RMgX \rightarrow RCH(OEt)_2 \xrightarrow{H^+} RCH{=}O$$

SOME UNUSUAL MODES OF REACTION

Benzylic Grignard reagents sometimes add carbonyl or other compounds at an 'allylic' position

e.g.

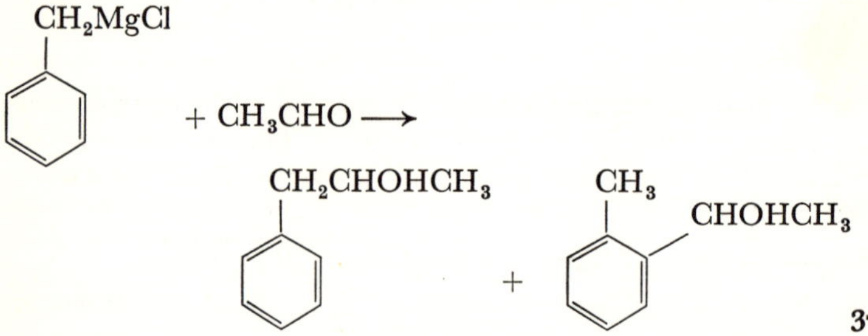

3-21

This can be represented mechanistically as follows:

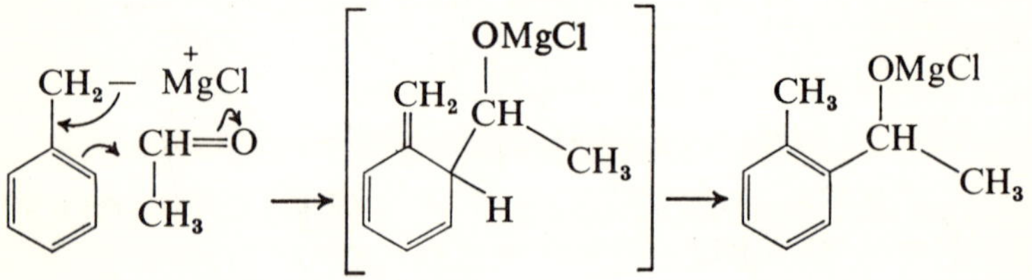

3-22

With 2,6-substituted benzyl Grignard reagents, formation of the methylene-dihydrobenzene derivative is assisted by relief of steric compression and becomes the predominant route:

e.g.

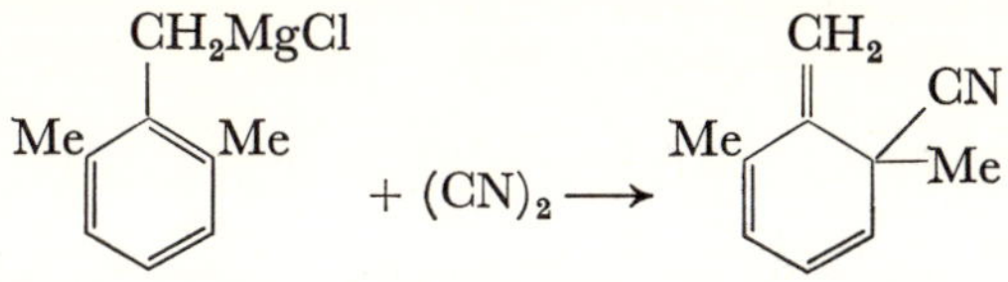

3-23

Although not strictly involving an organometallic reagent the reaction of N-pyrrolylmagnesium halides and similar reagents with alkyl halides may be compared with the above cases:

e.g.

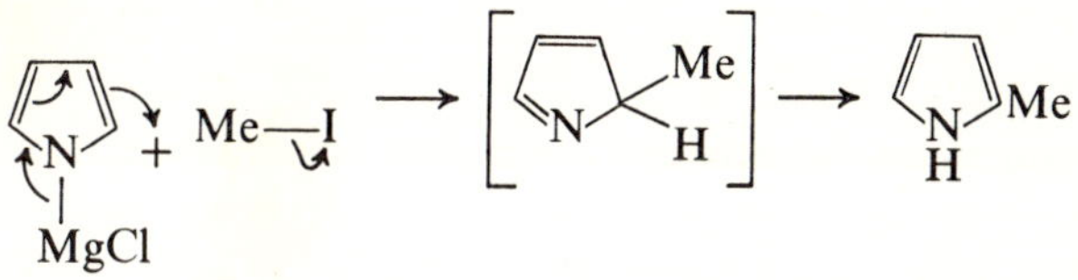

3-24

REACTIONS NOT INVOLVING THE HYDROCARBON LIGAND

When the metal–carbon bond is stable enough, a wide variety of displacements of other ligands are possible involving halide or any other groups attached to the metal. Those which lead to the formation of new metal carbon bonds have been included in Chapter 2 (Section B.9).

Groups IV and V provide the best examples of organometal halides of sufficient stability to undergo reactions reminiscent of other covalent halides, notably halocarbons. Thus the analogues in organometallic systems of the Wurtz reaction are provided by such examples as

$$Ph_3PbI + 2Na \rightarrow Ph_3PbNa + NaI$$

$$Ph_3PbNa + Ph_3PbI \rightarrow Ph_3Pb{-}PbPh_3 + NaI$$

Corresponding reactions occur with all trialkyllead halides and with similar derivatives of germanium and tin. But in contrast to the Wurtz reaction the cleavage of the product $R_3M{-}MR_3 + 2Na \rightarrow 2R_3MNa$ occurs in all these cases (not only the above example which might be compared with the special case of hexaphenyl-ethane). Hence the formation of either R_3MNa or $R_3M{-}MR_3$ can be controlled completely by the ratio of sodium to halide.

Acidification of such sodio-derivatives yields the corresponding germanes and stannanes,

e.g. $R_3SnNa + N\overset{+}{H}_4\overset{-}{Cl} \rightarrow R_3SnH + NaCl + NH_3$

but triphenylplumbylsodium yields the ammonium salt $Ph_3Pb^-NH_4{}^+$ and the rather unstable plumbanes have only been obtained by direct reduction of the halides with suitable hydrides,

e.g. $Me_3PbCl + KBH_4 \xrightarrow{\text{liq. NH}_3} [Me_3PbBH_4] \rightarrow$
$$Me_3PbH + BH_3NH_3$$

This method is of general utility, being applicable, for example, to the formation of stibines:

e.g. $Me_2SbBr + Li[B(OMe)_3H] \rightarrow Me_3SbH + LiBr + B(OMe)_3$

and to the reduction of di- and trihalides

$$Bu_2PbCl_2 + LiAlH_4 \rightarrow Bu_2PbH_2$$
$$MeSnCl_3 + LiAlH_4 \rightarrow MeSnH_3$$

The trihydrides of Ge and Sn have also been obtained from germane and stannane by the sequence

$$MH_4 + Na \xrightarrow{\text{liq. NH}_3} MH_3Na \xrightarrow{\text{RI}} RMH_3$$

Although the trialkylgermyllithium and -sodium react in most respects like organo–lithium and sodium reagents (cf. p. 45) the tin analogues frequently do not. Thus whereas water converts Ph_3GeNa to Ph_3GeH as expected, Ph_3SnLi affords chiefly the distannane $Ph_3SnSnPh_3$. With benzophenone, the germyl compound again behaves 'normally':

$$Ph_3GeLi + Ph_2C{=}O \rightarrow Ph_3GeC(OH)Ph_2$$

but the stannyl compound undergoes oxidation giving the benzophenone lithium ketyl and ultimately benzhydrol and the distannane:

$$2Ph_3SnLi + 2Ph_2C{=}O \rightarrow Sn_2Ph_6 + 2Ph_2C{-}OLi$$

Disodio-compounds of tin are also known, e.g. Me_2SnNa_2, and these may be obtained by addition of excess of sodium to dialkyltin dihalides in liquid ammonia. Polymeric dialkyltin is an intermediate:

e.g. $$nMe_2SnBr_2 + 2nNa \rightarrow (Me_2Sn)_n + 2nNaBr$$

$$(Me_2Sn)_n + 2nNa \rightarrow 2nMe_2SnNa_2$$

The disodio-compounds are obtained as deep red solutions which undergo the expected alkylation reactions.

In group V only the unstable deep red solutions of Ph_2BiNa and no alkyl analogues have been described.

The cleavage of symmetrical metal–metal bonds occurs readily, not only with alkali metals and other strong reducing agents, but also under oxidizing conditions. The antimony derivatives are less stable than the group IV compounds. Thus not only the alkyl derivatives (Me_4Sb_2 is spontaneously inflammable) but also the tetra–aryl compounds react readily with oxygen:

$$Ph_2SbSbPh_2 + O_2 \rightarrow Ph_2Sb—O—O—SbPh_2$$

Hexaphenyldilead is oxidized by neutral permanganate (in acetone) to give triphenyllead hydroxide:

$$Ph_3Pb—PbPh_3 + KMnO_4 + H_2O \rightarrow Ph_3PbOH$$

All such compounds react with halogens but the reaction of the hexaphenyldistannane with iodine:

$$Ph_3Sn—SnPh_3 + I_2 \rightarrow 2Ph_3SnI$$

is relatively slow and the germanium analogue is even less reactive.

The hydrides add to carbon–carbon bonds (cf. p. 21) and other multiple bonds:

e.g. $$Et_3SnH + Ph—N{=}C{=}O \rightarrow Et_3SnN(Ph)CHO$$

They are useful reducing agents capable, e.g. of reducing acid chlorides to aldehydes and ketones to alcohols. Such reactions have been studied most with the stannanes.

e.g. $$Ph_3SnH + PhCOCl \rightarrow PhCHO + Ph_3SnCl$$

$$Ph_2SnH_2 + PhCH{=}CHCHO \rightarrow Ph_2Sn + PhCh{=}CHCH_2OH$$

The hydrides decompose more or less readily to give hydrogen or alkanes. Thus Ph_2SnH_2 decomposes rather readily to $Ph_2Sn + H_2$; monohydrides R_3SnH are more stable, but the lead compound

Me_3PbH decomposes above $-100°$ to CH_4 (and probably Me_3Pb—
$PbMe_2H$) and the antimony derivative Me_2SbH disproportionates
at room temperature according to

$$2Me_2SbH \rightarrow Me_2Sb—SbMe_2 + H_2$$

When the dihydrides interact with the corresponding dihalides,
hydride-halides are formed, at least in the tin series:

e.g. $Bu_2SnH_2 + Bu_2SnCl_2 \xrightarrow[\text{temp.}]{\text{room}} 2Bu_2SnHCl$

With beryllium alkyls, tin hydride complexes exchange hydrogen
for alkyl

e.g. $Me_2Be + Et_3SnH \rightarrow MeBeH + Et_3SnMe$

Nucleophilic displacements of halogens and other groups are
possible in a wide variety of organometallic complexes. Thus the
fluoro-aluminium compounds, R_2AlF, are obtained from the
corresponding chlorides by heating with NaF in hydrocarbon
solvents. The ionic dialkylthallic halides, $R_2Tl^+X^-$, are sufficiently
stable in water to be convertible with silver oxide to the corresponding hydroxides, R_2TlOH. These water soluble compounds are
at least partially ionized and strongly basic. Treatment of the
same halides with alkoxides gives the dimeric alkoxides $(R_2TlOR')_2$.

The hydrolysis of organogermyl halides like that of the corresponding silanes gives oxides rather than hydroxides:

e.g. $2Et_3GeBr + 2NaOH \rightarrow (Et_3Ge)_2O + 2NaBr + H_2O$

$Ph_2GeBr_2 + 2NaOH \rightarrow (Ph_2GeO)_n$

The diphenylgermanium oxide is a polymer, the corresponding
alkyls are usually cyclic tetramers or trimers

e.g.

3·25

The corresponding tin and lead compounds are stable as the
hydroxides. Thus Me_3SnOH, Et_3PbOH, $Et_2Pb(OH)_2$ and similar
compounds are all obtained from the corresponding halides with
dilute aqueous alkali.

The dialkyltin dihalides yield polymeric oxides, e.g. $(Et_2SnO)_n$, and the trialkyltin oxides, e.g. $(Et_3Sn)_2O$, are readily and reversibly formed from the corresponding hydroxides by loss of water.

Alkylmercuric halides yield the related weakly basic hydroxides, RHgOH, and antimony forms both mono- and dialkylantimony oxides, e.g. $(Me_2Sb)_2O$ and $(PhSbO)_n$.

Such oxides and hydroxides can be 'esterified'.

e.g. $$(R_3Ge)_2O + Ac_2O \rightarrow 2R_3GeOAc$$

$$Et_3SnOH + HOAc \rightarrow Et_3SnOAc$$

Examples of analogous sulphides are known and may be prepared either from the halides:

e.g. $$Ph_3PbCl + PrSH + Et_3N \xrightarrow[\substack{room \\ temp.}]{C_6H_6} Ph_3PbSPr + Et_3NHCl \atop [80\%]$$

or from the hydroxides or oxides,

e.g. $$(R_3Sn)_2O + 2R'SH \rightarrow 2R_3SnSR' + H_2O$$

$$Et_3PbOH + EtSH \rightarrow Et_3PbSEt + H_2O$$

Triphenyltin hydroxide reacts similarly with hydrogen cyanide:

$$Ph_3SnOH + HCN \rightarrow Ph_3SnCN + H_2O$$

and the insoluble lead analogue Ph_3PbCN precipitates even when KCN is used in the corresponding reaction.

With stronger acids these oxides and hydroxides yield largely ionic di- and trialkyltin salts. Several perchlorates, fluoroborates, sulphates and nitrates have been characterized:

e.g. $$Me_2SnO + HNO_3 \rightarrow Me_2Sn^{2+}(NO_3^-)_2$$

Ammonolysis with ammonia or amines follows a course closely similar to the above hydrolyses at least for Ge and Sn giving the appropriate amino and imino derivatives or their salts. Typical examples are:

$$Me_3SnBr + NH_3 \rightarrow [Me_3SnNH_3]^+Br^-$$

$$2Et_3GeBr + 3NH_3 \text{ (liq.)} \rightarrow (Et_3Ge)_2NH + 2NH_4Br$$

A more complex example is the reaction of dimethylgold iodide with ethylene diamine to give either mono- or dimeric products, the latter formed by cleavage only of the iodide bridges, but the former involving displacement of iodide out of the coordination sphere:

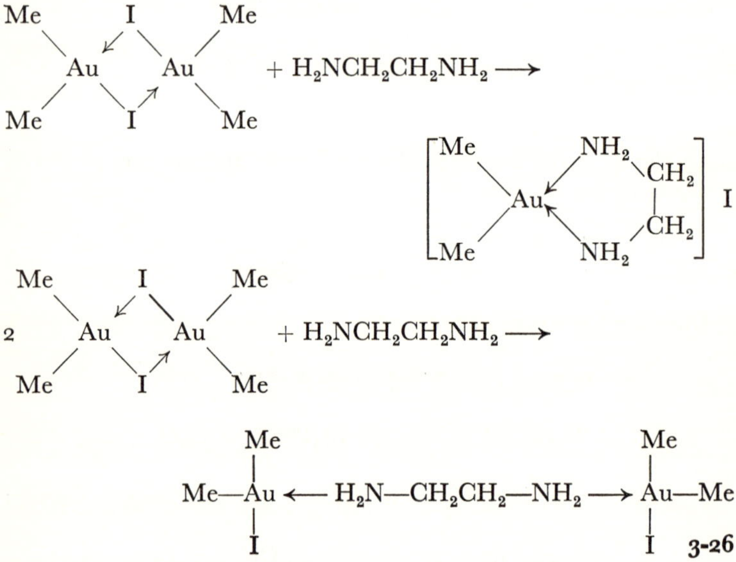

When tertiary amines are used the products are of necessity salts in which the halide has become ionic:

e.g. $$Me_3SnCl + C_5H_5N \rightleftharpoons [Me_3SnNC_5H_5]Cl$$

In this case an equilibrium is set up as is evident from the rise in conductivity. The same change has been used to study the equilibria

$$MClR(PR'_3)_2 + py \rightleftharpoons [MR(py)(PR'_3)_2]^+Cl^-$$

where $M = Pt$, Pd or Ni, R and R' are alkyl or aryl and py = pyridine. These square planar complexes exist in *cis*- and *trans*-configurations, the former reacting much faster due to the greater *trans*- labilizing effect of the phosphine ligands than of the R groups. Both the steric effect exerted by bulky R groups [e.g. for *cis*-PtClR(PEt₃)₂ the relative rates are 100,000:200:1 when R = Ph, o-tolyl and mesityl] and the much greater rates for the Ni and Pd than the Pt compounds [e.g. for *trans*-MCl(o-C_6H_4Me)(PEt₃)₂ they are in the ratio $5 \times 10^6 : 10^5 : 1$] are consistent with a mechanism involving intermediate addition of pyridine or solvent to give a 5-coordinate intermediate (Pt^{II} is generally less ready than Ni^{II} to go to higher coordination numbers).

Use of the corresponding nitrato complex,

$$trans\text{-}Pt(NO_3)(o\text{-}C_6H_4Me)(PEt_3)_2$$

in the same displacement reaction leads to an isolable ionic nitrate $[Pt(o\text{-}C_6H_4Me)(py)(PEt_3)_2]NO_3$.

An apparently general type of addition $M-X + A{=}B \rightarrow M-A-B-X$ where $A{=}B$ is a $C{=}N$, $C{=}O$ or $C{=}S$ system, has been demonstrated with Sn—OR and Hg—OR derivatives.

e.g. $Bu_3SnOMe + Ph-N{=}C{=}O \rightarrow Bu_3SnNPh-\overset{\displaystyle O}{\overset{\displaystyle \diagup}{C}}-OMe$

$Bu_3SnOMe + RCH{=}O \rightarrow Bu_3Sn-OCHROMe$

$Hg(OMe)_2 + PhN{=}C{=}S \rightarrow Hg[S-C(OMe){=}NPh]_2$

MODIFICATIONS WITHIN THE ORGANIC LIGAND

Few alkyls or aryls are sufficiently stable to allow extensive modifications of the hydrocarbon ligand to be effected. Hydroxy-alkylgermanes, e.g. $Ph_3GeCHOHPh$ and $(Ph_3Ge)_2CHOH$, have been oxidized to the corresponding ketones $Ph_3GeCOPh$ and $Ph_3GeCOGePh_3$.

In the transition-metal series the amide group in

$$(CO)_5MnCH_2CONH_2$$

can be hydrolyzed by HCl without splitting the metal–carbon bond giving the very weakly acidic complex $(CO)_5MnCH_2CO_2H$. Under similar conditions the α-carboxylic ester $(CO)_5MnCO_2Et$ is hydrolyzed not to the corresponding acid, but to the cation $Mn(CO)_6^+$. Analogous reactions occur with the Fe, Mo and W compounds having $C_5H_5Fe(CO)_2-$ and $C_5H_5Mo(or\ W)(CO)_3-$ groups in place of the $(CO)_5Mn$-group. In these series it has also been shown that α-alkoxy groups are readily and reversibly replaced by chloride according to:

e.g. $C_5H_5Fe(CO)_2CH_2OR \underset{\text{base}}{\overset{\text{HCl}}{\rightleftharpoons}} C_5H_5Fe(CO)_2CH_2Cl + ROH$

Chapter 4

Metal Carbonyls, Isonitriles, Cyanides and Acetylides

The basic mode of bonding of these ligands has been discussed in Chapter 1. It is the purpose of this chapter therefore to consider their structures more extensively and to consider their general chemical characteristics. The free ligands have in common the possession of a lone electron pair on carbon; this can be donated to the metal in forming the primary, sigma-bond:

$$|\overset{-}{\text{C}}{\equiv}\overset{+}{\text{O}} \leftrightarrow |\text{C}{=}\text{O}; \quad |\overset{-}{\text{C}}{\equiv}\overset{+}{\text{N}}\text{R} \leftrightarrow |\text{C}{=}\text{N}{-}\text{R};$$

$$|\overset{-}{\text{C}}{\equiv}\text{N}; \quad |\overset{-}{\text{C}}{\equiv}\text{C}{-}\text{R}$$

However, the acetylide ion cannot accept back-donation as readily as the cyanide ion or the carbonyl and isonitrile groups. This will be evident by writing down the appropriate valence bond structures:

$$\overset{-}{\text{M}} \leftarrow \text{C}{\equiv}\overset{+}{\text{O}} \leftrightarrow \text{M}{=}\text{C}{=}\text{O}; \quad \overset{-}{\text{M}} \leftarrow \text{C}{\equiv}\overset{+}{\text{N}}\text{R} \leftrightarrow \text{M}{=}\text{C}{=}\text{NR};$$

$$\overset{-}{\text{M}} \leftarrow \text{C}{\equiv}\text{N} \leftrightarrow \text{M}{=}\text{C}{=}\overset{-}{\text{N}}; \quad \overset{-}{\text{M}} \leftarrow \text{C}{\equiv}\text{C}{-}\text{R} \leftrightarrow \text{M}{=}\text{C}{=}\overset{-}{\text{C}}{-}\text{R}$$

It is seen that in the acetylide complex back-donation leads to a relatively unstable carbanionoid structure and this probably accounts at least in part for the relatively low stability of the acetylide complexes. Fulminates are very closely analogous to cyanides and may be considered as the N-oxides of cyanides in many complexes.

The analogy of the four groups is best illustrated by a series such as the tetrahedral nickel(0) complexes:

$$Ni(CO)_4, \ Ni(CNPh)_4, \ [Ni(CN)_4]^{4-}, \ [Ni(C{\equiv}CPh)_4]^{4-}$$

In each case the nickel atom (atomic number 28) attains formal inert gas configuration of electrons by the donation of a pair of electrons from each ligand group. In each case back-donation can be at its maximum since the nickel atom has 5 unshared pairs of electrons in the valency shell (although these are not all equally available for back-donation). The anionic ligands (CN, C≡CR) will, of course, form complexes equally or even more readily with the metals in higher oxidation states. Since they now neutralize the charge on the metal ion, back-donation is much less important. Thus Ni^{2+} gives the planar anions $[Ni(CN)_4]^{2-}$, $[Ni(CNO)_4]^{2-}$ and $[Ni(C{\equiv}CPh)_4]^{2-}$ in which only two units of negative charge must be dispersed from the metal atom. A metal carbonyl in an oxidation state higher than 0 will have a net positive charge and an unfavorable overall accumulation of positive charge on oxygen. Few such cations are known; the most notable are $Mn(CO)_6{}^{+}$ and $Re(CO)_6{}^{+}$ in which the octahedral symmetry may contribute to overall stability. Nitrogen being less electronegative than oxygen accepts such positive charge more readily. Hence back-donation in isonitrile complexes is less marked than in carbonyls and the preference for low oxidation states is also less pronounced. Thus in the first row of transition metals only Cr and Ni are known to form zerovalent isonitrile complexes, $Cr(CNR)_6$ and $Ni(CNR)_4$, whereas Mn, Fe, Co and Cu readily form complexes in the 1 or even 2 oxidation state: $Mn(CNR)_6{}^{+}$ and $Mn(CNR)_6{}^{2+}$, $Fe(CNR)_6{}^{2+}$, $Co(CNR)_5{}^{+}$, $Co(CNR)_5{}^{2+}$ and $Cu(CNR)_4{}^{+}$.

Moreover, anionic isonitrile complexes are not known whereas the metal carbonyls $Cr(CO)_6$, $Mn_2(CO)_{10}$, $Fe(CO)_5$ and $Co_2(CO)_8$ may be reduced to such species as $Cr(CO)_5{}^{2-}$, $Mn(CO)_5{}^{-}$, $Fe(CO)_4{}^{2-}$ and $Co(CO)_4{}^{-}$. Once again it will be seen that only those species with E.A.N. equal to that of the next inert gas are formed. In the neutral carbonyls this state is attained by the alternation of mono- and dimeric species, the latter having metal–metal bonds, while in the ionic series we have alternately singly and doubly charged ions. Stable electronic configuration combines with stable octahedral structure in the ions $M(CO)_6{}^{-}$ formed by vanadium, niobium and tantalum of which only the first has yielded a neutral carbonyl, $V(CO)_6$. This is one of the few but notable exceptions to the 'inert gas rule' among metal carbonyls. Its failure to attain this electronic configuration must be ascribed to the unfavourable change from octahedral 6-coordination to a seven coordinate structure which would arise if a metal–metal bond were to form between two such $V(CO)_6$ radical-molecules.

METAL CARBONYLS

1   Preparation and structure

The basic methods of preparation are outlined in Chapter 2. These lead to the neutral carbonyls mentioned above and their known analogues in the later transition series (Mo, W, Tc, Re, Ru and Os). In addition, they lead to carbonyl halides of Re, Ru, Os, Rh, Ir, Pd, Pt and Au. Here we consider the preparation of additional carbonyls and the structures of the carbonyls. All the hexa-carbonyls (V, Cr, Mo and W) have the expected octahedral structures. This is shown most simply by the appearance of a single carbonyl-stretching frequency at or near 2000 cm^{-1} in the infrared. It has been amply confirmed by x-ray and electron diffraction and other physical studies.

Manganese, technetium and rhenium carbonyls have $M(CO)_5$ groups joined by metal–metal bonds so that each metal atom has a somewhat distorted octahedral configuration,

e.g.

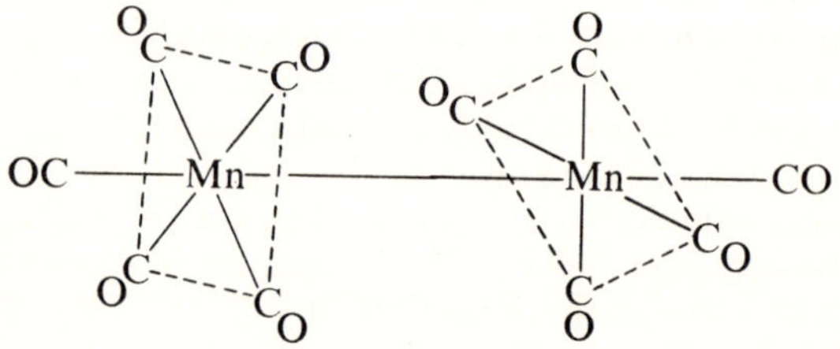

4-1

The carbonyl groups not lying on the metal–metal axis are slightly bent and these groups as a whole are bent away from the adjacent metal atom. It may be assumed that similar structures apply to the mixed carbonyls derivable from these metals,

e.g. $(CO)_5Mn—Re(CO)_5$ and $(CO)_5Mn—Co(CO)_4$.

Along with many related compounds, iron pentacarbonyl is now accepted as having a trigonal-bipyramid structure. This yellow liquid (b.p. 103°, m.p. −20°) on irradiation with sunlight (or ultraviolet light) deposits very insoluble golden-yellow crystals of $Fe_2(CO)_9$. The structure of this enneacarbonyl is well established from the x-ray work of Powell and Ewens (1939), as shown:

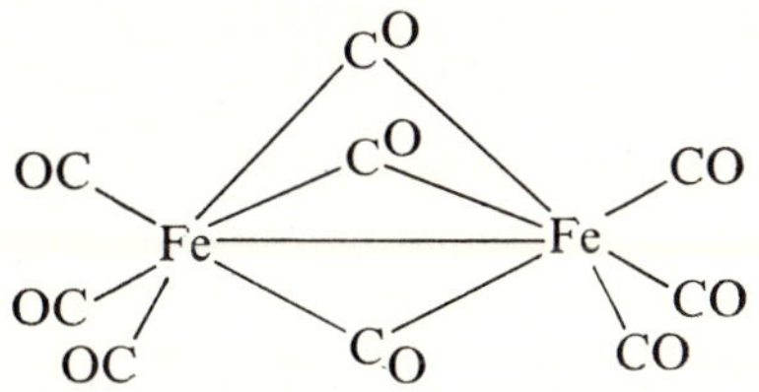

4-2

It may be regarded as made up of two octahedra with a common face through the centre of which the metal atoms are joined. The three 'ketonic' bridging carbonyls Fe—C—Fe (with =O on the C) are clearly distinguished in the infrared spectrum ($\nu = 1831$ cm^{-1}) from the terminal carbonyls ($\nu = 2087, 2023$ cm^{-1}). Despite their suggestive carbonyl absorption, the structural resemblance to ketones is purely formal and such bridging carbonyls do not show the chemical reactions of ketones. The insolubility of enneacarbonyldi-iron places it apart from all other neutral carbonyls which are generally soluble in organic solvents. This unexplained property has led several workers to repeat and confirm Powell's structure determination. Ruthenium and osmium analogues are not known.

The third iron carbonyl $Fe_3(CO)_{12}$ is obtained by the reduction of iron pentacarbonyl to the anion $Fe(CO)_4^{2-}$, or its equivalent, followed by oxidation,

e.g. $Fe(CO)_5 + OH^- \rightarrow HFe(CO)_4^- + CO_2$

$3HFe(CO)_4^- + 3MnO_2 + 3H^+ \rightarrow Fe_3(CO)_{12} + 3Mn(OH)_2$

The Ru and Os analogues have the symmetrical triangular structures shown for the osmium compound. The iron compound is shown by its Mössbauer spectrum to be less symmetrical, two of the metal atoms being different from the third. Structure determination by x-ray methods is complicated by disorder in the crystal lattice, but by combining the available results with data for the anion

$HFe_3(CO)_{11}^-$ the structure shown has been deduced.

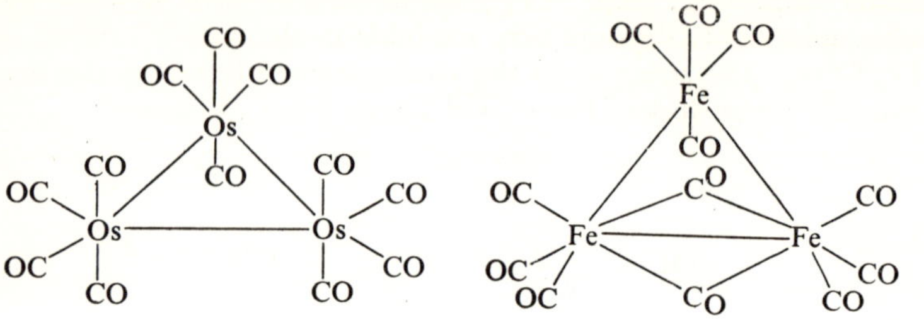

4·3

Mention must be made here of a compound which, though not a pure carbonyl, is closely related to the polymeric carbonyls: the iron carbonyl carbide $Fe_5(CO)_{15}C$ which has the structure shown and is obtained as a minor product in the reaction of dodecacarbonyltri-iron with acetylenes.

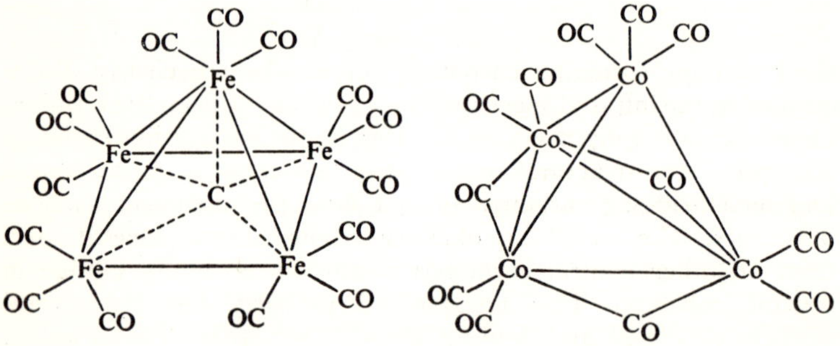

4·4

The cobalt group forms carbonyls $M_2(CO)_8$ and $M_4(CO)_{12}$. Octacarbonyldicobalt has two carbonyl bridges and its structure is derivable from that of enneacarbonyldiiron by substitution of the metal atoms and removal of one bridging CO group. This 'vacant' position may be responsible for the relatively high reactivity of this carbonyl and particularly for the formation from it of such complexes as the aluminium bromide adduct, $Co_2(CO)_8AlBr_3$. In solution the bridged form is in equilibrium with an isomer having eight terminal CO groups.

The dodecacarbonyl is found to have the structure shown with three bridging CO groups and one unique cobalt atom. There is a mixed carbonyl in which this apical cobalt tricarbonyl group is replaced by the group $HFe(CO)_3$. Rhodium forms a carbonyl

$Rh_6(CO)_{16}$ which has the metal atoms arranged octahedrally as shown with two terminal CO groups on each metal atom and four triply bridging CO groups over alternate faces.

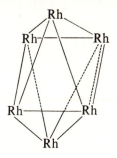

4·5

In the nickel group neither Pd nor Pt have yielded simple carbonyls so that the well-known tetrahedral $Ni(CO)_4$ is the only representative. However, the phosphine substituted carbonyls $Ni(CO)_2(PPh_3)_2$ and $Ni(CO)(PPh_3)_3$ have somewhat unstable Pt analogues.

2   Reactions

All the neutral metal carbonyls are reducible to carbonylate ions and the variety of such reduced species is greater than that of the carbonyls themselves. Thus nickel carbonyl gives $[Ni_2(CO)_6]^{2-}$, $[Ni_3(CO)_8]^{2-}$, $[Ni_4(CO)_9]^{2-}$ and $[Ni_5(CO)_9]^{2-}$ and iron gives three carbonyls but four anions: $Fe(CO)_4^{2-}$, $Fe_2(CO)_8^{2-}$, $Fe_3(CO)_{11}^{2-}$ and $Fe_4(CO)_{13}^{2-}$.

The structures of each of these anions have been determined. The ion $Fe(CO)_4^{2-}$ is tetrahedral and thus iso-structural with the isoelectronic $Co(CO)_4^-$ and $Ni(CO)_4$. The dimeric ion has a metal–metal bond, but no bridging carbonyls. It is thus very different in structure from the neutral $Fe_2(CO)_9$. The tri-iron anion in the $HFe_3(CO)_{11}^-$ form has the structure shown with the hydrogen probably symmetrically placed between two iron atoms. Structures of this type occur in other hydrocarbonyl anions, notably the Cr, Mo and W compounds $[(CO)_5M—H—M(CO)_5]^-$ in which the hydrogen bond is the only link between the two metal atoms.

The $Fe_4(CO)_{13}^{2-}$ ion has the remarkable structure shown in which the four metal atoms lie at the corners of a tetrahedron, the apical iron being different from the other three. One carbonyl group is shared between all the three latter iron atoms. Similar examples of CO groups bonded to 3 nickel or 3 cobalt atoms occur among the cyclopentadienyl and benzene complexes (see pp. 129, 138).

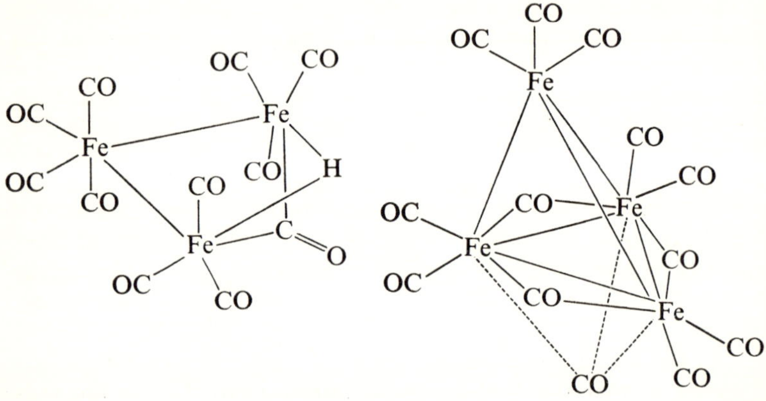

4·6

Reduction is easiest with the dimeric (or polymeric) carbonyls where cleavage of the metal–metal bond is involved. It is conveniently effected with sodium amalgam,

e.g. $Co_2(CO)_8 + 2Na \rightarrow 2NaCo(CO)_4$

Where loss of carbon monoxide is involved either similar reducing agents may be used or alkalis may cause disproportionation to the anion and carbon dioxide (see $HFe(CO)_4^-$ above). With liquid ammonia as the base, urea rather than carbon dioxide results, as in

$$Fe_2(CO)_9 + 4NH_3 \xrightarrow{20°} (NH_4)_2[Fe_2(CO)_8] + CO(NH_2)_2.$$

Chromium, molybdenum and tungsten carbonyls are reduced to the dimeric $[M^{-I}]$ anion by $NaBH_4$ in liquid ammonia

$$2Mo(CO)_6 + NaBH_4 \xrightarrow[60°]{NH_3} Na_2[Mo_2(CO)_{10}]$$

whereas in diglyme the same reaction produces the corresponding monosodium salt:

$$2W(CO)_6 + NaBH_4 \xrightarrow{diglyme} Na[W_2H(CO)_{10}]$$

Further reduction to the monomeric $[Cr^{-II}]$ anion is best effected with sodium in liquid ammonia

$$Cr(CO)_6 + 2Na \rightarrow Na_2Cr(CO)_5 + CO$$

The reaction with bases may also cause disproportionation of the metal,

e.g. $Fe_3(CO)_{12} + 3$ en $\xrightarrow{90°}$ $[Fe \, en_3][Fe_2(CO)_8] + 4CO$

The complexity of the anion formed from any of the iron carbonyls has been shown to depend on both the base strength and the temperature.

The conjugate acids of these carbonylates, the corresponding hydrocarbonyls, have been obtained from many of these ions, but some are too unstable to be isolated.

These hydridocarbonyls have hydrogen directly attached to the metal atom. Although in most x-ray structure determinations this hydrogen atom cannot be located directly, the distribution of other groups frequently allows its position to be deduced. Thus, in the complex $OsHBr(CO)(PPh_3)_3$ it must clearly occupy the 'vacant'

4·7

octahedral position indicated by the dotted line. More direct evidence comes from nuclear magnetic resonance measurements. Hydrogen atoms attached to metal give very high field maxima, e.g. at $17·5\tau$ in $HMn(CO)_5$ and 20τ in $HCo(CO)_4$. Broad line n.m.r. measurements have given direct estimates of metal hydrogen distances. Perhaps the best available value is that of $1·28 \pm 0·01$ Å in $HMn(CO)_5$. Metal hydrogen stretching frequencies in the infrared have also been noted in many cases. These can occur at widely varying frequencies, depending on the nature of the metal and are best recognized by comparing the spectra of the hydride and deuteride.

The carbonyl hydrides vary in acidity: $HCo(CO)_4$ is said to be comparable to a strong mineral acid; $HMn(CO)_5$ has pK ~ 7. Yet all give reactions characteristic of hydrides, apparently implying ionization to H^- as well as H^+. Thus they are powerful reducing

4

agents converting acetylenes to olefins to alkanes, or ketones to alcohols,

e.g. $$Me_2CO + H_2Fe(CO)_4 \rightarrow Me_2CHOH,$$

and carbon tetrachloride to chloroform. Another characteristic reaction of the hydrogen in such hydrides is with mercuric halides:

$$M—H + HgBr_2 \rightarrow M—HgBr + HBr$$

The same halomercury derivatives are accessible from the sodium salts of the hydrocarbonyls and the largely covalent mercury 'salts', e.g. $Hg[Co(CO)_4]_2$, are among the most stable derivatives of these carbonylates. Alkylmercuri-derivatives, e.g. $EtHgTa(CO)_6$, and bi-metallic complexes with many other metals and organometallic groups have been prepared, e.g. $Ph_3GeMn(CO)_5, H_2Ge[Mn(CO)_5]_2$, $Me_2Sn[Mn(CO)_5]_2$, $[Bu_2SnFe(CO)_4]_2$, $(Ph_3PAu)_2Fe(CO)_4$, $[PbFe(CO)_4]_n$, $AcOPbCo(CO)_4$.

Formation of a co-ordinate bond from carbonylate ions as donors has been demonstrated by the preparation of borane complexes of Re and Mn:

$$Et_4N[H_3B\leftarrow Re(CO)_5]; \quad Na[H_3B\leftarrow Mn(CO)_4PPh_3]$$

Oxidation of metal carbonyls with halogens, or in suitable cases (see Chapter 2) direct preparation from metal halides leads to the halocarbonyls:

e.g. $$Mn_2(CO)_{10} + Br_2 \rightarrow 2BrMn(CO)_5$$
$$Fe(CO)_5 + I_2 \rightarrow [Fe(CO)_5I]I \rightarrow CO + I_2Fe(CO)_4$$

Pseudohalogens do not always react similarly. Thus thiocyanogen $(SCN)_2$, does not convert decacarbonyldimanganese to the thiocyanato complex, $(CO)_5Mn—S—C\equiv N$. The latter is however obtained by the reaction:

$$(CO)_5MnNa + ClSCN \rightarrow (CO)_5MnSCN$$

Replacement of CO groups in this product by various other ligands, L, is accompanied by rearrangement of the SCN group:

$$(CO)_5MnSCN + 2L \rightarrow 2CO + (CO)_3Mn(L)_2NCS$$

The complexes of the isothiocyanato series so formed are recognized by the presence of a peak near 810 cm^{-1} in their infrared spectra, attributable to the CS group. The pentacarbonylthiocyanatomanganese has no absorption between 780 and 860 cm^{-1}. Distinction in the C—N stretching region is less clear-cut, the thiocyanato complexes absorbing at only slightly higher frequency (near 2150 cm^{-1}) than the isothiocyanato compounds.

Perfluoroalkyl iodides behave as pseudohalogens in their reactions with carbonyls:

e.g. $$C_2F_5I + Fe(CO)_5 \rightarrow CO + C_2F_5Fe(CO)_4I$$

No simple carbonyl halides of nickel are known and only phosphine substituted carbonyl halides of cobalt. Group VI metal carbonyls are completely decomposed by halogens, but react with halide ion, without oxidation, by substitution of CO to give halocarbonylate ions of the metal:

e.g. $$Mo(CO)_6 + KI \rightarrow K[Mo(CO)_5I] + CO$$

also formed by the action of iodine on the carbonylates:

e.g. $$Na_2[Cr_2(CO)_{10}] + I_2 \rightarrow 2Na[Cr(CO)_5I]$$

From this chromium compound, the remarkable, blue, paramagnetic, neutral $Cr(CO)_5I$ has been obtained by further treatment with iodine:

$$2Na[Cr(CO)_5I] + I_2 \rightarrow 2NaI + 2Cr(CO)_5I$$

Some of the carbonyl halides readily lose carbon monoxide on heating to give halogen-bridged dimers,

e.g.

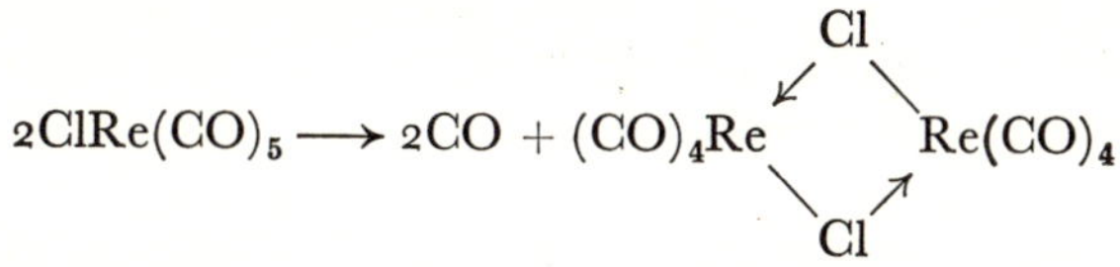

$$2ClRe(CO)_5 \longrightarrow 2CO + (CO)_4Re\underset{\displaystyle Cl}{\overset{\displaystyle Cl}{\diagup\diagdown}}Re(CO)_4$$

The reverse addition of CO will occur under pressure and other ligands also cleave such bridged complexes readily:

e.g.

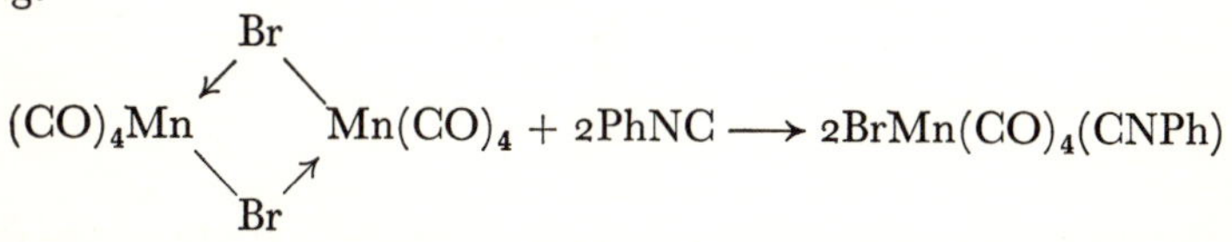

$$(CO)_4Mn\underset{\displaystyle Br}{\overset{\displaystyle Br}{\diagup\diagdown}}Mn(CO)_4 + 2PhNC \longrightarrow 2BrMn(CO)_4(CNPh)$$

Although the halogen atoms are essentially covalently bound in such carbonyl halides, the electron-withdrawing effect of the halogen atoms leads to a significant reduction of back-donation of electrons to the carbonyl groups and hence higher C—O stretching frequencies in the infrared. The highest frequencies are attained in the carbonyl fluorides and in the cationic carbonyls, e.g. those, $M(CO)_6^+$, of Mn and Re obtainable by the action of carbon monoxide on the halocarbonyls in the presence of aluminium halides to facilitate halide removal. Conversely, electron-donating ligands lower the C—O stretching frequencies and the lowest values are observed in the carbonylate ions. Thus we may compare the series:

$$Mn(CO)_6^+, \quad Cr(CO)_6 \quad \text{and} \quad V(CO)_6^-$$
$$2090 \qquad\quad 1981 \qquad\quad 1859 \text{ cm}^{-1}$$

or with the same metal:

$$Mn(CO)_6^+ \qquad\qquad BrMn(CO)_5 \qquad\qquad Mn_2(CO)_{10}$$
$$2090 \qquad\qquad 2064, 2017 \qquad\qquad 2063, 2028, 1997$$
$$Mn_2(CO)_6 \, (diars)_2* \qquad\qquad Mn(CO)_5^-$$
$$1944, 1937, 1885 \qquad\qquad 1895, 1863 \text{ cm}^{-1}$$

Analogous to the carbonyl halides, and frequently by direct displacement of the halogen, we can prepare a range of other derivatives, e.g. carbonyl cyanides, thiocyanates, mercaptides, etc. The sulphides are most commonly found in the form of bridged complexes of which the iron compounds have been most closely studied. Among the simplest compounds of this type are the mercaptides $Fe_2(CO)_6(SR)_2$ which exist in two isomeric, but interconvertible, series with the alkyl groups either *cis-* or *trans-* with respect to the four-membered Fe—S—Fe—S ring:

4-8

In the analogous sulphide $[SFe(CO)_3]_2$ an S—S group acts as the symmetrical bridging group between two iron atoms. The iron–iron distance in this substance is 2·55 Å, but the bond between these

* 'diars' = o-phenylene-bis-dimethylarsine, $o\text{-}C_6H_4(AsMe_2)_2$.

two atoms is best thought of as a 'bent bond' formed by overlap of orbitals projecting along the dotted lines in the diagram, giving each iron atom a distorted octahedral arrangement.

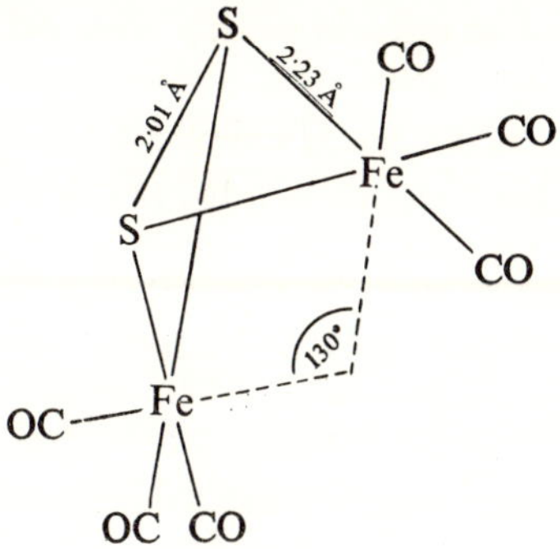

4-9

Related oxy- and hydroxy-complexes are known for group VI metals and for rhenium:

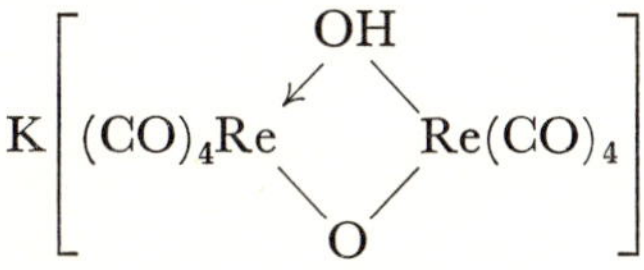

$$K\left[(CO)_4Re\begin{matrix} OH \\ \nwarrow \\ \\ O \end{matrix}Re(CO)_4\right]$$

4-10

When nitric oxide reacts with a halometal carbonyl it replaces halogen and CO. The reaction has been used for manganese and platinum carbonyl halides and with various hydrocarbon derivatives.

e.g.

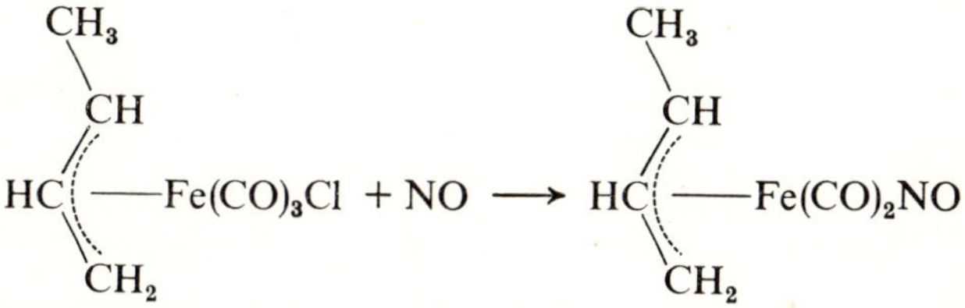

4-11

With the less polar iodides, addition of a halogen acceptor (Ag, Ag$^+$) becomes advantageous.

Direct reaction of metal carbonyl with nitric oxide provides routes to $Co(CO)_3NO$ [from $Co_2(CO)_8$] and $Fe(CO)_2(NO)_2$ [from $Fe_2(CO)_9$ or $Fe_3(CO)_{12}$] which form an iso-electronic and isosteric series with nickel carbonyl and with the anions $Co(CO)_4^-$ and $[Fe(CO)_3NO]^-$. The latter is readily obtained from iron carbonyl and alkaline nitrite:

$$Fe(CO)_5 + NO_2^- \rightarrow [Fe(CO)_3NO]^- + CO + CO_2$$

A further, but rather unstable member of this series is the manganese compound $Mn(CO)(NO)_3$. This metal also forms a mononitrosyl $Mn(CO)_4NO$, presumably isostructural with $Fe(CO)_5$. In all these compounds nitric oxide may be regarded as a 3-electron donor.

Other common ligands which can replace carbon monoxide directly are 2-electron donors and thus replace CO without major structural change. This is true of the closest analogues of CO, the isonitriles (Chapter 2, Section B.11). The most widely studied carbonyl replacements are those by phosphines and related tri-valent compounds of P, As and Sb. Their reactivity decreases in the order $PCl_3 > PF_3 > P(OR)_3 > PR_3 > AsR_3 > SbR_3$ and the degree of substitution observed follows the same order. Thus PF_3 and $P(OR)_3$, being better electron acceptors, tend to replace more CO groups than PR_3. Chelating di- and tri-phosphines and arsines have frequently been used to obtain more extensive substitution than occurs with the mono-phosphines or arsines. Thus o-phenyl-enebisdimethylarsine [o-$C_6H_4(AsMe_2)_2$] can replace all CO groups from nickel and up to four from iron and from the group VI metals. Several 7-coordinate complexes have been obtained by halogenation of the resultant molybdenum and tungsten complexes,

e.g. $Mo(CO)_4(diars) + I_2 \rightarrow Mo(CO)_3(diars)I_2$

$Mo(CO)_2(diars)_2 + Br_2 \rightarrow [Mo(CO)_2(diars)_2Br]Br$

Although amines are similar as ligands in some respects to phosphines and arsines, their greater basicity frequently leads to a different reaction pattern and their inability to accept back-donation of electrons favours the formation of cationic complexes. Thus we may contrast the reactions

$$ClMn(CO)_5 + 2Ph_3As \rightarrow ClMn(CO)_3(AsPh_3)_2 + 2CO$$

and $ClMn(CO)_5 + 2NH_3 \rightarrow [Mn(CO)_4(NH_3)_2]^+Cl^- + CO$

With both iron and cobalt carbonyls disproportionation in-variably results.

e.g. $3Co_2(CO)_8 + 12NH_3 \rightarrow 2[Co(NH_3)_6][Co(CO)_4]_2 + 8CO$

(cf. also p. 91).

Nickel carbonyl behaves similarly with the more strongly basic amines,

e.g. $5Ni(CO)_4 + 3H_2NCH_2CH_2NH_2 \rightarrow$

$$[Ni(C_2H_8N_2)_3][Ni_4(CO)_9] + 11CO$$

This tendency is reduced with amines in which the nitrogen is part of an aromatic system and hence capable of accepting some back-donation from the metal. Thus, nickel carbonyl reacts with o-phenanthroline to give a neutral complex, $Ni(CO)_2(o\text{-phen})$, as do the isoelectronic nitrosocarbonyls, $Co(NO)(CO)_3$ and $Fe(NO)_2(CO)_2$ giving $Co(NO)(CO)(o\text{-phen})$ and $Fe(NO)_2(o\text{-phen})$ respectively.

Other groups which can replace carbon monoxide directly include sulphur dioxide, which with enneacarbonyldi-iron gives a product believed to have the SO_2 as bridging group:

$$Fe_2(CO)_9 + SO_2 \rightarrow CO + Fe_2(CO)_8SO_2$$
$$[18\%]$$

Halide (X^-) and various other $[N_3^-, SCN^-, (CN)_3C^-, \text{etc.}]$ anions displace one CO group from neutral or cationic carbonyls (cf. p. 93).

e.g. $\qquad W(CO)_6 + [Et_4N]N_3 \rightarrow Et_4N[W(CO)_5N_3]$

$\qquad Mn(CO)_5X + [Et_4N]X \rightarrow Et_4N[Mn(CO)_4X_2]$

Cyanide readily replaces more than one carbonyl group. However, accurate choice of reaction conditions may adequately control the product formed. Thus, in liquid ammonia solution, $Co(CO)_3NO$ reacts with one mole of potassium cyanide at $20°$, with two moles at $60°$ and at $120°$ the last CO group is replaced to give $K_3[Co(CN)_3NO]$.

Both this replacement, and the reverse substitution of cyanide by carbon monoxide have been used to obtain a variety of mixed cyano-carbonylate ions. The group VI carbonyls $M(CO)_6$ and even their anions $M_2(CO)_{10}^{2-}$ react to give successively the ions $[M(CO)_5CN]^-$, $[M(CO)_4(CN)_2]^{2-}$ and $[M(CO)_3(CN)_3]^{3-}$. The next member of this series, $[M(CO)_2(CN)_4]^{4-}$, is obtained by displacement of α,α'-bipyridyl from $M(CO)_2(bipy)_2$. Nickel carbonyl reacts similarly with two moles of potassium cyanide giving $K(Ni(CO)_3CN]$ and $K_2[Ni(CO)_2(CN)_2]$. The latter is also obtainable from the complex nickel(0) cyanide, $K_4[Ni(CN)_4]$ with carbon monoxide and a nickel(I) cyanocarbonyl has been prepared similarly:

$$K_4[Ni_2(CN)_6] + 2CO \xrightarrow{\text{liq. NH}_3} 2K_2[Ni(CN)_3CO]$$

As a relatively poor π-acceptor, CN is readily replaced and careful control of conditions is necessary to avoid complete replacement of CN by CO in such reactions.

It has been established that both unimolecular dissociation of metal carbonyls (SN1) and bimolecular displacement mechanisms (SN2) are involved in different examples of the substitution processes discussed in this section. Kinetic studies have been carried out in a number of cases both of exchange of CO using $C^{14}O$ and of the replacement of CO by appropriate ligands. Thus the exchange of carbon monoxide is first order in carbonyl and independent of carbon monoxide for, e.g., $Ni(CO)_4$, $Co_2(CO)_8$, $Mn(CO)_5X$, $Cr(CO)_6$ and several of their derivatives. The rate decreases as CO groups are replaced by phosphines corresponding to the increasing strength of the remaining M—C bonds. In the halomanganese carbonyls it decreases in the order $Cl > Br > I$, the corresponding rates being in the ratio $200 : 8 : 1$ and in each case one carbonyl group (that *trans* to halogen) exchanges more slowly than the other four.

Dissociative mechanisms have similarly been demonstrated for light-catalyzed substitutions of, for example, $Mo(CO)_6$ and $C_5H_5Mn(CO)_3$, whereas bimolecular substitution occurs in the carbon monoxide exchange of, for example, $C_5H_5Co(CO)_2$ and *cis*-$Fe(CO)_4I_2$ and in the displacements of CO by various ligands from $Fe(CO)_2(NO)_2$ and $Co(CO)_3NO$.

Where photolysis is employed to effect substitution the process is believed to involve dissociation of the type

$$M(CO)_n \xrightarrow{h\nu} M(CO)_{n-1} + CO$$

In the case of $W(CO)_6$, spectroscopic evidence for the product $W(CO)_5$ has been obtained by carrying out the irradiation at low temperature in a hydrocarbon glass. Pentacarbonyliron similarly yields $Fe(CO)_4$ which under ordinary conditions combines with the pentacarbonyl to give the enneacarbonyl.

$$Fe(CO)_4 + Fe(CO)_5 \rightarrow Fe_2(CO)_9$$

The greatly enhanced reactivity of the latter compared to $Fe(CO)_5$ may well be the result of thermal reversibility of this reaction.

Reactions of metal carbonyls with alkyl halides

The formation of perfluoroalkyl and σ-allylmetal carbonyl halides directly from metal carbonyls and halocarbons has been described in Chapter 2, Section B.12. With allyl halides the product may decompose to the corresponding diallyl and in many cases formation of such dimeric hydrocarbons has been described without isolation of, or even evidence for, the intermediacy of allyl complexes. Thus the reaction

$$2RCH{=}CH{-}CH_2X + Ni(CO)_4 \rightarrow$$
$$(RCH{=}CHCH_2{-})_2 + NiX_2 + 4CO$$

may be regarded as a general process and allylic acetates have been used as well as halides.

Simple alkyl halides appear unreactive, but dihalides with electron-withdrawing groups react similarly with iron carbonyl and many other carbonyls:

e.g. $2Ph_2CCl_2 + 2Fe(CO)_5 \rightarrow Ph_2C{=}CPh_2 + 2FeCl_2 + 10CO$

Ethyl dibromomalonate eliminates only one bromine to give the ferric chelate of bromomalonic ester:

$$6Br_2C(COOEt)_2 + 5Fe(CO)_5 \rightarrow$$
$$2Fe[BrC(COOEt)_2]_3 + 3FeBr_2 + 25CO$$

With cobalt carbonyl or the anion, $Co(CO)_4^-$, $1,1,1$-trihalo-alkanes CYX_3 react to give cobalt complexes, $(CO)_9Co_3CY$ where Y may be alkyl, aryl or CO_2R groups or halogen atoms:

e.g. $CH_3CH_2CBr_3 + 3Co(CO)_4^- \rightarrow$
$$CH_3CH_2C[Co(CO)_3]_3 + 3Br^- + 3CO$$

When Y is of the form RCH_2, the products are identical with those resulting from the action of acids on the acetylene complexes $Co_2(CO)_6(RC{\equiv}CH)$:

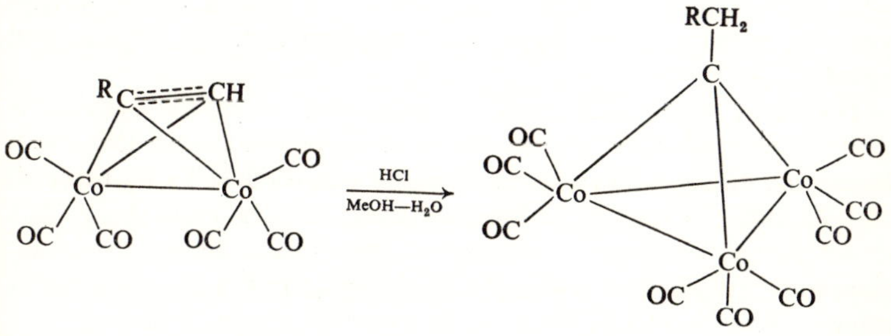

4-12

Bromine decomposes these complexes to give back the halide $YCBr_3$.

Reaction of metal carbonyls with metal alkyls

Group VI metal carbonyls add alkyl or aryllithium thus: $M(CO)_6 + RLi \rightarrow [(CO)_5MCOR]Li$, where M = Cr, Mo or W and R is, for example, Me or Ph. The products are hydrolzed by dilute acid to give the hexacarbonyls + the aldehyde RCHO and the formation of benzaldehyde + benzil from nickel carbonyl and phenylmagnesium bromide may follow a similar course. Of greatest interest, however, is the reaction of the above salts with alkyl halides,

e.g.

$$[(CO)_5MoCOCH_3]^- + MeI \longrightarrow I^- + (CO)_5Mo \rightleftarrows C \underset{Me}{\overset{OMe}{<}}$$

The formulation of such products as derived from the carbene $:C \underset{Me}{\overset{OMe}{<}}$ has been established on the basis of x-ray diffraction study.

CYANIDES AND ISOCYANIDE COMPLEXES

The simple salt-like cyanides formed by the main-group metals must be considered outside the scope of this volume. We are concerned here with those cyanides in which the metal is covalently bound to the carbon atom of a cyanide group and more especially with the complex cyanides of the transition metals which can be assumed to have some degree of π-bonding between carbon and metal.

The range of properties and bonding types among the cyanides is wide. Although CN^- is the ion of a fairly weak acid the alkali metal and thallous derivatives must be regarded as ionic, those of Na, K and Rb having sodium chloride lattices with the anions either freely rotating or disordered (but changing to an ortho-rhombic modification with all CN groups parallel at low temperature). The Cs and Tl compounds have CsCl type lattices.

Largely covalent structures are established for the cyanides of the Ni, Cu and Zn groups, with a tendency for the metal to be bonded to both ends of the cyanide group. Thus AgCN forms long chains: —Ag—C—N—Ag—C—N— and Cd and Zn form 3-dimensional networks in which each metal atom is linked tetrahedrally to four others by M—C—N—M bridges. A single unit cell is shown in the figure (Zn or Cd = ●; C = ●; N = ○)

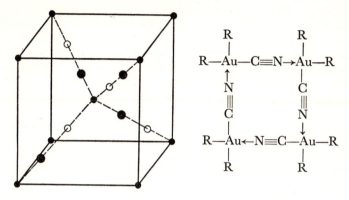

4·13

Mercuric cyanide differs in forming a molecular crystal in which the slightly bent units ($\angle$C—Hg—C $= 171°$; N—C—Hg $= 173°$)

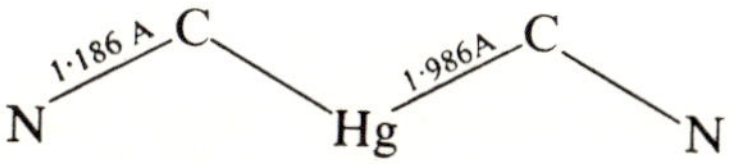

are so arranged that each Hg atom interacts with two nitrogens of neighboring molecules (at 2·70 Å distant).

Gold forms inter alia the tetrameric dialkylgold cyanides. For the diethyl compound the planar structure shown (R = Et) has been demonstrated crystallographically. Among the complex cyanides, silver(I) forms the salt $K[Ag(CN)_2]$ which has a linear anion in which silver is probably linked to carbon whereas Cu^I forms $K_3[Cu(CN)_4]$ containing the tetrahedral $Cu(CN)_4{}^{3-}$ ion which is iso-electronic with $Ni(CO)_4$.

On the other hand the barium salts $Ba[M(CN)_4]$ of Pt, Pd and Ni contain planar anions. It may be assumed that the last of these rearranges to a tetrahedral form during its reduction by potassium in liquid ammonia to the Ni^0 derivative:

$$K_2[Ni^{II}(CN)_4] + 2K \xrightarrow{NH_3} K_4[Ni^0(CN)_4]$$

The hexacyanides $Fe(CN)_6{}^{4-}$, $Fe(CN)_6{}^{3-}$, $Co(CN)_6{}^{3-}$ and $Cr(CN)_6{}^{3-}$ when present as the free ions, as, for example, in

$K_4Fe(CN)_6$. $3H_2O$ or in $[Co(NH_3)_6][Co(CN)_6]$, possess regular octahedral structures. But other salts of these ions, and expecially the transition metal ferro- and ferricyanides undoubtedly contain M—C—N—M' groups. Thus spectroscopic evidence indicates the presence of Fe—C≡N → Ni groups in $K_2NiFe(CN)_6$ and pigments of the Prussian blue class must contain 3-dimensional networks of Fe—C≡N → Fe groups. When $KFeCr(CN)_6$ is prepared from $K_3Cr(CN)_6$ it is obtained as a brick-red substance with infrared maxima at 2168 cm^{-1} (and 2113 cm^{-1}) similar to $Cr(CN)_6{}^{3-}$ itself. Heating to 100° converts this substance to a green form with a maximum at 2092 cm^{-1} considered characteristic of ferrocyanides. It is believed that in this isomerization the CN groups flip over, converting Fe←N≡C—Cr units to Fe—C≡N→Cr.

The chromicyanide ion like the nickelocyanide is reducible in liquid ammonia to the analogue of the corresponding carbonyl:

$$K_3[Cr^{III}(CN)_6] + 3K \xrightarrow{NH_3} K_6[Cr^0(CN)_6]$$

The other elements in the chromium group, Mo and W can coordinate up to eight cyanide groups the salts $K_4M(CN)_8 \cdot 2H_2O$ having the metal atom surrounded by eight carbons disposed at the corners of a dodecahedron; the M—C—N groups are linear with Mo—C = 2·15 and C—N = 1·15 Å.

Fulminato complexes corresponding to the complex cyanides have been described for Fe^{II}, Ni^{II} and Co^{III}:

e.g.
$$CoSO_4 + NaCNO \xrightarrow[H_2O]{air} [Co(CNO)_6]^{3-}$$

Mixed cyanofulminato complexes have also been obtained,

e.g.
$$[Fe(CN)_5NH_3]^{3-} + CNO^- \rightarrow [Fe(CN)_5(CNO)]^{4-}$$

As sodium salts these crystallize from water as polyhydrates, e.g. $Na_2[Ni(CNO)_4] \cdot 5H_2O$; $Na_4[Fe(CNO)_6] \cdot 18H_2O$, and their reduction leads directly to cyano complexes:

$$[Fe(CNO)_6]^{4-} + 12Fe(OH)_2 + 6H_2O \rightarrow$$
$$[Fe(CN)_6]^{4-} + 12Fe(OH)_3$$

$$Na_2[Ni(CNO)_4] + Na—Hg \xrightarrow{H_2O} Na_4[Ni_2(CN)_6]$$

Neutral cyano and fulminato complexes are readily formed by

displacement of some of the anionic ligands by phosphines or similar neutral ligands:

e.g. $[Ni(CN)_4]^{2-} + 2PEt_3 \rightarrow (Et_3P)_2Ni(CN)_2 + 2CN^-$

$[Pd(CNO)_4]^{2-} + 2PPh_3 \rightarrow (Ph_3P)_2Pd(CNO)_2 + 2CNO^-$

From the zerovalent complexes $K_4[Ni(CN)_4]$ and $K_6[Cr(CN)_6]$ the cyanide may be displaced completely by such ligands:

e.g. $K_4[Ni(CN)_4] + 4PPh_3 \rightarrow 4KCN + Ni(PPh_3)_4$

The reverse displacement, e.g. of o-phenanthroline, from the cations $[M(\text{o-phen})_3]^{2+}$ works with iron:

$$[Fe(\text{o-phen})_3]^{2+} + 2Y^- \rightarrow Fe(\text{o-phen})_2Y_2 + \text{o-phen}$$

where $Y = CN^-$ or CNO^-.

Nickel, in this case gives only the ionic complex

$$2[Ni(\text{o-phen})_3]^{2+} + 4CN^- \rightarrow [Ni(\text{o-phen})_3][Ni(CN)_4] + 2 \text{ o-phen}$$

Covalent cyano and fulminato complexes are also known in the form of the mixed alkylmetal derivatives of mercury,

e.g. $PhCH_2HgCNO,$

and of group IV metals, R_3MCNO and R_3MCN where $M = Ge$, Sn or Pb. The fulminates of this type are stable at room temperature, but rearrange on heating to the corresponding isocyanates.

The chemical evidence for the presence of metal-carbon bonds in the complex cyanides includes their facile direct alkylation to isonitrile complexes. This has been exploited most with ferrocyanides which are methylated by methyl sulphate or iodide to $Fe(CNMe)_4(CN)_2$ or, under more vigorous conditions, to the $[Fe(CNMe)_6]^{2+}$ ion. The dichloride of the latter reverts to the neutral complex on heating:

$$[Fe(CNMe)_6]Cl_2 \rightarrow Fe(CN)_2(CNMe)_4 + 2MeCl$$

Similar methylation has been employed to convert, for example, cobalticyanide to $Co(CN)_3(CNMe)_3$ and $K[C_5H_5Mo(CO)_2(CN)_2]$ to $[C_5H_5Mo(CO)_2(CNMe)_2]I$.

The reaction proceeds particularly smoothly with benzyl bromide providing an excellent route to the tetra-, penta- and hexakis-benzylisocyanide complexes of iron:

e.g. $K_4Fe(CN)_6 + 5PhCH_2Br \rightarrow [Fe(CN)(CNCH_2Ph)_5]Br + 4KBr$

It is also possible to interchange alkyl groups by treatment of the isonitrile complexes with appropriate alkyl halides,

e.g. $[Fe(CNMe)_6]Br_2 + PhCH_2Br \rightarrow$
$$Fe(CN)_2(CNCH_2Ph)_4 + [Fe(CN)(CNCH_2Ph)_5]Br$$

a process which must depend on the ready reversibility of the later alkylation stages

e.g. $[Fe(CN)(CNR)_5]X + R'X \rightleftharpoons [Fe(CNR')(CNR)_5]X_2 \rightleftharpoons$
$$[Fe(CN)(CNR')(CNR)_4]X + RX$$

Alkylations with MeI or Me_2SO_4 have been described for $Ag_2[Cd(CN)_4]$, CuCN, $K_3[Cr(CN)_6]$, $Ag_4[Mo(CN)_8]$ and many other similar cyanides. In most of these cases the products are complex and ill-defined, but methylation of the cyanide groups always occurs and free methylisocyanide can be liberated from the products. More clearly defined products result from addition of isocyanides to the metal salt. Thus CuCN adds up to three moles of RNC giving $Cu(CN)(CNR)_3$ while CuCl can give both the neutral complexes $CuCl(CNR)_3$ and the ionic $[Cu(CNR)_4]Cl$.

The group VI metal salts only react under reducing conditions (cf. p. 56) to give the neutral $M(CNR)_6$ complexes. In the case of manganese, where both $[Mn^I(CNR)_6]^+$ and $[Mn^{II}(CNR)_6]^{2+}$ are stable ions, the latter have only been obtained by oxidation (Br_2, HNO_3, etc.) of the Mn^I complexes. In alkaline medium the Mn^{II} complexes disproportionate back to the lower oxidation state, probably at the expense of part of the ligand:

$$13[Mn(CNR)_6]^{2+} + 14OH^- \rightarrow$$
$$12[Mn(CNR)_6]^+ + 6RNCO + Mn(OH)_2 + 6H_2O$$

In the case of iron, although methylation of ferrocyanide affords the hexakis–isonitrile cation $[Fe(CNMe)_6]^{2+}$, the addition of isonitriles to ferrous salts leads only to the introduction of four molecules of the ligand giving $[Fe(CNR)_4]^{2+}$. Apart from these and the mixed carbonylisocyanide complexes (p. 47), the isonitrile analogues of the nitrosocarbonyls $Fe(CO)_2(NO)_2$ and $Co(CO)_3(NO)$ are also known. They may be obtained by displacement of CO from these carbonyls, or, in the case of iron, by either displacement of sulphide from Roussin's red salt:

$$K_2[Fe_2(NO)_4S_2] + 4RNC \rightarrow 2Fe(CNR)_2(NO)_2 + K_2S_2$$

or reaction of tetrakis–isocyanide–iron(II) salts with hydroxylamine:

$$[Fe(CNR)_4]^{2+} + 4NH_2OH \rightarrow$$
$$Fe(CNR)_2(NO)_2 + 2CNR + 2NH_4^+ + 2H_2O$$

Cobalt forms an interesting and varied array of isocyanide complexes. Whereas its chloride and bromide react with four ligand molecules to give $Co(CNR)_4X_2$ as blue violet products with one unpaired electron, which give conducting solutions and hence probably contain square planar $[Co(CNR)_4]^{2+}$ ions with dsp^2 hybridized metal, the corresponding iodides occur additionally in a diamagnetic form. The latter is probably dimeric, like the rhodium analogue $[Rh_2I_2(CNPh)_8]I_2$. With iodine-bridged structures, (4–14) these would be analogous to the dimeric halocarbonylmanganese

4-14

$X_2Mn_2(CO)_8$. Dimeric structures have been demonstrated for the pentakis–isocyanidecobalt(II) ions obtained when cobalt perchlorate reacts with such ligands:

$$2Co(ClO_4)_2 + 10RNC \rightarrow [Co(CNR)_5]_2(ClO_4)_4$$

X-ray structure determination on the methyl isocyanide complex shows these derivatives to be isosteres of decacarbonyldimanganese, the two halves being joined by a metal–metal bond (Co—Co = $2\cdot74$ Å) while the Co—C—NR groups deviate from linearity to about the same extent ($\sim6°$) as many metal carbonyl groups. They are reduced by hydrazine to the yellow, diamagnetic Co^I compounds, $[Co(CNR)_5]ClO_4$. The rhodium(I) derivatives in contrast to those of cobalt(I) are of the form $[Rh(CNR)_4]X$. They have a strong tendency to solvate and are highly coloured though diamagnetic.

Nickel, palladium and platinum halides all yield neutral bis-isocyanide complexes $M(CNR)_2X_2$ which correspond to the platinum chlorocarbonyl, $Pt(CO)_2Cl_2$. But unlike the nickel and palladium derivatives, the platinum compounds also exist in the ionic form $[Pt(CNR)_4][PtX_4]$, where X = halogen or CN.

Apart from the ready formation of the Ni^0 derivatives either from $Ni(CO)_4$ (p. 47) or from Ni^{II} under reducing conditions, palladium also forms a zerovalent complex. This is obtained when the diiodo complex is treated with alkali in the presence of excess of free isocyanide:

$$Pd(CNR)_2I_2 + 2KOH + RNC \rightarrow$$
$$Pd(CNR)_2 + KI + RNCO + H_2O$$

The brown, air-stable, diamagnetic and very insoluble products, $Pd(CNR)_2$, have no analogues among the metal carbonyls, but react with phosphites with partial or complete displacement of isocyanide to give the tetra-coordinate $Pd(CNR)[P(OR')_3]_3$ and $Pd[P(OR)_3]_4$. They also dissolve in liquid isocyanides, possibly forming $Pd(CNR)_{3\text{ or }4}$ and react with iodine to give back $Pd(CNR)_2I_2$.

Isonitriles, like carbonyls can be bridging ligands, as has been shown by the following preparation of a cyclopentadienyliron complex of this type

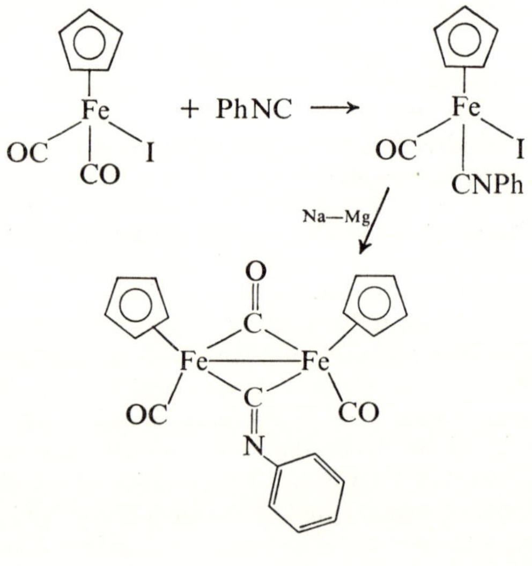

4·15

As in the case of the carbonyls, the bridging ligand is characterized by infrared absorption at much lower frequency. Thus, whereas typical terminal isocyanide groups have maxima above 2100 cm^{-1} (e.g. $Ni(CO)_3(CNMe)$ at 2190 cm^{-1}; the above iodide at 2137 cm^{-1}) the bridging isocyanide in the above complex probably gives rise to the peak which occurs at 1704 cm^{-1}.

Isocyanide complexes of rare earth metals have been obtained by simple addition to the tricyclopentadienyls $(C_5H_5)_3M$, of ytterbium, holmium and terbium. Thus

$$(C_5H_5)_3Ho + CNC_6H_{11} \rightarrow (C_5H_5)_3HoCNC_6H_{11}.$$

The products are sublimable crystalline solids with CN absorption maxima at 2205 cm^{-1}.

ACETYLIDE COMPLEXES

Both palladium and platinum form zerovalent acetylide complexes, analogous to the above bis-isonitrile palladium, when their cyanide complexes are treated with potassium acetylide and potassium metal in liquid ammonia solution:

$$K_2[M(CN)_4] + 2K + 2KC\equiv CR \rightarrow 4KCN + K_2[M(C\equiv CR)_2]$$
$$\text{where } M = Pd \text{ or } Pt$$

When air is passed into the solution containing the yellow pyrophoric Pt^0 complex and excess acetylide, re-oxidation leads to the Pt^{II} complex, $K_2[Pt(C\equiv CR)_4]$ cf. p. 51.

The nickel(0) complex contains 4 acetylide groups and may be formed by potassium in liquid ammonia reduction of the Ni^{II} derivative, $K_2[Ni(C\equiv CR)_4]$. The Ni^I complex $K_6[Ni_2(C\equiv CR)_8]$ is isosteric with $(Fe_2(CO)_8)^{2-}$ and is obtained by simultaneous displacement of cyanide and carbonyl groups from

$$K_4[Ni_2(CN)_6(CO)_2].$$

Cobalt, iron and manganese give complexes in oxidation states II and III. Those of cobalt and iron correspond closely to the corresponding cyanides, the Fe^{II} and Co^{III} derivatives being yellow and diamagnetic, while the Fe^{III} and Co^{II} complexes are paramagnetic and highly coloured. Interconversion occurs in liquid ammonia by air oxidation and alkali metal reduction,

e.g. $$K_4[Fe(C\equiv CH)_6] \underset{K}{\overset{O_2/NH_3}{\rightleftarrows}} K_3[Fe(C\equiv CH)_6]$$

In the case of manganese the divalent ion forms only an outerorbital (sp^3) complex with four ligand molecules $K_2[Mn(C\equiv CR)_4]$

in which the metal retains 5 unpaired electrons in the half-filled 3d shell, in contrast to the cyanide $[\mathrm{Mn(CN)}_6]^{4-}$. During its oxidation two more ligand ions are added:

$$\mathrm{K_2[Mn(C{\equiv}CH)_4] + 2KC{\equiv}CH \xrightarrow[NH_3]{O_2} K_3[Mn(C{\equiv}CH)_6]}$$

Cuprous ions yield both $\mathrm{K[Cu(C{\equiv}CR)_2]}$ and $\mathrm{K_2[Cu(C{\equiv}CR)_3]}$ while Zn, Cd and Hg give compounds of the type $\mathrm{K_2[M(C{\equiv}CR)_4]}$ analogous to their cyanides. Examples of this type of complex include the spiro- compounds from o-diethynylbenzene:

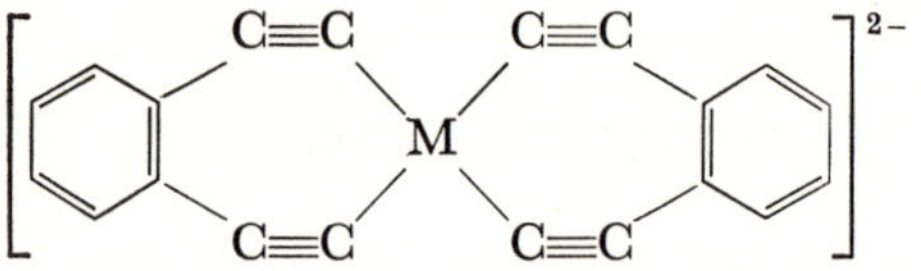

4-16

The formation of these, rather than polymeric acetylides, is remarkable in view of the angular strain imposed on the acetylene grouping.

Chapter 5

'μ-Complexes'

2-ELECTRON DONORS

The simplest examples of this class as well as the first to be described and to have their structures recognized are the platinum-ethylene complexes referred to in Chapter 1. Other mono-olefins give analogous complexes, e.g. $K[(CH_3CH{=}CH_2)PtCl_3]$. These

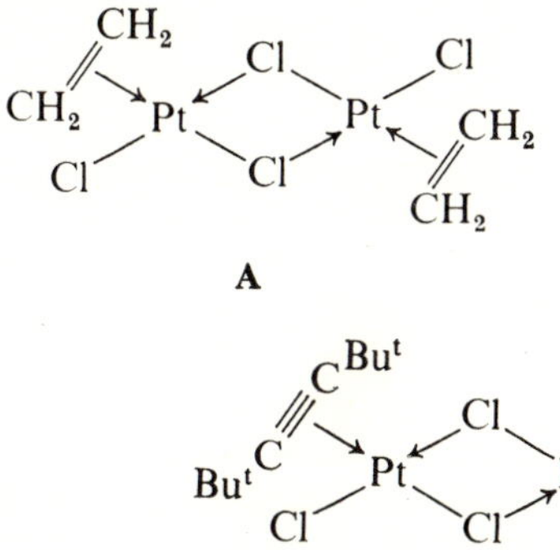

A

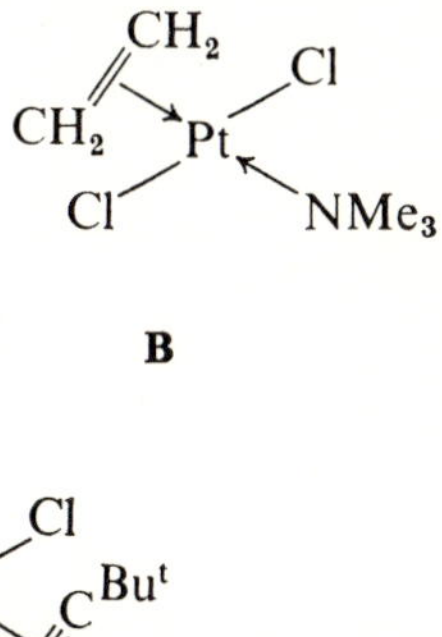

B

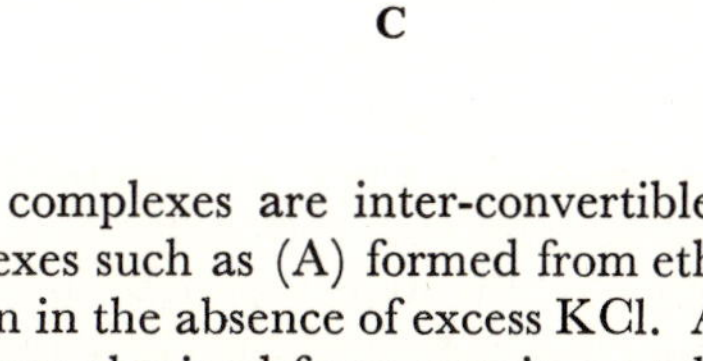

C

Zeise salt type complexes are inter-convertible with the dimeric covalent complexes such as (A) formed from ethylene and K_2PtCl_4 in acidic solution in the absence of excess KCl. Analogous products (e.g. C) have been obtained from certain acetylenes.

Various electron donor ligands, e.g. tert.-amines, convert these compounds to monomeric products, (e.g. B), by cleavage of the halogen bridges. To obtain complexes of comparable stability from Pd, Ru, or Os it is necessary to use a chelating diolefin. 1,5-Cyclooctadiene has a particularly suitable configuration and has been much used. Thus it affords, on simple treatment with the appropriate halides, the complexes of Pd^{II}, Rh^{I} and Ru^{II} shown.

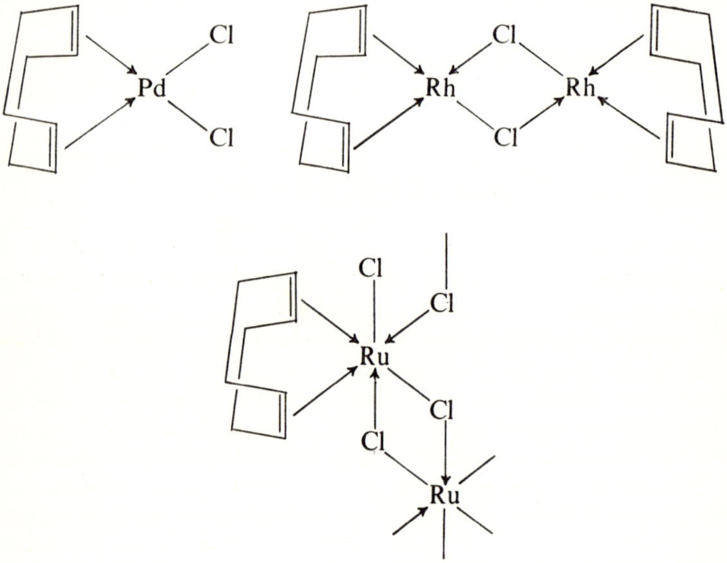

5-2

The last is polymeric with chloride bridges from each Ru atom to two others. Both it and the dimeric Rh complex suffer the bridge splitting reaction with donor ligands described for Pt. Thus triphenylphosphine converts the Rh complex to square planar $C_8H_{12}Rh(Cl)PPh_3$ and p-toluidine converts the Ru compound to octahedral $C_8H_{12}RuCl_2(p\text{-}H_2NC_6H_4Me)_2$.

Ingenious use of the reversible formation of platinum olefin complexes has been made by Cope for the resolution of olefins, notably *trans*-cyclooctene and *trans*-cyclononene. By exchange with the ethylene complex of the type (5—1,B) but containing an optically active amine such as α-phenylethylamine, the racemic olefin yields the diastereoisomeric complexes:

e.g. $PtCl_2(PhCHMeNH_2)(C_2H_4) + C_8H_{14} \rightarrow$

$$PtCl_2(PhCHMeNH_2)(C_8H_{14}) + C_2H_4.$$

These are then separated and individually decomposed with potassium cyanide or triphenylphosphine to liberate the active olefin:

e.g. $PtCl_2(PhCHMeNH_2)(C_8H_{14}) + 4KCN \rightarrow$

$$K_2Pt(CN)_4 + 2KCN + PhCHMeNH_2 + C_8H_{14}$$

$$PtCl_2(PhCHMeNH_2)(C_9H_{16}) + 2PPh_3 \xrightarrow{Ac_2O}$$

$$(Ph_3P)_2PtCl_2 + PhCHMeNH_2 + C_9H_{16}$$

The speed of the last reaction allows isolation of even the optically unstable cyclononene without extensive racemization.

Silver(I) and copper(I) also form complexes with both mono and di- (or poly-) olefins and with acetylenes. They vary in stoicheiometry, but both silver nitrate and silver perchlorate will commonly complex with two molecules of a simple olefin or one of a diene. In several examples which have been studied crystallographically the metal atom is bonded unsymmetrically to two olefins. The bonding is weak, the olefin being readily regenerated (e.g. by heating or treatment with aqueous NaCl), and the perturbation of the carbon-carbon double bond is sufficient only to lower its i.r. stretching frequency by c. 50 cm^{-1}. The latter figure compares with c. 150 cm^{-1} for the platinum complexes. The copper complexes are markedly less stable than those of silver and many have been studied only in solution in equilibrium with the free components.

Other metals bond to simple olefins or even dienes only when linked simultaneously to other strongly π-bonding ligands (e.g. CO, C_5H_5) and generally in low oxidation states. Only Ni^0 has been observed bonded to olefins alone. It may bond to either 2, 3 or 4 such groupings as in the bis-acrylonitrile complex, the cyclododecatriene complex and the bis-cycloocta-1,5-diene complex shown

$$
\begin{array}{c}
CN \\
/ \\
CH_2{=}CH \\
\downarrow \\
Ni \\
\uparrow \\
CH{=}CH_2 \\
/ \\
NC
\end{array}
$$

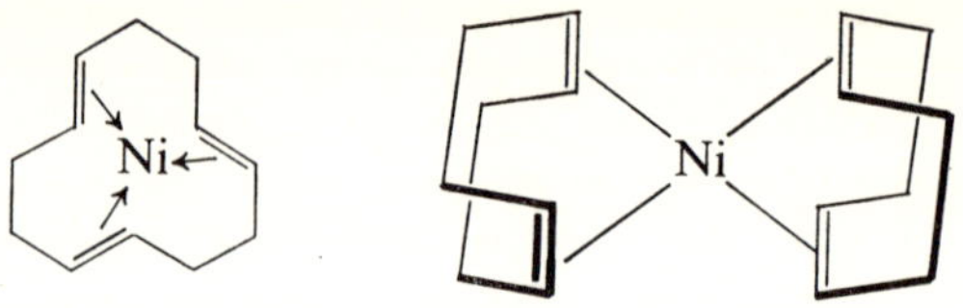

5-4

These can be prepared inter alia by the sequence of displacements:

$$Ni(CO)_4 \xrightarrow{CH_2=CHCN} Ni(CH_2=CHCN)_2 \xrightarrow{C_{12}H_{18}}$$

$$NiC_{12}H_{18} \xrightarrow{C_8H_{12}} Ni(C_8H_{12})_2$$

The electron deficient acrylonitrile complex is pyrophoric in air and readily adds further ligands, e.g. two moles of triphenyl-phosphine:

$$Ni(CH_2=CHCN)_2 + PPh_3 \rightarrow (Ph_3P)Ni(CH_2=CHCN)_2 \xrightarrow{PPh_3}$$

$$(Ph_3P)_2Ni(CH_2=CHCN)_2$$

Both the phosphine adducts are still very air sensitive.

The bis-cycloocta-1,5-diene complex and the analogous bis-duroquinonenickel as well as the mixed duroquinone-nickel-diene complexes are much more stable substances; the last can readily

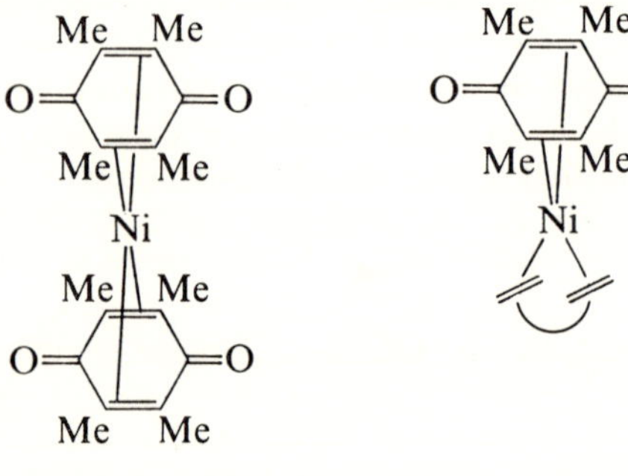

5-5

be prepared from the bis-duroquinone complex by replacement of one molecule of the quinone. It has been shown that the ease of such replacement, as well as the stability of the product increase in the series:

cyclooctatetraene < bicyclo[2,2,1]heptadiene < dicyclopenta-diene < 1,5-cyclooctadiene, and that conjugated dienes do not give analogous products. Similarly, molybdenum carbonyl reacts much more readily with unconjugated, chelating dienes than with conjugated dienes to give products of the type $(diene)Mo(CO)_4$. On the other hand displacement of CO from cyclopentadienyl-cobalt dicarbonyl by dienes:

5-6

appears to occur with equal ease with conjugated and unconjugated dienes. Except in one or two special cases iron carbonyl gives stable products only with conjugated dienes. Since the resultant diene-iron tricarbonyls appear to have a largely delocalized electron system in the diene residue, they must be regarded as having 4-electron donor ligands rather than 2 separate 2-electron donor ligands and are treated more fully below (p. 120). Manganese in the few diene complexes known is also linked to a conjugated system.

Nevertheless both the iron and manganese groups can form quite stable complexes with mono-olefins. The neutral iron complexes $(CO)_4Fe \leftarrow (olefin)$ are most stable and most readily prepared (see p. 48) when the olefin is conjugated with an electron-withdrawing group, e.g. CN, CO_2Et, etc. Conjugation with a second double bond is sufficient to yield a product of reasonable stability and butadiene with enneacarbonyldi-iron affords both the mono- and bis-tetracarbonyliron complexes:

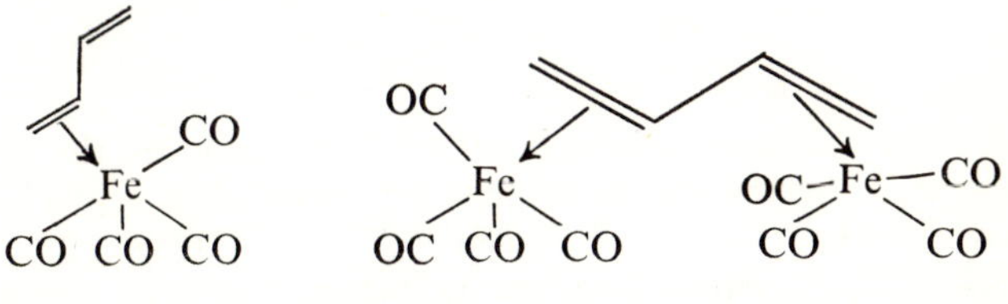

5-7

The former readily loses carbon monoxide to give the tricarbonyl $C_4H_6Fe(CO)_3$ in which the metal atom is linked to both double bonds.

The fumaric acid complex has been resolved via its brucine salt into the optically active forms, having $[\alpha]_D^{25} \pm593°$ (in acetone):

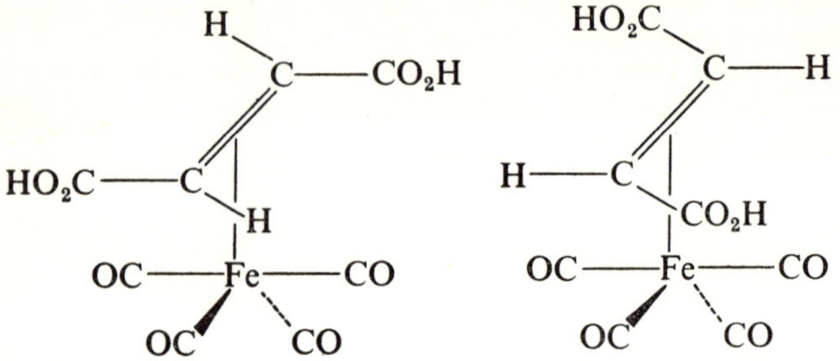

5-8

Manganese and rhenium in the form of the groups $C_5H_5M(CO)_2$ and chromium in $ArHCr(CO)_2$ from mono-olefin (or acetylene) complexes of good stability which may be exemplified by

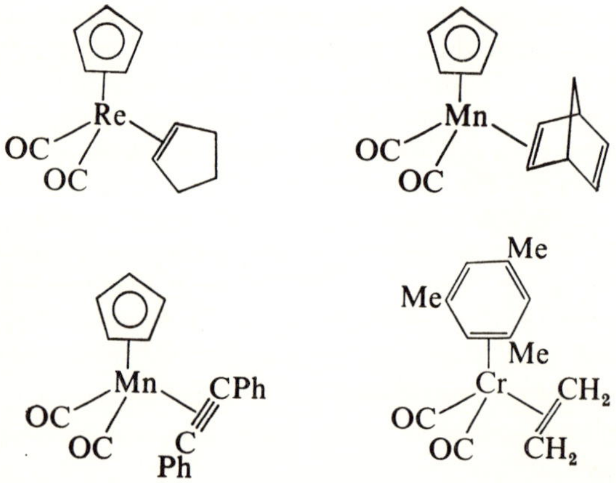

5-9

The other complexes formed with simple olefins are the cationic complexes in which the olefin may be regarded as replacing one CO in the ions $Mn(CO)_6^+$, $C_5H_5Fe(CO)_3^+$, $C_5H_5Mo(CO)_4^+$ and $C_5H_5W(CO)_4^+$. Apart from the preparation of such compounds from the corresponding halides (p. 50) they have been obtained by hydride abstraction from the corresponding alkyls,

e.g. $C_5H_5Fe(CO)_2$—CH_2CH_3 + $Ph_3C^+BF_4^-$ $\longrightarrow$

$$\left[C_5H_5Fe(CO)_2 \longleftarrow \begin{matrix} CH_2 \\ \| \\ CH_2 \end{matrix} \right]^+ BF_4^- + Ph_3CH$$

The reaction is reversible, the cationic olefin complexes being converted to neutral alkyls by sodium borohydride. Another method is the protonation of σ-allyl complexes,

e.g. $C_5H_5Mo(CO)_3$—CH_2CH=CH_2 + H^+ $\longrightarrow$

$$\left[C_5H_5Mo(CO)_3 \xleftarrow{\quad} \begin{array}{c} CH_2 \\ \| \\ CHCH_3 \end{array} \right]^+$$

3-ELECTRON DONORS

When the same σ-allyl complex is irradiated, it is transformed to the corresponding π-allyl complex:

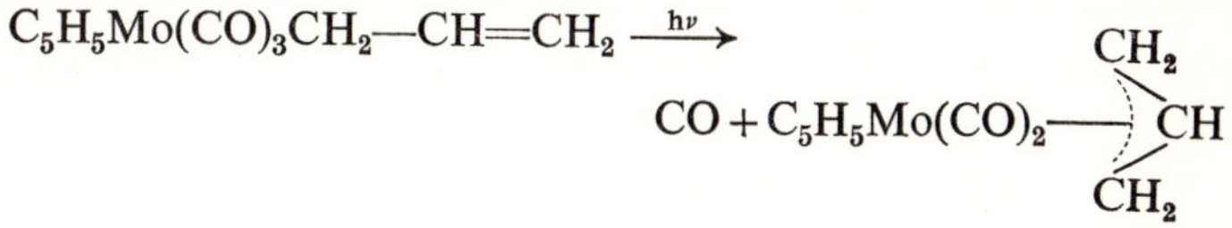

$$C_5H_5Mo(CO)_3CH_2\text{—}CH\text{=}CH_2 \xrightarrow{\ h\nu\ } $$

$$CO + C_5H_5Mo(CO)_2 \text{—} \begin{array}{c} CH_2 \\ CH \\ CH_2 \end{array}$$

With σ-allylpentacarbonylmanganese, the same change merely requires warming:

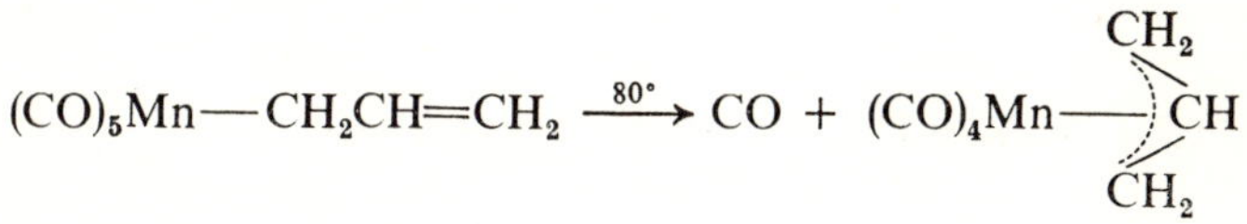

$$(CO)_5Mn\text{—}CH_2CH\text{=}CH_2 \xrightarrow{\ 80°\ } CO + (CO)_4Mn\text{—}\begin{array}{c} CH_2 \\ CH \\ CH_2 \end{array}$$

and in the case of the cobalt analogue it occurs so readily that only the π-complex is isolated when tetracarbonyl-cobaltsodium is treated with allyl bromide, although the σ-compound must be intermediate:

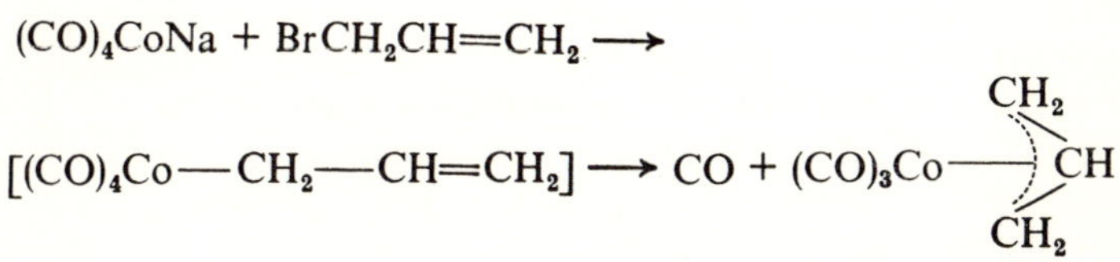

$$(CO)_4CoNa + BrCH_2CH\text{=}CH_2 \longrightarrow$$

$$[(CO)_4Co\text{—}CH_2\text{—}CH\text{=}CH_2] \longrightarrow CO + (CO)_3Co\text{—}\begin{array}{c} CH_2 \\ CH \\ CH_2 \end{array}$$

In all these simple allyl compounds and in their homologues the allylic group is bonded symmetrically (cf. p. 9) to the metal as a 3-electron donor. This was first deduced from their nuclear magnetic resonance spectra, but has been amply confirmed by detailed structure determination of several allyl complexes, e.g. the chloropalladium complex:

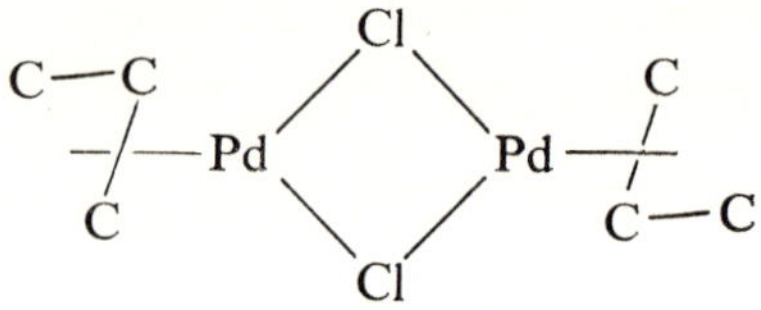

$$\textbf{5-10}$$

In this the C—C distances are equal. The C—C—C planes are not exactly perpendicular to the Pd-Cl plane, but inclined at an angle which leads to equal distances from Pd to the three carbon atoms. This compound and its bromo- analogue are obtainable from sodium chloropalladite and allyl alcohol or chloride a reaction which involves a formal disproportionation of the latter reagent (part of which must be oxidized to acrolein). Even direct reaction of palladium metal and allyl bromide affords this complex:

$$Pd + CH_2{=}CHCH_2Br \rightarrow \tfrac{1}{2}(C_3H_5PdBr)_2$$

and allenes can add palladous chloride to give 2-chloroallyl derivatives:

e.g.

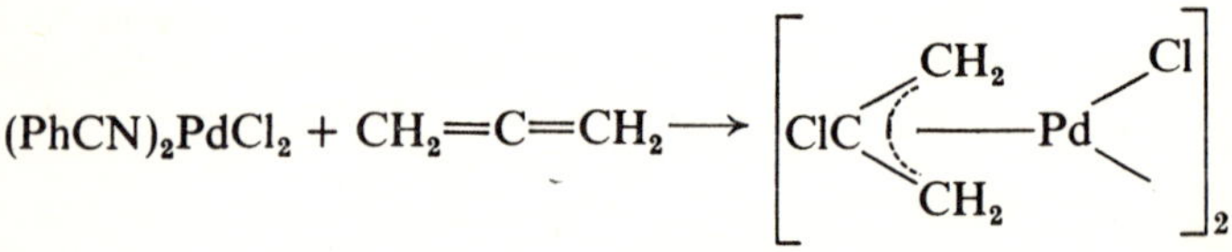

$$\textbf{5-11}$$

The reaction of palladous chloride with propylene (5-12) is best

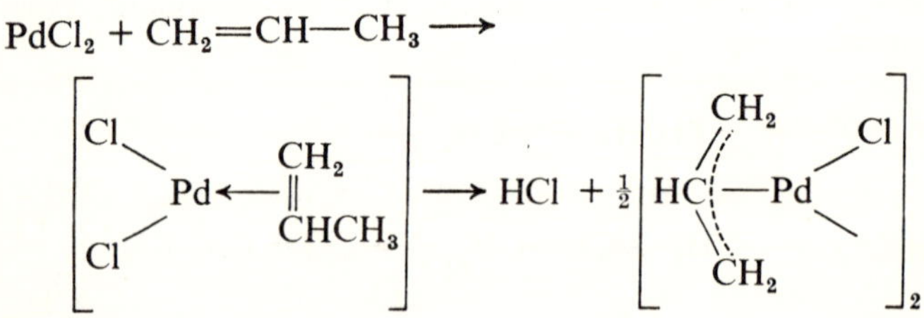

$$\textbf{5-12}$$

visualized as proceeding through an olefin complex of the type shown. This route is closely related to the Pd—Cu catalyzed olefin oxidation reactions discussed in Chapter 6.

The nickel analogue is readily formed from nickel carbonyl and allyl chloride or bromide.

$$2Ni(CO)_4 + 2CH_2{=}CHCH_2Br \xrightarrow[\text{reflux}]{C_6H_6} (C_3H_5NiBr)_2 + 8CO$$

The only known cyclopropenyl complex is obtained similarly:

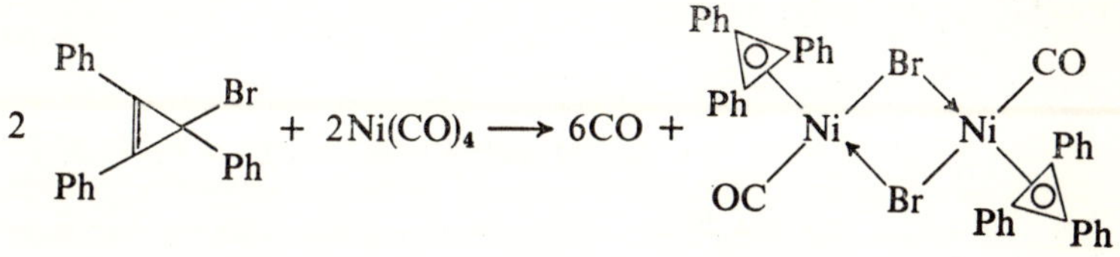

5-13

In contrast to the formation of this dicarbonyl complex, it is noteworthy that all the carbonyl groups are liberated in the above reaction of allyl bromide, despite the fact that in the product (as in the Pd compound) each metal atom is two electrons short of inert gas configuration. Similarly the dimeric halides do not add triphenylphosphine, but react with fission of the halide bridge to give $C_3H_5NiX(PPh_3)$. Although likewise having 34 electrons around nickel, the diallyl derivative $(C_3H_5)_2Ni$ is a considerably more reactive substance, which loses both hydrocarbon groups when treated with triphenylphosphine:

$$(C_3H_5)_2Ni + 4PPh_3 \rightarrow Ni(PPh_3)_4 + C_6H_{10}$$
$$\text{diallyl}$$

This diallyl complex is much less stable and more reactive than the 36-electron allylcyclopentadienyl nickel, (A). It is noteworthy that this stable complex results not only from allylnickel bromide and cyclopentadienylsodium, but also by direct displacement of a cyclopentadienyl by an allyl group when dicyclopentadienylnickel

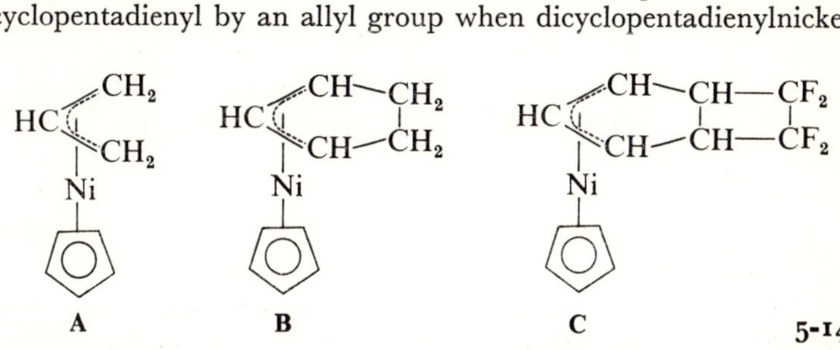

A   B   C   5-14

is treated with allylmagnesium bromide. The closely related complexes (B) and (C) result when dicyclopentadienylnickel is reduced with sodium amalgam or treated with tetrafluoroethylene. These examples illustrate the strong tendency to form complexes of this type.

Like the above nickel halide complex, the tricarbonyl-allyliron halides are conveniently prepared from iron carbonyls (preferably $Fe_2(CO)_9$) and allyl halides:

$$Fe_2(CO)_9 + CH_2{=}CHCH_2Br \rightarrow$$

$$C_3H_5Fe(CO)_3Br + CO + Fe(CO)_5$$

An alternative approach to higher homologues involves the protonation of diene-iron carbonyls. When tetracarbonyl-butadiene-iron is used this may be regarded as proceeding by the steps:

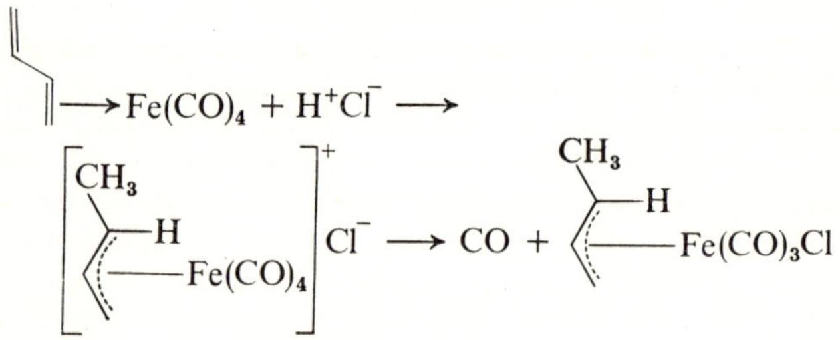

5-15

but no stable tetracarbonylallyliron cation has ever been isolated. Instead, the stable cation in this series appears to be the tricarbonyl-allyliron cation with only 34 electrons about the iron atom. This is formed as the perchlorate or fluoroborate when the corresponding acids are added to tricarbonylbutadiene–iron:

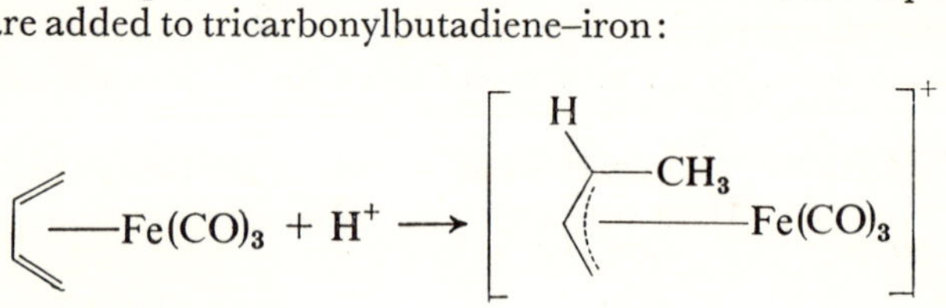

5-16

On the other hand there is also an example of a tricarbonyl-allyliron anion (36 electrons) formed by adding caesium fluoride to tricarbonylperfluorocyclohexadiene-iron:

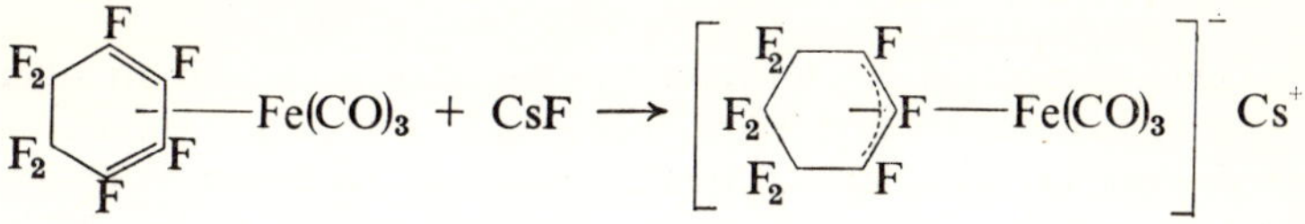

$$\text{5-17}$$

When the above proton addition is carried out using hydrogen chloride, the anion becomes covalently linked to the metal and an inversion of configuration occurs:

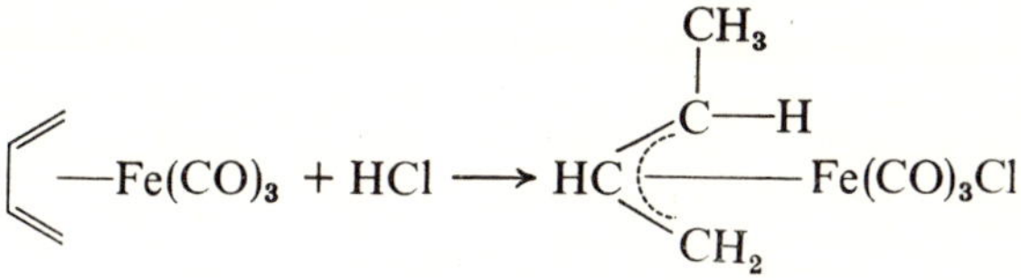

$$\text{5-18}$$

Thus whereas the cation preserves the configuration of the butadiene complex, the chloro-complex has the alternative 'syn'-configuration. Hence it is identical with both the complex from tetracarbonyl-butadiene-iron and that obtained by the action of crotyl chloride on enneacarbonyldi-iron (cf. p. 52). Mild reduction of the analogous tricarbonylallylchloro-iron, best effected by merely shaking with Al_2O_3, gives tricarbonylallyliron as an equilibrium mixture of the monomeric radical and the dimer:

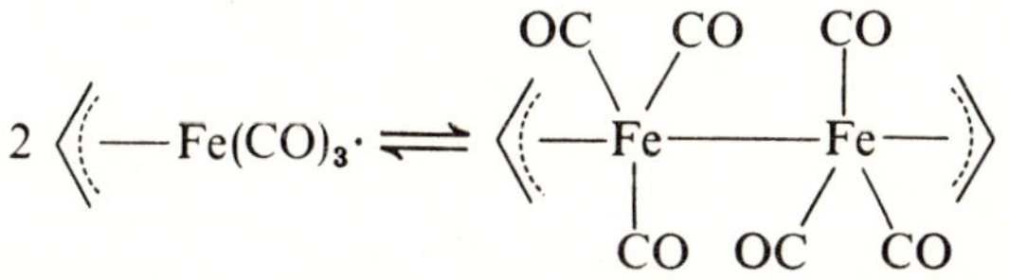

$$\text{5-19}$$

Neither the weakness of the metal-metal bond in this compound, compared, for example, to that in decacarbonyldimanganese nor the failure to form carbonyl bridges have been adequately explained.

4-ELECTRON DONORS

Diene complexes of iron have become known in large number. Although enneacarbonyldi-iron reacts under the mildest conditions, most work has been done by treating dienes with pentacarbonyliron at temperatures in the range 130–200°. Under such conditions dienes in which the double bonds are separated by one or two CH_2 groups isomerize to give tricarbonyliron complexes of the corresponding conjugated dienes. Tricarbonylbutadiene-iron is the prototype of this class, but a large number of derivatives are known. In these the diene may be part of a ring and may have a wide variety of substituents, e.g. alkyl, alcoholic, aldehyde, acid or ester groups.

Additional double bonds remain unaffected. Thus in both the cycloheptatriene and tropone (=cycloheptatrienone) complexes shown, one double bond may be reduced catalytically without affecting the bonding to the metal.

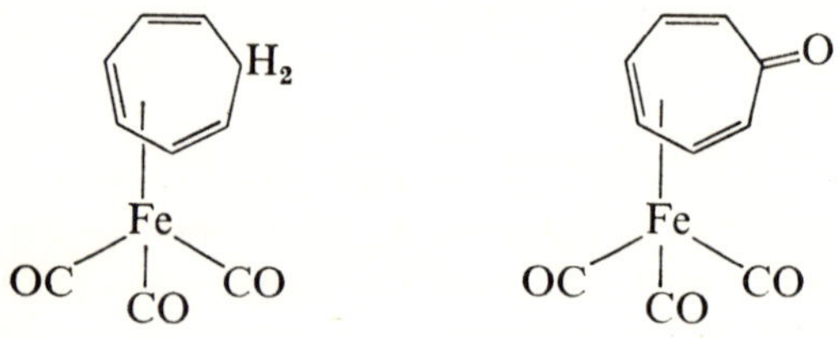

5-20

Cyclo-octatetraene gives complexes both with one and with two $Fe(CO)_3$ groups. The structures, determined by x-rays, have not only revealed that in each case the iron atoms are bonded to a

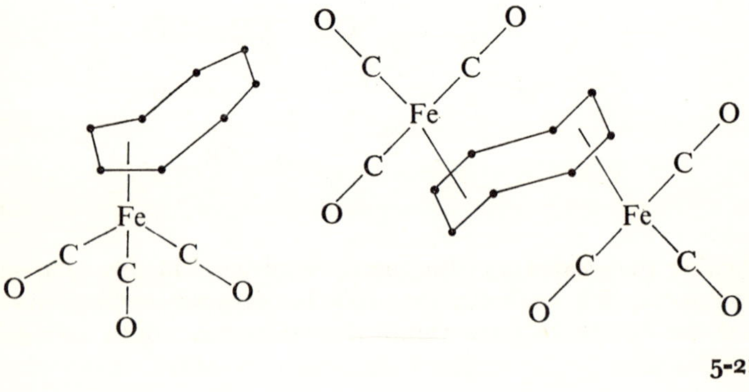

5-21

conjugated diene system in exactly the same manner as in tricarbonylbutadiene-iron, but that the ring adopts the configurations shown, contrasting sharply with the 'tub' shape adopted by the free hydrocarbon.

Tropone complexes of the type shown above, were first observed as products of the reaction of iron carbonyls with acetylenes. They form together with a wide variety of other products depending on the nature of the acetylene, the carbonyl and the conditions used. Several others have iron bonded to diene systems. Thus cyclopentadienone complexes are readily formed, of which the 2,5-diphenyl derivative from phenylacetylene is a typical example:

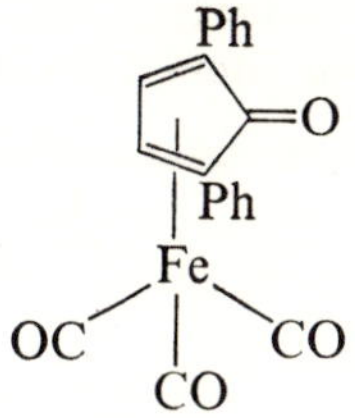

5-22

Another type are the di-iron compounds in which one iron atom is linked to a diene system that is itself part of a ferracyclopentadiene ring. The prototype of this class is the compound (5-23) obtained

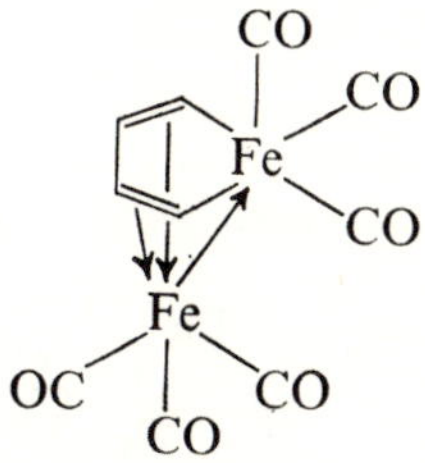

5-23

(12% yield) from acetylene itself on warming (65°) with $Fe_3(CO)_{12}$ and also from pentacarbonyliron and thiophene with expulsion of sulphur. The dihydroxy-derivative (R = H) is formed when acetylene is absorbed by solutions of $NaHFe_2(CO)_8$. In this case only two carbons are derived from the acetylene and substituted acetylenes (RC≡CR) give analogous products which on mild oxidation give the cyclic diacyliron derivative shown. Even bonds

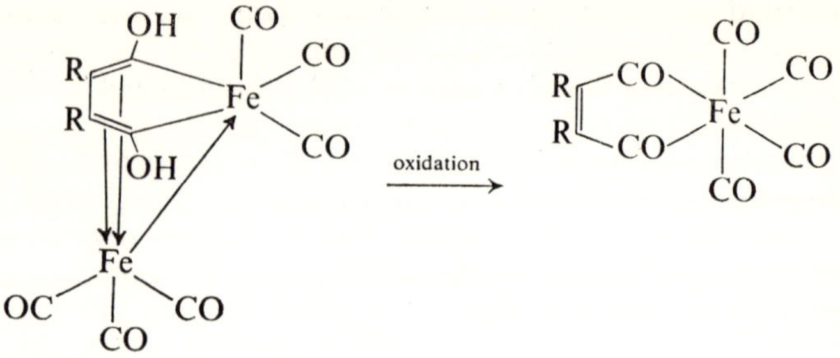

5-24

which are part of an aromatic ring can be linked as components of a diene system to an iron atom as in the ferra-indene analogue:

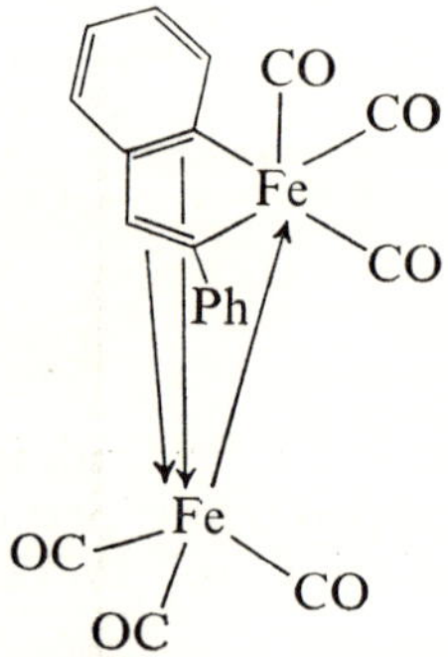

5-25

The tetraphenylferracyclopentadiene complex has been subjected to a number of degradations in which the ring-iron atom is lost.

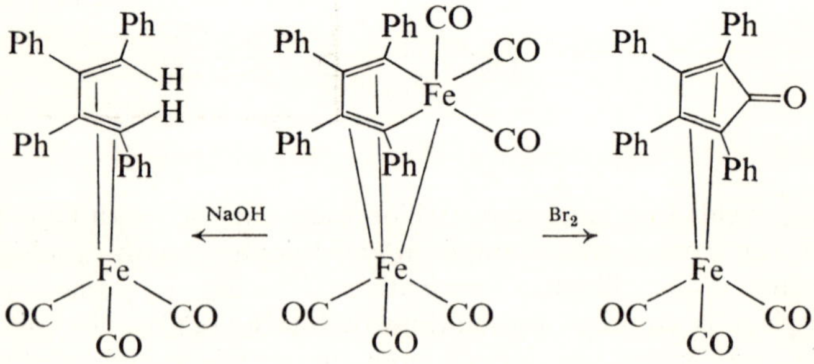

5-26

Thus sulphur displaces both metal atoms and gives tetraphenyl-thiophene. Irradiation or caustic alkali cause reductive cleavage to give tricarbonyltetraphenylbutadiene-iron, while bromine in acetic acid causes CO insertion to give the tetraphenylcyclopentadienone (tetracyclone) complex, also obtained directly from iron carbonyls with either tolane or tetracyclone. The latter is one of the few conjugated dienes which have been shown to give such complexes also with hexacarbonylmolybdenum which reacts to give dicarbonyl-bis(tetracyclone)molybdenum.

The wide variety of complexes which have been obtained from carbonyls of iron and tolane also include the two isomeric tri-iron complexes (I) and (II). The latter (II) is unique at the time of

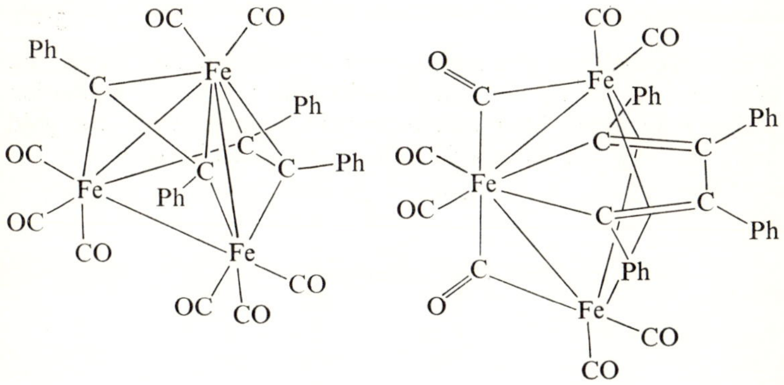

I   II

5-27

writing as an example of a complex in which the same π-electron system serves to bond two metal atoms on either side of the hydro-carbon system. The former (I), which is intermediate in the forma-tion of the second isomer, is the only example, with iron, in which the acetylene itself has not been modified in reacting with the carbonyl. Although an alkyne possesses four π-electrons the overlap of its π-orbitals with suitable orbitals of a single metal atom clearly presents steric problems. The simplest situation is probably that where the acetylene bonds to two metal atoms as above or as in the dicyclopentadienyldinickel complexes obtained by treating either dicarbonyldicyclopentadienyldinickel or dicyclopentadienylnickel

5

with suitable acetylenes:

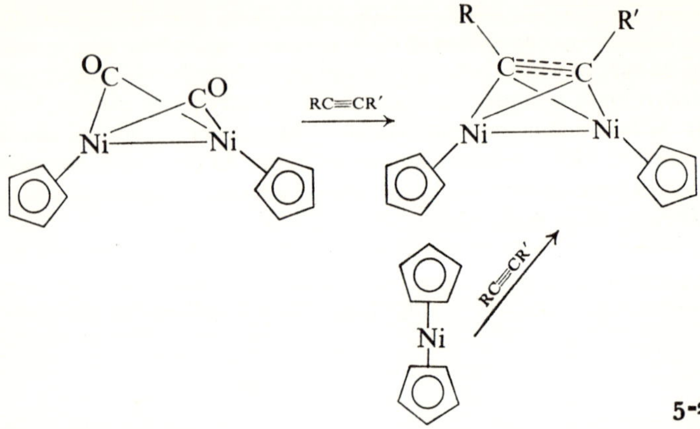

5-28

A related cobalt complex is discussed in Chapter 6. Acetylenes can, of course, use merely one pair of π-electrons (cf. p. 111), a situation which may apply inter alia to certain copper, silver and gold acetylides, e.g. the tetrameric $Bu^t C \equiv CAu$ formulated as

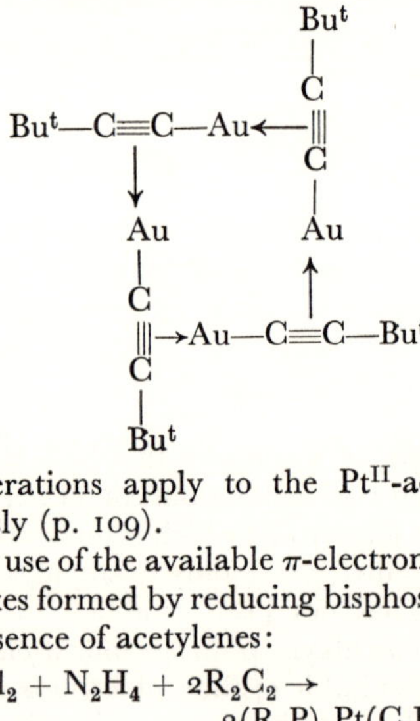

5-29

Similar considerations apply to the Pt^{II}-acetylene complexes discussed previously (p. 109).

However, fuller use of the available π-electrons may be postulated in the Pt^0 complexes formed by reducing bisphosphine-platinum(II) halides in the presence of acetylenes:

$$2 \, cis\text{-}(R_3P)_2PtCl_2 + N_2H_4 + 2R_2C_2 \rightarrow$$
$$2(R_3P)_2Pt(C_2R_2) + N_2 + 4HCl$$

and in the molybdenum and tungsten carbonyl complexes $M(CO)(C_2R_2)_3$.

The 4-π-electron ligand of greatest theoretical interest is undoubtedly the cyclobutadiene system. As tetraphenylcyclobutadiene, this was recognized to be present in yet another of the complexes from iron carbonyls and tolane and the chloro-palladium complex is readily obtained from the same acetylene and solutions

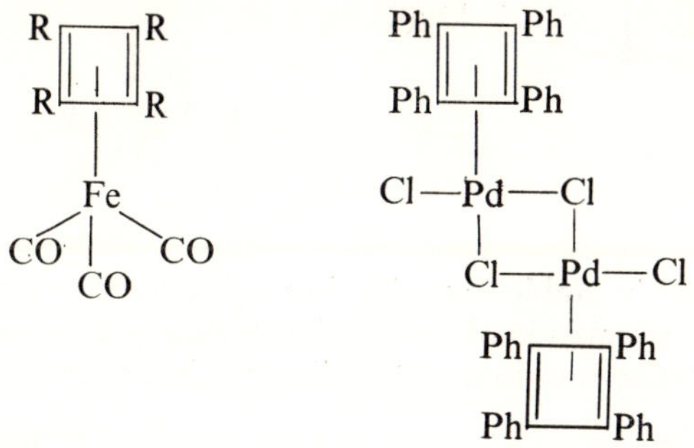

5-30

of palladous chloride. The ligand so formed can be transferred to other metals, e.g. in the reactions:

$$[C_4Ph_4PdBr_2]_2 \; + \; Fe(CO)_5 \xrightarrow{\text{xylene}} C_4Ph_4Fe(CO)_3 \qquad (88\%)$$

$$[C_4Ph_4PdBr_2]_2 + (C_5H_5)_2Co \xrightarrow{\text{xylene}} C_4Ph_4CoC_5H_5 \qquad (12\%)$$

$$[C_4Ph_4PdBr_2]_2 \; + \; Ni(CO)_4 \xrightarrow{\text{benzene}} C_4Ph_4NiBr_2 \qquad (47\%)$$

$$[C_4Ph_4PdBr_4]_4 \; + \; Co_2(CO)_8 \xrightarrow[25°]{CH_2Cl_2} C_4Ph_4Co(CO)_2Br \qquad (60\%)$$

The product of the last reaction is strongly paramagnetic despite its formal krypton configuration of electrons. The first recognized cyclobutadiene complex was the nickel compound obtained by Criegee and Schröder when they treated dichlorotetramethylcyclobutene with nickel carbonyl:

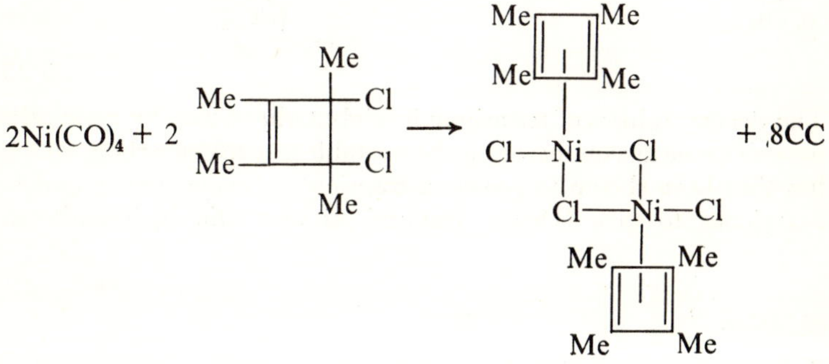

$$2Ni(CO)_4 + 2 \qquad \longrightarrow \qquad + \, .8CC$$

5-31

A similar reaction has yielded the unsubstituted iron compound:

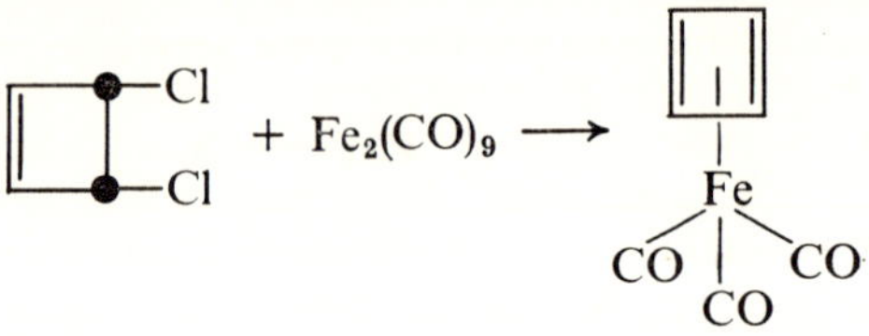

5-32

This remarkably stable complex has a reactive aromatic cyclo-butadiene ring, capable of undergoing a variety of typical electro-philic substitution reactions. The following illustrates this reactivity.

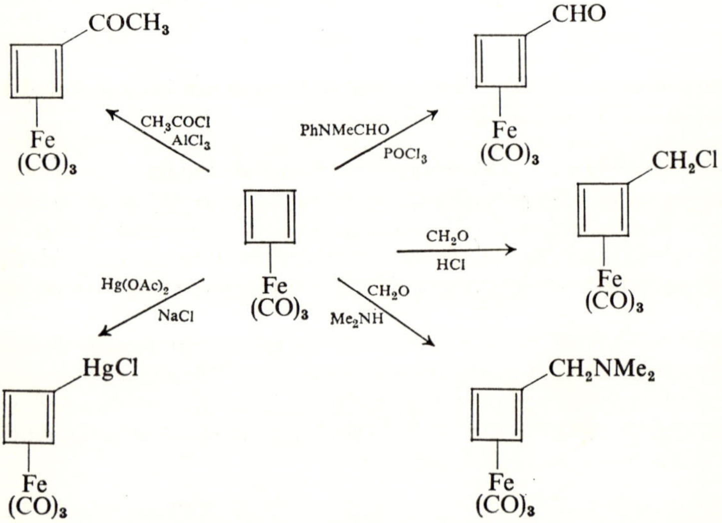

5-33

The decomposition of tricarbonylcyclobutadiene-iron by ceric salts provides a means of liberating the unstable free hydrocarbon, which has thus been shown to possess a transient existence and to add to acetylenes to give 'Dewar isomers' of aromatic hydrocarbons:

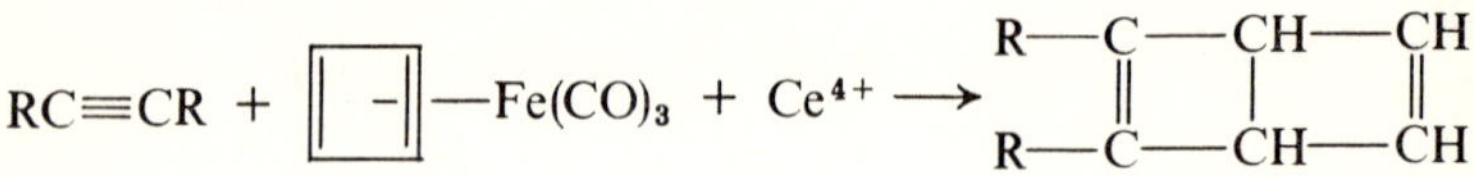

5-34

5-ELECTRON DONORS

The strong tendency of cyclopentadiene to yield cyclopentadienyl-metal complexes makes it one conjugated diene which does not normally yield diene complexes. Even tetracyclone complexes can be formulated as substituted cyclopentadienyl complexes. Thus the iron compound (cf. p. 122) may be written as

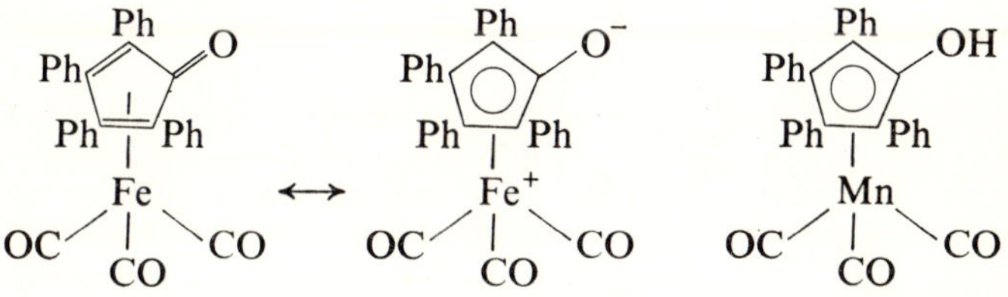

5-35

and with decacarbonyldimanganese, tetracyclone reacts to give an unstable product which reacts with water to give tricarbonyl-hydroxytetraphenylcyclopentadienyl-manganese. When the methylene carbon of cyclopentadiene is disubstituted as in the spiran (A) or the fulvene (D) reaction with enneacarbonyldi-iron affords the diene complexes (B) and (E). But on heating the former (B)

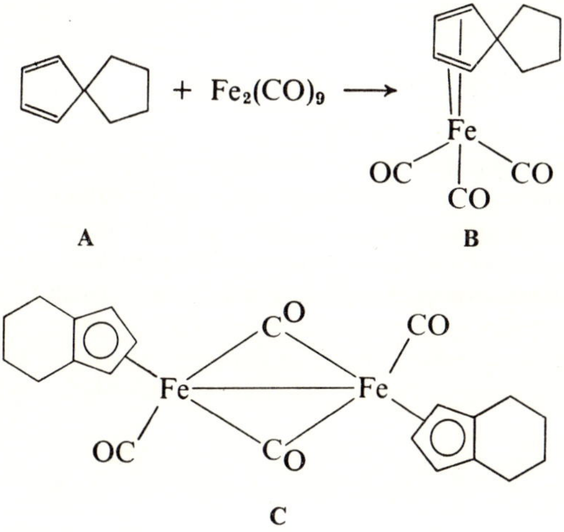

5-36

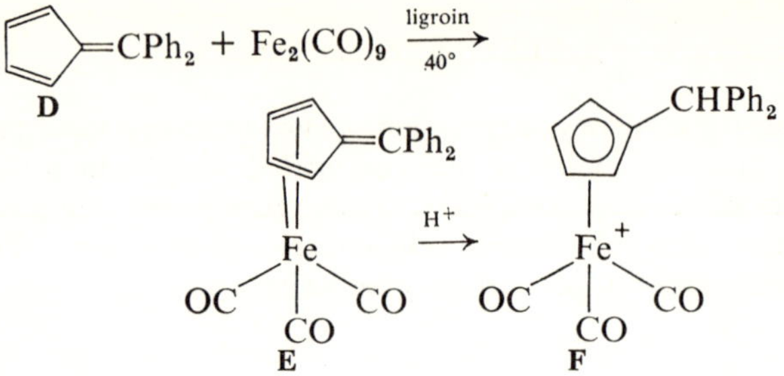

$$\text{D} \quad \bigotimes=CPh_2 + Fe_2(CO)_9 \xrightarrow[40°]{\text{ligroin}}$$

5-36

rearranges to the tetrahydrobenzocyclopentadienyl complex (C). The tendency of the fulvene complex to go over to a cyclopentadienyl complex is apparent from its ready protonation to give the cation (F).

With simple cyclopentadienes the formation of cyclopentadienyl complexes involves loss of hydrogen. This occurs at the expense of cyclopentadiene and may be formulated, e.g. in the reaction with octacarbonyldicobalt, as:

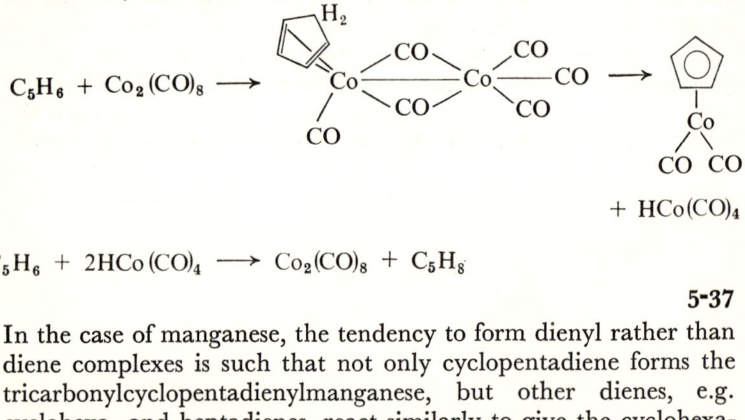

$$C_5H_6 + 2HCo(CO)_4 \longrightarrow Co_2(CO)_8 + C_5H_8$$

5-37

In the case of manganese, the tendency to form dienyl rather than diene complexes is such that not only cyclopentadiene forms the tricarbonylcyclopentadienylmanganese, but other dienes, e.g. cyclohexa- and heptadienes, react similarly to give the cyclohexa- and heptadienyl complexes (n = 1 and 2 respectively):

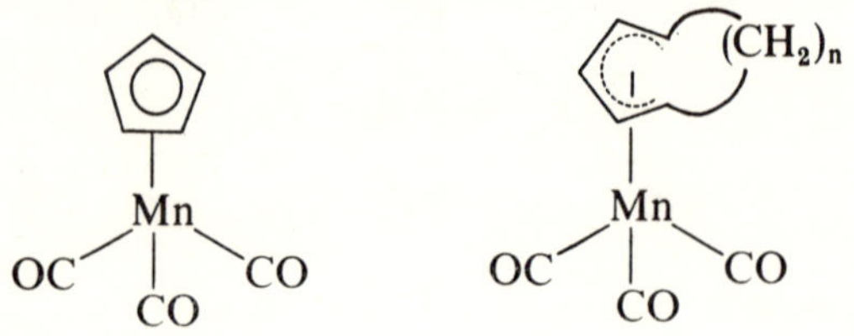

5-38

The full range of carbonylcyclopentadienyl complexes obtainable from metal carbonyls of first row transition elements is shown below.

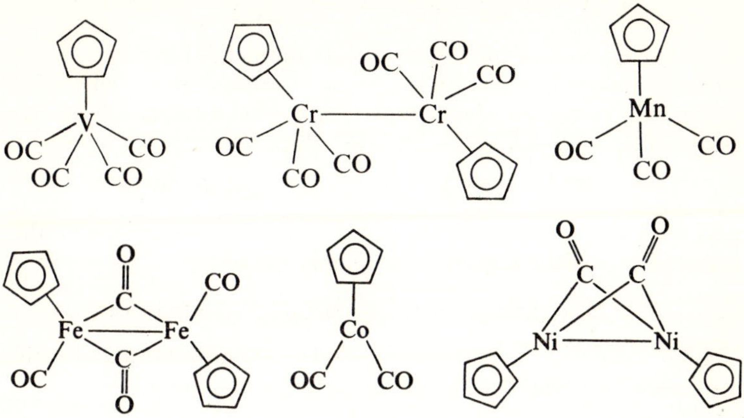

5-39

The nickel compound must be made by reaction of the carbonyl with dicyclopentadienylnickel rather than cyclopentadiene:

$$(C_5H_5)_2Ni + Ni(CO)_4 \rightarrow [C_5H_5Ni(CO)]_2 + 2CO$$

On more prolonged heating this reaction affords the dark green trinuclear complex in which two carbonyl groups are linked to all three metal atoms on either side of the nickel plane. The vanadium

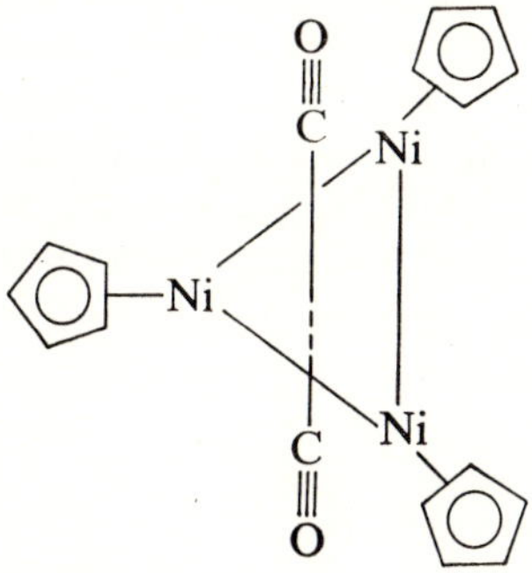

5-40

and manganese compounds are best obtained by treating the dicyclopentadienyls of these metals with carbon monoxide, and in the case of cobalt both the following steps are readily reversible:

$$Co_2(CO)_8 \underset{CO}{\overset{C_5H_6}{\rightleftharpoons}} C_5H_5Co(CO)_2 \underset{CO}{\overset{C_5H_6}{\rightleftharpoons}} (C_5H_5)_2Co$$

With few exceptions the heavier transition metals have been shown to form analogous compounds. In many ways all these behave like the metal carbonyls themselves. Thus the dimeric species are oxidized by halogens to monomeric halocarbonyls,

e.g. $\quad [C_5H_5Mo(CO)_3]_2 + Br_2 \rightarrow 2C_5H_5Mo(CO)_3Br$

and with the exception of the nickel compound, they are readily reduced by sodium amalgam to anionic species:

e.g. $\quad [C_5H_5W(CO)_3]_2 + 2Na \rightarrow 2[C_5H_5W(CO)_3]^-Na^+$

Similar reduction succeeds with the relatively unstable and reactive vanadium compound with loss of carbon monoxide:

$$C_5H_5V(CO)_4 + 2Na \rightarrow [C_5H_5V(CO)_3]^{2-}(Na^+)_2 + CO$$

On treatment with air in the presence of hydrogen chloride, this same carbonyl yields the oxydichloride $C_5H_5VOCl_2$. The greater stability of the latter may be attributed to its formal 6-coordinate structure whereas the tetracarbonyl is formally 7-coordinate.

Both the tetracarbonylvanadium and the very stable tricarbonyl-manganese complex have been shown to undergo substitution reactions. These are discussed below (p. 145) with those of ferrocene.

Although the above carbonyls are the most closely studied monocyclopentadienyl metal compounds, a wide variety of others are known. Thus Pt, Pd and Ni all form nitrosylcyclopentadienyl derivatives C_5H_5MNO. The Pt and Pd compounds are difficult to obtain and unstable in contrast to the (isoelectronic) allylcyclo-dienyl derivatives $C_5H_5MC_3H_5$ (cf. p. 117). But the nickel compound is stable and obtainable from most other cyclopentadienyl-nickel compounds by treatment with nitric oxide.

e.g.

$$(C_5H_5)_2Ni + NO \longrightarrow \quad \overset{\displaystyle\bigcirc}{\underset{\underset{NO}{|}}{\underset{Ni}{|}}} \quad \longleftarrow (C_5H_5NiCO)_2 + NO$$

5-41

When the bridged alkylthio complex is the starting material, both replacement of thiol and of cyclopentadienyl groups can take place so that the product is a mixture of the cyclopentadienylnickel nitrosyl and of the thiolnickel nitrosyl $[EtSNiNO]_n$:

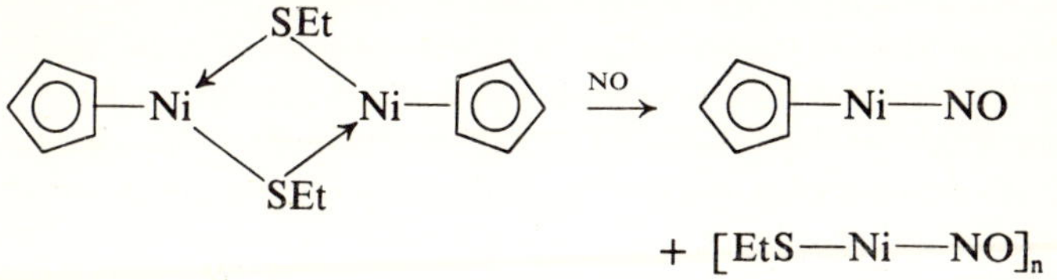

$$+ [EtS—Ni—NO]_n$$

5-42

On the other hand the latter on reaction with cyclopentadienyl-sodium suffers replacement of EtS but not of NO:

$$C_5H_5Na + [EtS-NiNO] \rightarrow NaSEt + C_5H_5NiNO$$

A variety of other nitrosyl complexes from other metals include such chromium compounds as the dinitrosyl chloride $C_5H_5Cr(NO)_2Cl$, obtained from chromic chloride, cyclopentadienylsodium and nitric oxide, and the bridged dimeric $(C_5H_5)_2Cr_2(NO)_4$ related structurally to the carbonyliron complex $(C_5H_5)_2Fe_2(CO)_4$:

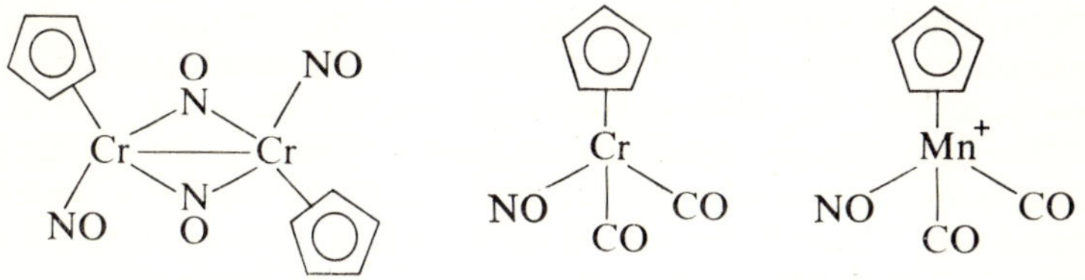

5-43

There are also several mixed carbonyl-nitrosyls such as the iso-electronic Cr and Mn compounds shown, the former obtained from $C_5H_5Cr(CO)_3^- + NO$ and the cationic manganese complex by the action of nitrous or nitric acid on tricarbonylcyclopentadienyl-manganese.

Several alkoxy(cyclopentadienyl) derivatives of titanium are known. Thus a mixture of tetrabutyl titanate and titanium tetrachloride on reaction with cyclopentadiene and a base gives $C_5H_5Ti(OBu)_2Cl$ thus:

$$2C_5H_6 + Ti(OBu)_4 + TiCl_4 + 2Et_3N \xrightarrow{C_6H_6}$$
$$2C_5H_5Ti(OBu)_2Cl + 2Et_3N \cdot HCl$$

The related trihalides $C_5H_5MX_3$ are known both with Zr and Ti and the latter has been shown to be intermediate in forming the dicyclopentadienyl derivative:

$$C_5H_5MgBr + TiCl_4 \rightarrow C_5H_5TiCl_3 \underset{TiCl_4}{\overset{C_5H_5Na}{\rightleftharpoons}} (C_5H_5)_2TiCl_2$$

Whereas the yellow trihalide is a compound of only moderate stability, the red dicyclopentadienyldichloro-titanium is one of the most stable cyclopentadienyl complexes known. This despite its formal coordination number 8 and the possession of at most 16 electrons in the valence shell. The one related compound in which titanium reaches 18 outer electrons is the dicarbonyl $(C_5H_5)_2Ti(CO)_2$ obtained by treating the dichloride with cyclopentadienylsodium and carbon monoxide. It is the only known CO complex of a group IV metal.

Other reactions of this dichloride include its smooth conversion with aryl or alkyllithium to dialkyls (or aryls),

e.g. $(C_5H_5)_2TiCl_2 + 2MeLi \rightarrow 2LiCl + (C_5H_5)_2TiMe_2$

The dimethyl derivative is stable in air, but decomposes on heating and is reduced by hydrogen (without catalyst) to an unstable green compound believed to be the neutral complex $(C_5H_5)_2Ti$. The intermediate oxidation state of Ti^{III} is fairly readily reached by direct reduction of the dichloride to the purple $(C_5H_5)_2TiCl$. This is less stable than the dihalide, but more stable than the Ti^{II} complex, so that stability here follows closely that normally encountered for the different oxidation states of the metal.

The second and third row transition elements have yielded analogous compounds only in their preferred oxidation states, usually as bis-cyclopentadienylmetal halides. Thus Zr and Hf, like Ti, form $(C_5H_5)_2MX_2$, but have not yielded products in lower oxidation states. Niobium and tantalum give $(C_5H_5)_2MX_3$. Molybdenum and tungsten not only form related halides, $(C_5H_5)_2MX_2$ and $[(C_5H_5)_2MX_3]^+$, but by borohydride reduction of these, also the hydrides $(C_5H_5)_2MH_2$. These remarkable compounds are basic, dissolving in acids to give $[(C_5H_5)_2Mo(or\ W)H_3]^+$ and the analogous rhenium compound behaves similarly:

$$(C_5H_5)_2ReH + H^+ \rightleftharpoons [(C_5H_5)_2ReH_2]^+$$

Technetium forms a dimer $(C_5H_5)_2Tc\text{-}Tc(C_5H_5)_2$, rather than a hydride, by reaction of $TcCl_4$ with C_5H_5Na.

The dicyclopentadienyl, $(C_5H_5)_2Ti$, is the first member of the series $(C_5H_5)_2M$ known for all first-row transition metals, but only for Ru and Os in the iron group among the heavier elements. The peak of stability is reached in this group and the aromaticity of

ferrocene, $(C_5H_5)_2Fe$, and its Ru and Os analogues is discussed
separately, below (p. 145). Among ionic compounds comparable
(or even higher) stability is reached in the cobalt group with the
ions $(C_5H_5)_2M^+$ of Co, Rh and Ir. Only in these and the iron
group metallocenes, among the $(C_5H_5)_2M$ species is the inert gas
configuration reached exactly. It is exceeded in the neutral
dicyclopentadienylcobalt $(C_5H_5)_2Co$, which is therefore extremely
sensitive to air, undergoing oxidation to the ion $(C_5H_5)_2Co^+$. This
and related ions are precipitated by those anions (e.g. I_3^-, BPh_4^-,
reineckate, picrate, etc.) which typically precipitate large univalent
cations like K^+ and Cs^+. In the cobalt case the hygroscopic simple
bromide can be obtained by fuming the tribromide almost to
dryness with hydrobromic acid and removing the last of the water
and hydrogen bromide in a vacuum desiccator.

Reduction of the ions $(C_5H_5)_2M^+$ (M = Co, Rh, Ir) to the
neutral complexes $(C_5H_5)_2M$ is possible, if with some difficulty.
While the cobalt compound is thermally stable, the Rh and Ir
derivatives (obtained by dry fusion of the salts $(C_5H_5)_2M^+PF_6^-$
with metallic sodium) are stable only if trapped at liquid air
temperature. At room temperature they dimerize to products
having the structure:

5-44

When reduction is carried out with reagents capable of providing
hydride ion, e.g. $NaBH_4$, the closely related complexes $C_5H_5MC_5H_6$
(M = Co, Rh or Ir; X = H) are formed. These owe their

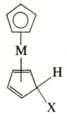

5-45

stability to the retention of inert gas configuration about the metal atom. A wide range of substituted compounds of the same type may be obtained by use of other anions, e.g. the alkyl anions of organo-lithium compounds. The entering group X has been found to occupy the position remote from the metal atom.

Dicyclopentadienylnickel, which has an E.A.N. of 38, is a diamagnetic and moderately air-stable green crystalline solid. It can be oxidized to the yellow cation $(C_5H_5)_2Ni^+$ with 37 electrons about the metal (and hence paramagnetic with one unpaired electron) but does not undergo further oxidation without complete breakdown; thus a nickel(IV) ion $(C_5H_5)_2Ni^{2+}$ which would be isoelectronic with $(C_5H_5)_2Co^+$ and $(C_5H_5)_2Fe$ is not known.

Ferrocene itself undergoes oxidation to the ferricinium ion $(C_5H_5)_2Fe^+$, with an ease comparable to other Fe^{II}-Fe^{III} oxidations. The blue paramagnetic salts of this ion are moderately stable, but are decomposed by alkalis which lead to partial destruction, the remainder being reduced back to ferrocene.

The ferricinium ion is an intermediate in the oxidative breakdown of ferrocene by bromination:

$$C_{10}H_{10}Fe + \tfrac{1}{2}Br_2 \rightarrow C_{10}H_{10}Fe^+Br^- \xrightarrow{Br_2} FeBr_3 + 2C_5H_5Br_5$$

The only other conditions under which a complete and smooth cleavage of the ferrocene system has been shown to occur, is by reduction. Catalytic hydrogenation to iron and cyclopentane requires extremely vigorous conditions, but reaction with alkali metals and amines occurs at room temperature,

e.g. $C_{10}H_{10}Fe + 2Li \xrightarrow{EtNH_2} Fe + 2C_5H_5Li$

One cyclopentadiene ring can however be displaced smoothly using aromatic hydrocarbons in the presence of aluminium chloride. Thus with benzene

$$(C_5H_5)_2Fe + C_6H_6 + AlCl_3 + HCl \xrightarrow{Al}$$

$$[C_5H_5FeC_6H_6]^+AlCl_4^- + C_5H_6$$

The product on reduction with sodium borohydride gives cyclo-hexadienylcyclopentadienyliron, an analogue of ferrocene in which one cyclopentadienyl group is replaced by another dienyl ligand:

$$C_5H_5FeC_6H_6^+ + H^- \longrightarrow$$

5-46

The reaction proceeds analogously with substituted benzene complexes and with the tricarbonylbenzenemanganese cation, $C_6H_6Mn(CO)_3^+$ to give the corresponding cyclohexadienyl series. Cycloheptadienyl- as well as open-chain dienyliron complexes have been obtained as the tricarbonyl cations by three methods:

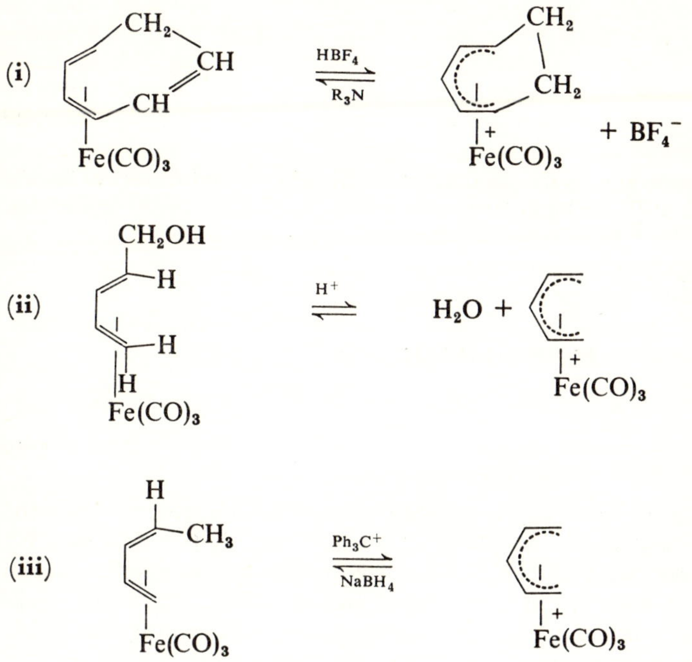

5-47

It is noteworthy that whereas the method (ii) proceeds with geometrical inversion, the hydride abstraction (iii) only proceeds if the CH group involved already possesses the correct orientation.

6- AND 7-ELECTRON DONORS

While the cycloheptatriene complex involved in reaction (i) above is only a 4-electron (i.e. diene) complex (cf. p. 120), all 3 double bonds become involved when the same and similar trienes are linked to a metal of the Cr group. In this sense the complexes formed by

$$M(CO)_6 + C_7H_8 \longrightarrow 3CO +$$

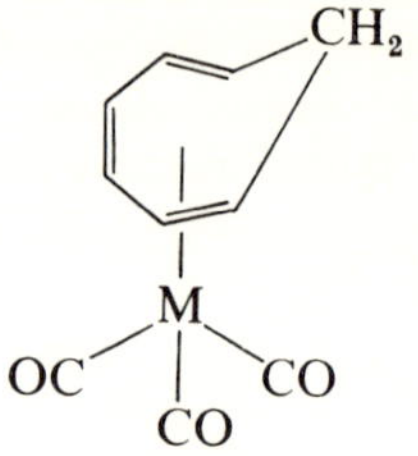

5-48

benzene and its simple derivatives may be viewed merely as special cases of triene ligands:

$$M(CO)_6 + RC_6H_5 \longrightarrow$$

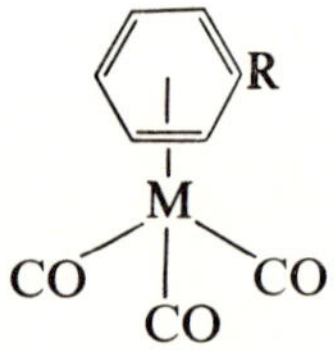

5-49

There are however, a number of notable differences: Thus the cycloheptatriene complexes of all three metals (Cr, Mo and W) are red, whereas the benzene compounds are pale yellow. The former have 3, the latter only 2 strong carbonyl stretching peaks in the infrared. The triene complexes are considerably less stable than the arene complexes in the case of chromium, but the order is apparently reversed with Mo and W.

Tricarbonylarenechromiums have been obtained with a wide variety of substituents R, with fused polycyclic aromatics and with thiophene. The latter compound as well as the naphthalene and

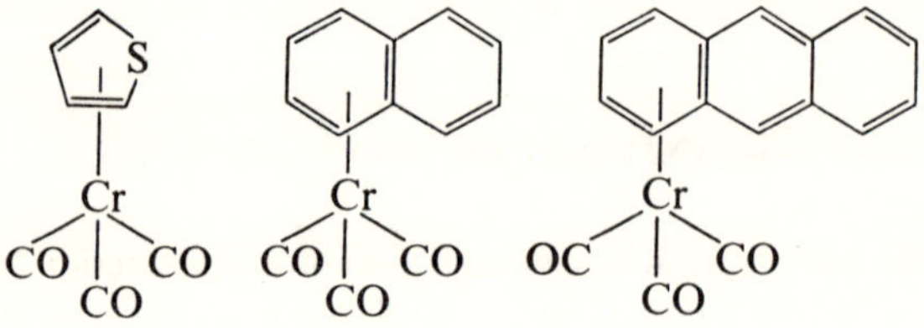

5-50

phenanthrene complexes are all red and moderately stable, but the purple anthracene complex only retains marginal stability.

In tricarbonylbenzenechromium and its alkyl derivatives the preferred conformation as revealed by x-ray crystallographic studies is the staggered form (A). However the anisole and o-toluidine complexes have been shown to have the eclipsed structures

| A | B | 5·51 |

(B; X = OMe; R = H and X = NH$_2$; R = Me respectively). If we consider the chromium atom to be bonded octahedrally, the three orbitals directed towards the ring point towards the electron-rich carbon atoms *ortho* and *para* to the methoxy- and amino groups in the latter case (B), but to the centres of three π-bonds in structure (A).

The reactivity of the arene system itself in these complexes shows the effect of the tricarbonylchromium group in a manner which varies with the reaction studied. A general electron-withdrawing effect may be deduced from the enhanced acidity of both phenol and benzoic acid when bonded to this group, as well as the correspondingly reduced basicity of aniline in its complex. This effect is perhaps most marked in the case of nucleophilic reactions, e.g. the smooth conversion of tricarbonylchlorobenzenechromium under very mild conditions to the anisole complex:

$$(C_6H_5Cl)Cr(CO)_3 + MeOH \xrightarrow[\substack{boiling \\ MeOH}]{NaOAc} (C_6H_5OMe)Cr(CO)_3$$

Yet, electrophilic substitution is not markedly hindered and may indeed likewise be facilitated. The possible reactions are limited by the stability of the complex under suitable reaction conditions. But Friedel-Crafts acetylation proceeds smoothly:

$$C_6H_6Cr(CO)_3 + CH_3COCl \xrightarrow[CS_2]{AlCl_3} CH_3COC_6H_5Cr(CO)_3$$

Mono-arene complexes of other metals include the interesting trimeric benzene-cobalt carbonyl cation obtained from octa-carbonyldicobalt via its aluminium bromide complex $Co_2(CO)_8 \cdot AlBr_3$:

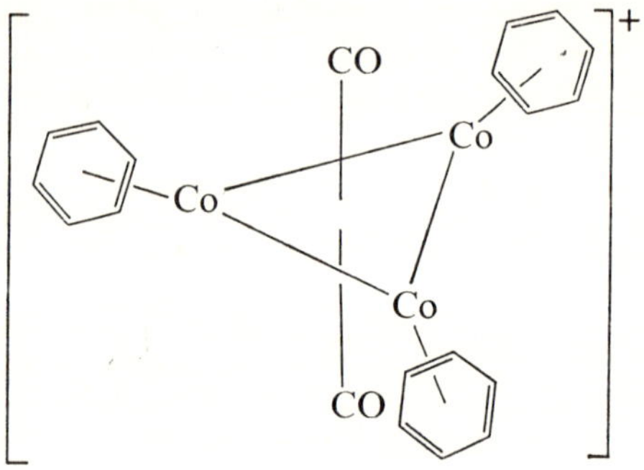

5-52

Benzene cyclopentadienyls $C_6H_6MC_5H_5$ are known for Cr and Mn and while the former is paramagnetic being one electron short of inert gas configuration, the manganese compound, though attaining the E.A.N. of 36, is equally unstable.

Bis-arene chromiums were first obtained by Hein and his co-workers from the reaction of chromic chloride with phenylmag-nesium bromide. But their correct formulation was first suggested by Onsager and confirmed by the degradative studies of Zeiss as well as Fischer and Hafner's alternative synthesis (see p. 57) of the parent compound bis-benzene chromium. From both methods salts of the stable bis-arenechromium(I) cations are first isolated; the diamagnetic neutral complexes are readily obtained on re-duction:

$$(ArH)_2Cr^+ \underset{O_2/H^+}{\overset{Na_2S_2O_4}{\rightleftharpoons}} (ArH)_2Cr$$

It is now recognized that Hein's method involves the spontaneous rearrangement of di- or triphenylchromium,
e.g.

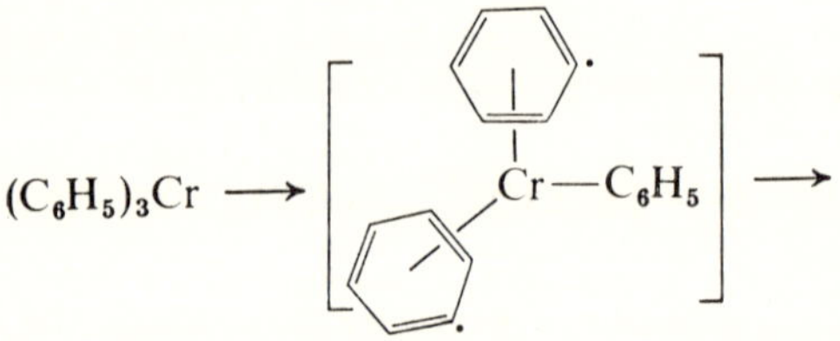

$(C_6H_5)_3Cr \longrightarrow \left[\begin{array}{c} \\ Cr-C_6H_5 \\ \end{array} \right] \longrightarrow$

5-53

Thus what was once described as 'triphenylchromium bromide' is now known to be the bromide of the above benzene diphenyl chromium(I) ion and 'pentaphenylchromium hydroxide' is similarly the phenoxide of the bis-diphenylchromium cation. Formation of the latter from triphenylchromium implies simultaneous formation of the bis-benzenechromium cation, which was demonstrated.

The Fischer-Hafner method of synthesis has been extended not only to Mo and W in the same group as Cr, but to numerous other transition metals. In this way, VCl_4 yields the red-brown V^0 complex $(C_6H_6)_2V$, iso-electronic with $(C_6H_6)_2Cr^+$. Rhenium readily affords the yellow cation $(C_6H_6)_2Re^+$, iso-electronic with the yellow-green $(C_6H_6)_2W$, but the corresponding manganese complex is unknown, although the bis-hexamethylbenzene derivative $(C_6Me_6)_2$-Mn^+ has been described. The greater stability of complexes of this type when bearing electron-donating groups is quite general. It is apparent in, for example, the low stability of $(C_6H_6)_2Fe^{2+}$ compared to $(1,3,5-Me_3C_6H_3)_2Fe^{2+}$ and in the isolation of $(C_6Me_6)_2Co^{2+}$, $(C_6Me_6)_2Co^+$ and their Rh analogues.

The aromatic ligands are readily displaced from all these complexes by other donors. Thus dibenzenechromium exchanges ligands with chromium carbonyl in

$$(C_6H_6)_2Cr + Cr(CO)_6 \rightarrow 2C_6H_6Cr(CO)_3$$

and loses both benzene rings when treated with phosphorus trifluoride:

$$(C_6H_6)_2Cr + 6PF_3 \rightarrow 2C_6H_6 + Cr(PF_3)_6$$

An oxidative displacement of the rings has been described using di-tert.-butyl peroxide:

$$(C_6H_6)_2Cr + 2Bu^tOOBu^t \rightarrow 2C_6H_6 + Cr(OBu^t)_4$$

The effect of the metal on the aromaticity of the benzene ring has been studied in the case of bisbenzenechromium. Its sensitivity to oxidation and to Lewis acids severely limits the possible reactions. Metalation with amylsodium has however been shown to occur and to give both mono- ($C_6H_6CrC_6H_5Na$) and di-sodio derivatives which undergo the expected further reactions with carbon dioxide, alkyl halides, etc.

An attempt has also been made to study the relative reactivity of the benzene and cyclopentadiene rings in the mixed benzene-cyclopentadienylchromium. Reaction with acetyl chloride and aluminium chloride leads to a remarkable expansion of the six-membered ring (which also occurs with the manganese analogue):

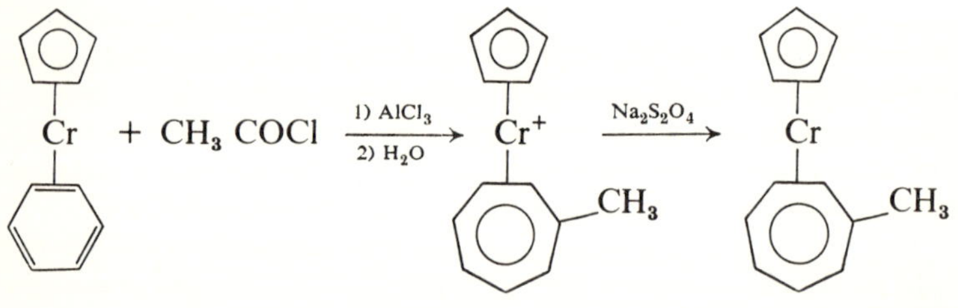

5·54

The same product can be obtained by direct displacement of the benzene ring with methylcycloheptatriene, again using aluminium chloride as a catalyst:

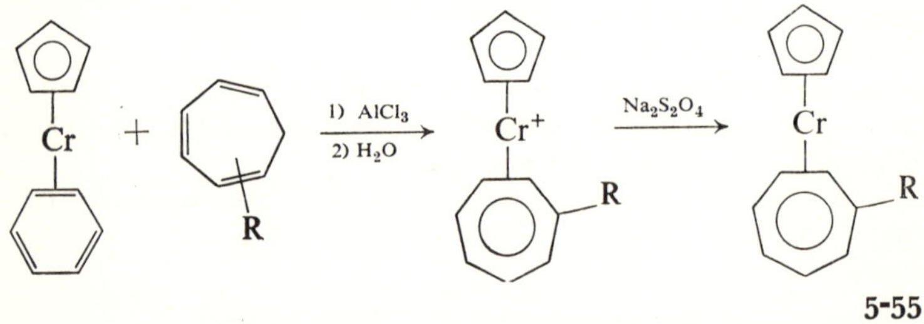

5·55

This route works equally well with cycloheptatriene to give the unsubstituted complex ($R = H$) which is isomeric with dibenzenechromium. Cycloheptatrienylcyclopentadienylchromium can clearly be regarded as having the 7-membered ring as a ligand donating 7 electrons and this must be true of the tricarbonylvanadium complex conveniently obtained from the hexacarbonyl:

$$V(CO)_6 + C_7H_8 \rightarrow C_7H_7V(CO)_3$$

It is convenient to regard this ligand as a 7-electron donor even in the cationic complexes $C_7H_7M(CO)_3{}^+$ of Cr, Mo and W. These are readily obtained by the reversible hydride abstraction from the triene complexes

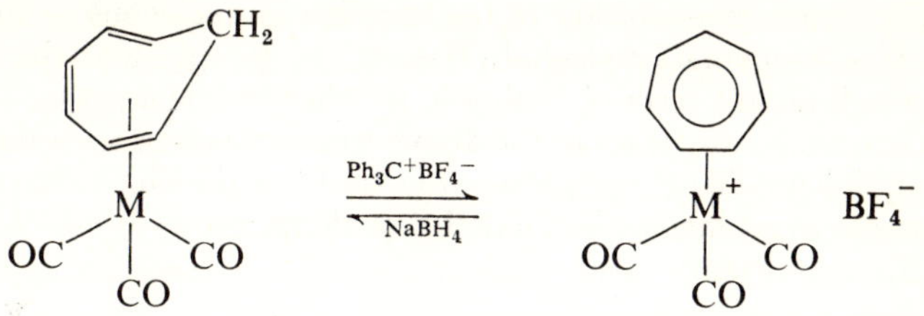

5-56

The reformation of triene complexes occurs not only with hydride, but with other anions capable of adding to the ring. Many examples have been studied in the chromium series and it is established that the anion invariably adds from the less hindered side to give the exo-isomer:

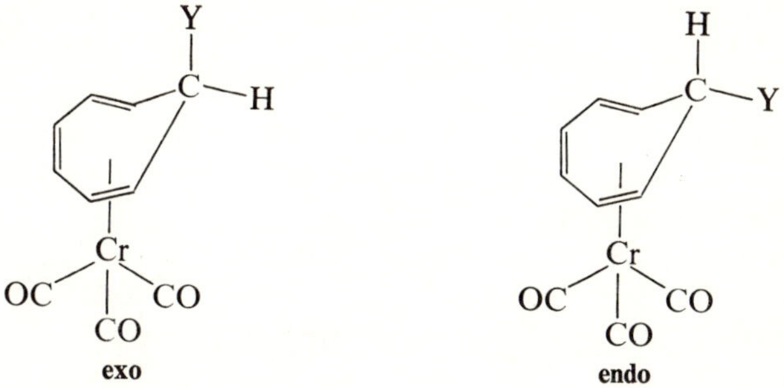

exo   endo   5-57

On the other hand the alternative, endo-isomer is the usual product when such substituted cycloheptatriene complexes are prepared from the hexacarbonyl or other carbonyl derivatives of chromium and the substituted triene.

e.g.

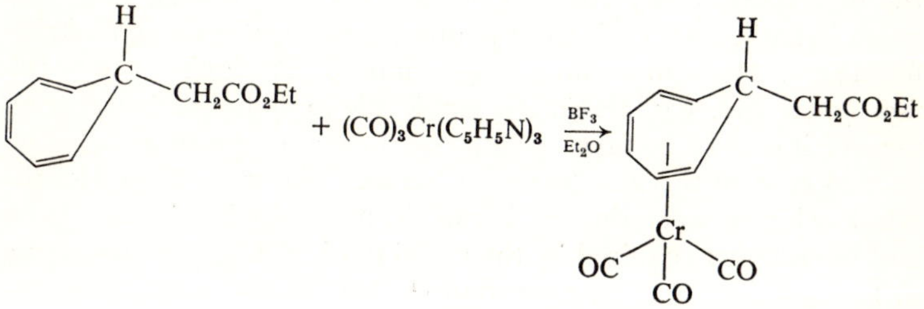

5-58

Presumably this is because the preferred equatorial conformation of the substituent is maintained during complex formation.

The above exo-addition of nucleophiles is analogous to that of the bis-cyclopentadienylcobalt(I) salts (cf. p. 133) and the same pattern is almost certainly followed in other analogous cases. Thus it is instructive to compare the above transformations with those of the cycloheptadienyl complexes of Fe and Mn (in which the stereochemical assignments are made by analogy):

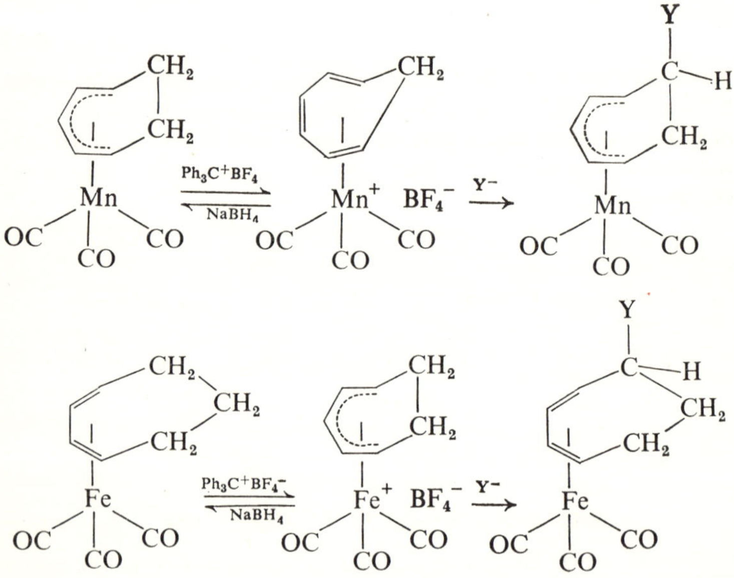

5·59

It will have been observed that although this chapter contains the description of hydrocarbon complexes with a wide variety of other ligands, metal tricarbonyl groupings occur with remarkable frequency. Without wishing to attribute special significance to this fact (there are, e.g. numerous stable di- and tetracarbonyl complexes), it may be useful to summarize the main types of tricarbonyls encountered in the first transition series. The table illustrates the relationship between the number of electrons supplied by the ligand and the number required by the metal (with 3CO groups supplying 6) to reach inert gas configuration (E.A.N. = 36).

TABLE 3

(A)

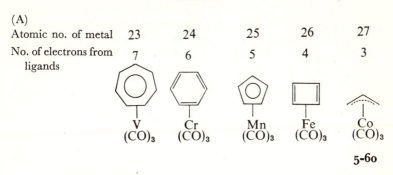

Atomic no. of metal	23	24	25	26	27
No. of electrons from ligands	7	6	5	4	3
	V (CO)$_3$	Cr (CO)$_3$	Mn (CO)$_3$	Fe (CO)$_3$	Co (CO)$_3$

5-60

(B)   Tricarbonyl cyclopentadienyls with metal in the appropriate oxidation state to have 25 electrons:

V^{2-} (CO)$_3$ Cr$^-$ (CO)$_3$ Mn (CO)$_3$ Fe$^+$ (CO)$_3$

5-61

CARBAMETALLIC COMPOUNDS

At the time of writing, only preliminary descriptions are available of this class of metallocene analogues in which the (1)-2,3-dicarbollyl group (A), $B_9C_2H_{11}$, takes the place of the cyclopentadienide ion. The parent ion $(B_9C_2H_{11})^{2-}$ is generated by treatment of $(CH_3)_3\overset{+}{N}H$ $B_9C_2H_{12}^-$ with sodium hydride. Reaction of this ion with ferrous salt yields the remarkably stable, diamagnetic, $[Fe(B_9C_2H_{11})_2]^{2-}$ analogous to ferrocene. This may be air-oxidized to the red, paramagnetic ferricinium analogue $[Fe(B_9C_2H_{11})_2]^-$, both being conveniently isolated as their tetramethylammonium salts. By using a mixture of the disodium (1)-2,3-dicarbollide and sodium cyclopentadienide, M. F. Hawthorne and his coworkers have also obtained the complex $[C_5H_5FeB_9C_2H_{11}]^-$, and the purple crystalline neutral iron(III) complex obtained from this by oxidation. The structure (B) of the latter has been confirmed by an x-ray diffraction study. The configuration is eclipsed as in $(C_5H_5)_2Ru$ rather than staggered as in ferrocene and the iron-ring distances are almost identical for the dicarbollyl and cyclopentadienyl rings. The cobalticinium analogues $[Co^{III}(B_9C_2H_{11})_2]^-$ and $C_5H_5CoB_9C_2H_{11}$ have been obtained similarly and the former has been reduced with butyllithium to the purple cobaltocene analogue $[Co(B_9C_2H_{11})]^{2-}$.

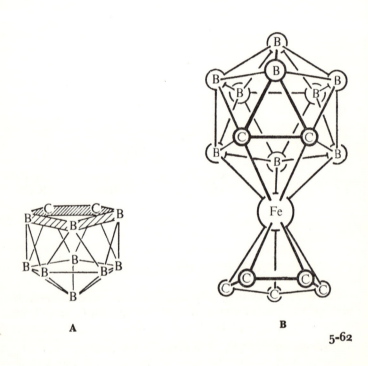

A   B

5-62

In addition, by reaction of the carbollide with $BrMn(CO)_5$ and $BrRe(CO)_5$, the complexes $[(B_9C_2H_{11})M(CO)_3]^-$, where $M = Mn$ or Re, have been obtained and isolated in high yield as their caesium salts. These are again immediately comparable to cyclopentadienyl analogues and many other complexes similarly related to cyclopentadienyl derivatives will undoubtedly prove accessible in the same way. Moreover, substituted (C-alkyl) carboranes have been employed in the same way and other carborane systems may well be found which simulate different hydrocarbons as π-bonding ligands.

AROMATICITY OF CYCLOPENTADIENYLS

Aromaticity in ferrocene was first demonstrated by its Friedel-Crafts acetylation and this reaction has been used to show that also the following monocyclopentadienyl complexes can undergo electrophilic substitution:

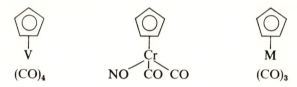

where M = Mn, Tc or Re

5-63

Of these only the manganese compound has been investigated extensively and among dicyclopentadienyls only brief studies of the Ru and Os analogues have supplemented the extensive work on ferrocene.

Comparative studies, again using the Friedel-Crafts acetylation, have established the following orders of increasing reactivities:

$$C_6H_6 < C_5H_5Mn(CO)_3 < MeC_5H_4Mn(CO)_3$$

$$< MeOC_6H_5 < (C_5H_5)_2Fe$$

and

$$(C_5H_5)_2Os < (C_5H_5)_2Ru < (C_5H_5)_2Fe$$

The extremely high reactivity of ferrocene is well illustrated by its acetylation under such mild conditions as heating with acetic anhydride containing phosphoric acid. Also by its susceptibility to the Mannich condensation (with CH_2O and secondary amines) and the Vilsmeier reaction (with $PhNMeCHO + POCl_3$), two reactions restricted in the benzene series to such reactive species as phenol:

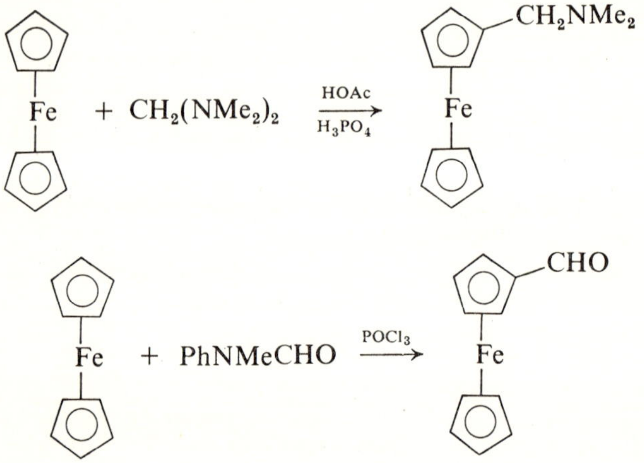

5·64

✱ The predominant formation of mono-substituted products in these reactions is evidence of the marked deactivation which is effectively transmitted to the unsubstituted ring. Further substitution to give the dialdehyde has not been accomplished in the Vilsmeier reaction and the bis-dimethylaminomethylderivative, $Fe(C_5H_4CH_2NMe_2)_2$, is only formed in poor yield in the aminomethylation process. Acylation on the other hand can smoothly be extended to give high yields of diacyl derivatives when aluminium chloride is employed as the Friedel-Crafts catalyst:

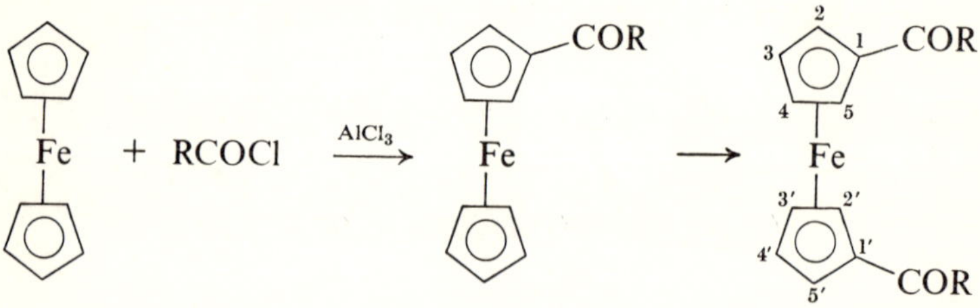

5·65

The catalytic or Clemmensen reduction of the acyl derivatives so produced is a valuable method of obtaining alkylferrocenes since Friedel-Crafts alkylations proceed much less smoothly.

That the two substituents in the diacylferrocenes and hence in the derived dialkyl compounds are in different rings has been proved both by independent synthesis of the latter from alkylcyclo-pentadienes and by various physical methods. 1,2-Diacetylferrocene has been shown to be a minor by-product in the di-acetylation. In common with other ferrocene derivatives in which one ring is unsubstituted, this compound has i.r. peaks close to 9 and to 10 μ which are absent in the 1,1'-isomer. Experience has shown that these two bands (respectively an antisymmetrical ring breathing and a C—H bending mode) can be used as a reliable indication of the presence of an unsubstituted ring.

Sodium borohydride converts 1,1'-diacetylferrocene to the corresponding diol which suffers very facile dehydration to a mixture of the two diastereoisomeric bridged ethers:

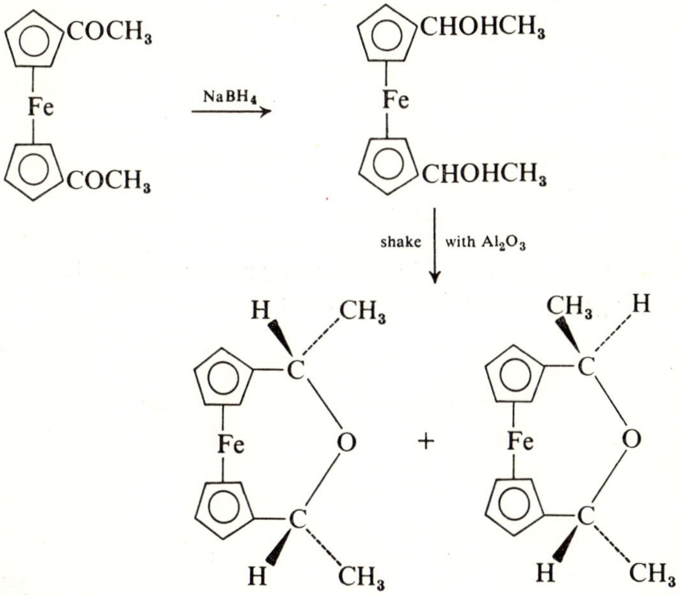

5-66

This is a particularly easy route to products in which the two rings are bridged. The first such system was obtained by the cyclization of ferrocenylpropionic acid:

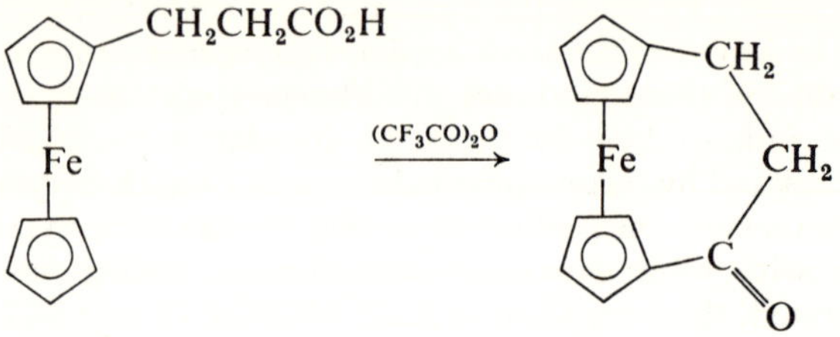

5-67

In contrast to this the next homologue cyclizes exclusively into the same ring. The resultant ketone was shown to be resolvable into optical isomers and it will be seen that no ferrocene derivative bearing two unlike substituents on the same ring is superimposable on its mirror image. Reduction of this ketone affords two alcohols one

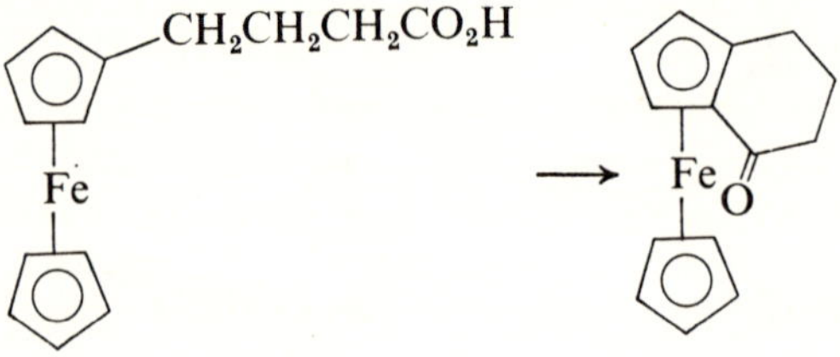

5-68

with its OH group on the side of the ring nearer the metal and one with this group remote from the metal:

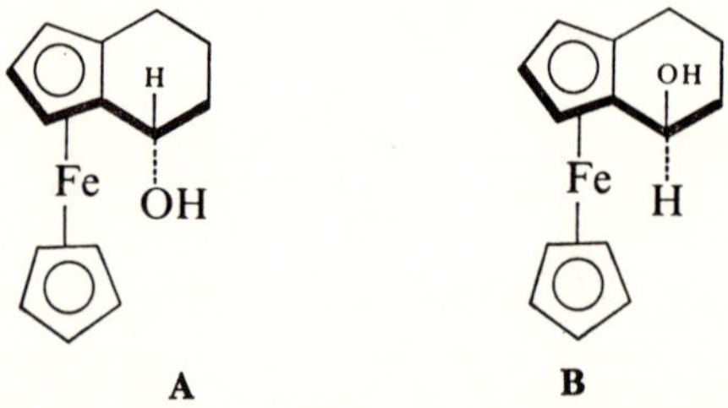

A   B

5-69

The solvolysis of the acetates of both these alcohols has been studied. In aqueous at 30° the acetate of isomer (B) solvolyzes 2500 times faster than the acetate of (A). Both give exclusively the exo-alcohol (B).

These facts are most readily accounted for by postulating inter-action of a filled non-bonding metal orbital with the carbonium ion formed. In the case of the exo-acetate such interaction can occur with the *incipient* carbonium ion and will therefore accelerate solvolysis. The solvolysis of the manganese derivatives $(CO)_3MnC_5H_4$-CHROAc is quite slow by comparison. That α-ferrocenylcar-bonium ions and analogous species are considerably stabilized is clearly established from a number of lines of investigation. Thus the relative rates of solvolysis of $C_5H_5MC_5H_4$CHMe—OAc where M = Os, Ru and Fe are 5·37, 1·36, 1·00. On this scale the rate for Ph_3COAc is 0·152 showing that the α-metallocenyl carbonium ions are substantially more stable than the triphenylmethyl carbonium ion. More qualitative evidence comes inter alia from the ease of addition of acids to vinylferrocene,

e.g. $C_5H_5FeC_5H_4CH{=}CH_2 + H^+N_3^- \rightarrow$

$$[C_5H_5FeC_5H_4\overset{+}{CH}CH_3] \rightarrow C_5H_5FeC_5H_4CHN_3CH_3$$

and even from the solubility of ferrocenecarboxyaldehyde in dilute acids:

$$C_5H_5FeC_5H_4CHO + HCl \rightleftharpoons C_5H_5FeC_5H_4CH{=}\overset{+}{O}H$$
$$\updownarrow$$
$$C_5H_5FeC_5H_4\overset{+}{C}H{-}OH$$

The best formulation of the carbonium ion is still a matter of dispute. Inter alia, arguments have been advanced in favour of a displace-ment of the ring bearing the carbonium ion relative to the metal so as to permit consideration of the structure:

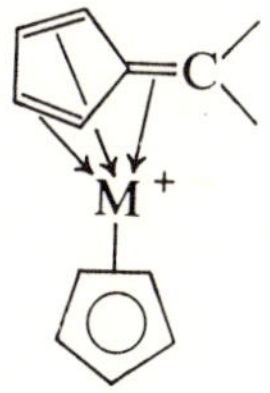

5-70

Such formulation may be compared with the stable ion

$$[C_5H_5FeC_6H_6]^+.$$

Alternatively the structure in which the ring is displaced in the opposite direction and in which the iron atom interacts only with a diene system:

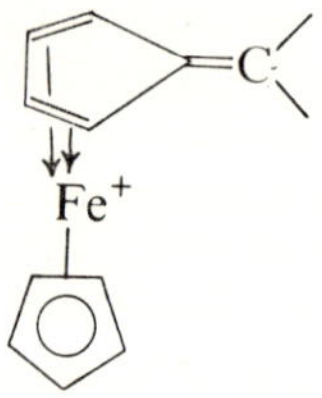

5-71

has been advanced and the related structure

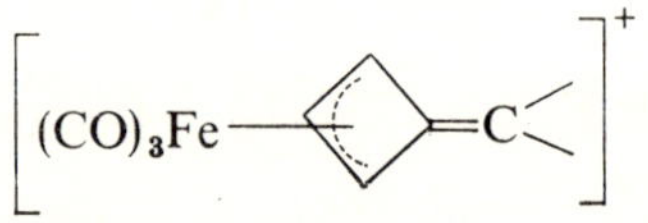

has been used to explain the stability of α-carbonium ions derived from tricarbonylcyclobutadiene-iron. The latter structure finds analogy in the tricarbonylallyliron cations (cf. p. 118).

This formulation may also be compared with the intermediate which we must write for electrophilic substitution of the metalocenes:

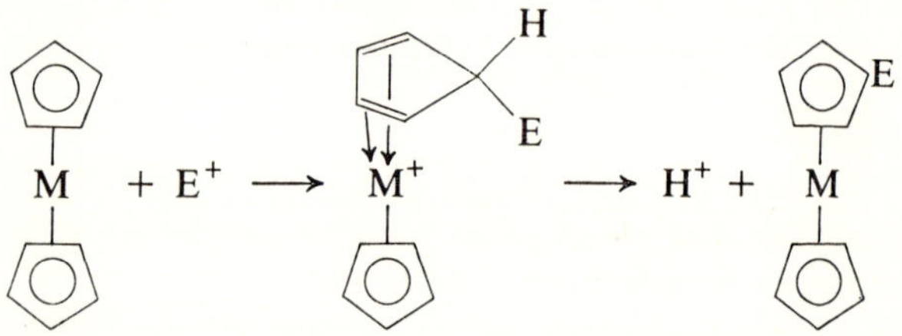

5-72

It will be observed that the intermediate can have two isomeric forms depending on the direction of attack of the electrophile (E^+). That attack from either side of the ring is possible has been demonstrated in ingenious fashion by Rosenblum, who synthesized the two stereoisomeric acids (5-73, A) and demonstrated that they could be

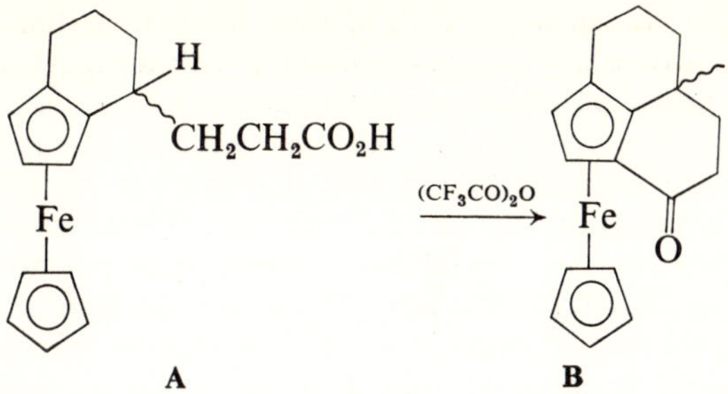

A   **B**   5-73

cyclized with comparable ease to the stereoisomeric tricyclic ketones shown. The intermediate acids were obtained by the sequence

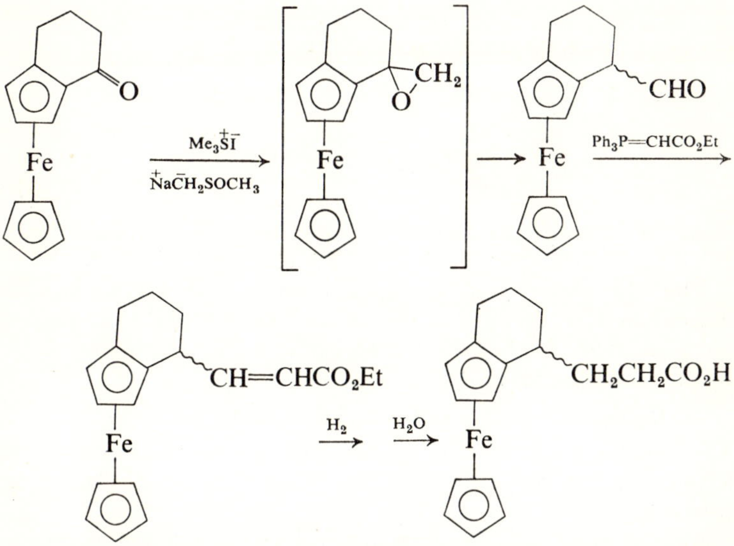

5-74

The possibility that electrophilic attack from the metal side may proceed via an intermediate of the form

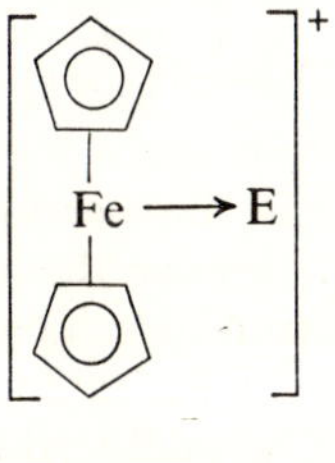

5-75

has been considered as a result of the observation that ferrocene dissolves in strong acids to give solutions with a high-field proton resonance peak consistent with such a structure ($E = H$). This formulation also provides a ready explanation of the mode of attack of free radicals. These appear incapable of substituting ferrocene, but readily attack ferricinium salts. The reaction pattern, however, shows strong resemblance to electrophilic reactions at least in regard to directive influences. If the free electron of the ferricinium ion is assumed to be in a metal orbital the first step of the reaction would be expected to be the radical-radical coupling:

5-76

Thus the intermediate so formed would be indistinguishable from the intermediate postulated above for electrophilic attack.

The most closely studied radical reaction is the arylation with diazonium salts. In this case the ferricinium ion and the free radical are generated together from ferrocene and the diazonium cation by the redox process:

$$C_{10}H_{10}Fe + ArN_2^+ \rightarrow C_{10}H_{10}Fe^+ + ArN_2 \cdot \rightarrow Ar \cdot + N_2$$

The resultant substitution yields both mono- and 1,1'-diaryl ferrocenes, but only traces of the other isomeric disubstitution products.

Another substitution process in which ferricinium ion formation plays a role is the condensation with formaldehyde in strong acid (HF or H_2SO_4). The initial steps may be represented as

$$C_{10}H_{10}Fe + CH_2O + H^+ \rightarrow C_{10}H_9FeCH_2OH + H^+ \rightarrow$$

$$C_{10}H_9FeCH_2\overset{+}{O}H_2 \rightarrow C_{10}H_9FeCH_2^+ + H_2O$$

When a large excess of ferrocene is used the resultant ferrocenylmethyl cation can substitute further in this to give diferrocenylmethane $(C_{10}H_9Fe)_2CH_2$. Under the usual conditions, however, the main product is diferrocenylethane. It is believed that the stable α-ferrocenylcarbonium ion tautomerizes to the ferriciniummethyl radical, $C_5H_5Fe^+C_5H_4CH_2\cdot$ [this is not a resonance form of the former ion, as the transformation involves the unpairing of electrons]. This radical now dimerizes to the bis-ferricinium ion $(C_5H_5Fe^+C_5H_4CH_2)_2$ which is reduced to the observed product during the work-up procedure.

Ease of oxidation to ferricinium ion prevents direct nitration or halogenation and attempts to carry out such reactions with tri-carbonylcyclopentadienylmanganese result in complete oxidative breakdown. Nitro- and halogenoferrocenes are however accessible by indirect methods which rely ultimately on metalation. Both the facile mercuration (see p. 37) and the lithiation may conveniently be used. The mercurated products are transformed by such reactions as:

$$C_{10}H_9FeHgCl \xrightarrow{Na_2S_2O_3} (C_{10}H_9Fe)_2Hg \xrightarrow{I_2} C_{10}H_9FeI$$

The lithio-compounds are most conveniently converted to halides via the boronic acids (also obtainable from ferrocene, boron trichloride and aluminium chloride):

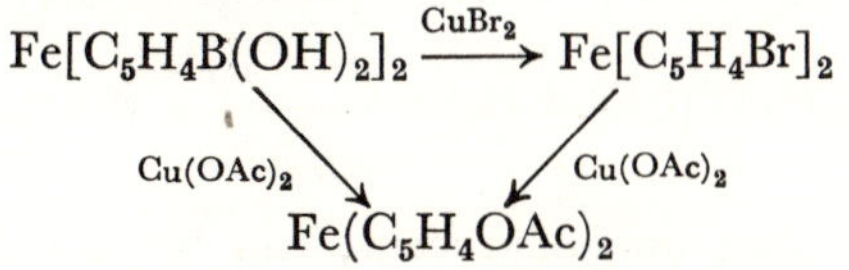

$$Fe[C_5H_4B(OH)_2]_2 \xrightarrow{CuBr_2} Fe[C_5H_4Br]_2$$

Cu(OAc)$_2$ $\searrow$ $\swarrow$ Cu(OAc)$_2$
$$Fe(C_5H_4OAc)_2 \qquad\qquad 5\text{-}77$$

These reactions yield both the halides and, via the acetates, the hydroxyferrocenes. The latter and the free aminoferrocenes are very unstable to air, due to the greater oxidizability conferred by such electron-donating substituents. The mono-amine is readily obtained by treating lithioferrocene with O-methyl-hydroxylamine:

$$C_5H_5FeC_5H_4Li + MeONH_2 \rightarrow LiOMe + C_5H_5FeC_5H_4NH_2$$

but the diamine has only been obtained in solution, most efficiently by the sequence

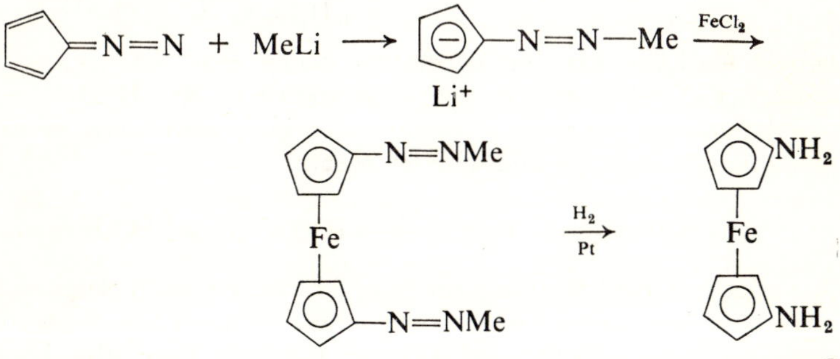

$$5\text{-}78$$

Nitro- and nitrosoferrocene are obtained by treating lithio-ferrocene with alkyl nitrate or nitrite:

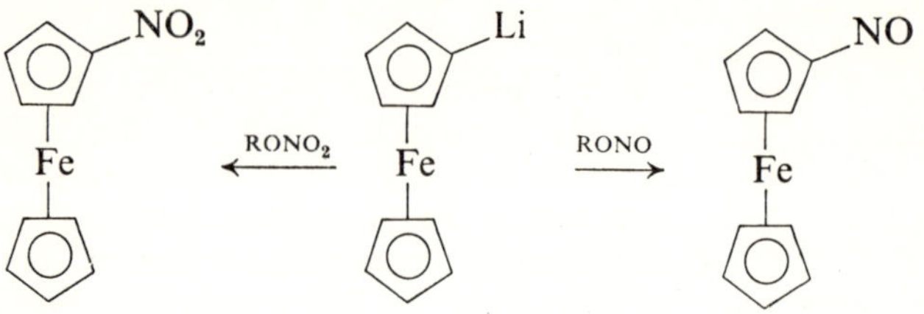

5·79

Both can be reduced to aminoferrocene which has also been obtained by Curtius degradation of ferrocene-carboxylic acid via the ester, hydrazide and azide. Tricarbonyl(aminocyclopentadienyl)manganese may be prepared similarly:

$$(CO)_3MnC_5H_4COCl \xrightarrow{NaN_3} (CO)_3MnC_5H_4CON_3 \xrightarrow[140°]{PhCH_2OH}$$

$$(CO)_3MnC_5H_4NHCOOCH_2Ph \xrightarrow[\substack{or \\ H_2/Ni}]{HBr/HOAc} (CO)_3MnC_5H_4NH_2$$

This amine, unlike aminoferrocene, can be diazotized, and the resultant diazonium chloride undergoes Sandmeyer-type reactions with mercuric halides but not with cuprous halides:

$$(CO)_3MnC_5H_4NH_2 + Am^iONO \xrightarrow[Pr^iOH]{HCl}$$

$$(CO_3)MnC_5H_4\overset{+}{N}\equiv N\ Cl^- \xrightarrow{HgCl_2} (CO)_3MnC_5H_4Cl$$

The violet solutions of ferrocenediazonium salts obtained by

$$C_{10}H_9FeLi + PhN_3 \longrightarrow C_{10}H_9FeN=N\cdot NHPh \xrightarrow[-40°]{H^+X^-}$$

$$C_{10}H_9FeN_2{}^+X^- + PhNH_3X$$

couple with phenols, but decompose above −20° to ferrocenyl halides (if X = halogen) or hydroxyferrocene (if X = HSO$_4$).

Sulphonation proceeds smoothly with both tricarbonyl cyclo-pentadienylmanganese and with ferrocene:

$$(CO)_3MnC_5H_5 + H_2SO_4 \xrightarrow{Ac_2O} (CO)_3MnC_5H_4SO_3H$$

A variety of further transformations of the resultant sulphonic acids have been carried out in both series. More or less elaborate transformations of other substitution products have also been effected. Among the key intermediates for these have been the quaternary ammonium salt, $C_5H_5FeC_5H_4CH_2\overset{+}{N}Me_3I^-$, derived from dimethylaminomethylferrocene (cf. p. 146) and the aldehydes of both series. The latter are perhaps most conveniently prepared by direct substitution with ethyl dichloromethyl ether, Cl_2CHOEt, in the presence of aluminium chloride. In the manganese series, the methyl substituted aldehydes have also been obtained by a Gatterman reaction:

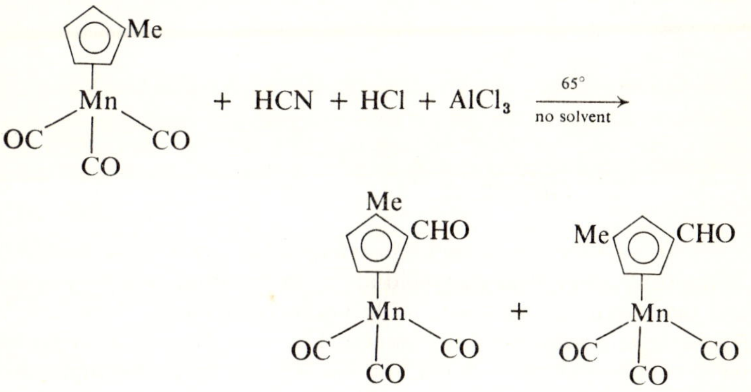

5-80

6

Chapter 6

Catalytic Processes

GENERAL CONSIDERATIONS

Direct uses of organometallic compounds are few in number. Tetraethyl- and tetramethyllead are manufactured on a large scale and employed as anti-knock additives in petroleum. Tricarbonyl-(methylcyclopentadienyl)manganese has very limited application for the same purpose. Ferrocene has activity in controlling combustion of various fuels, reducing carbon deposition (smokiness of flames), but practical utility based on this effect has not been established.

Biocidal activity of organo-tin, -lead, -mercury and arsenic compounds is well established. The antiseptic and especially fungicidal properties of di- and tri-alkyltin derivatives (e.g. dibutyltin chloride, tributyltin oxide) find varied uses in medicine, agriculture and in the treatment of textiles, etc. The antibiotic uses of organo-arsenicals (Ehrlich's 'Salvarsan' marks the beginning of modern chemotherapy) and the antiseptic use of such organo-mercurial preparations as 'Mercurochrome' (2,7-dibromo-4-hydroxymercurifluorescein) and 'Merthiolate' are largely superseded by other drugs.

The other uses are indirect—as synthetic intermediates or as catalysts. The former have been discussed in Chapter 3, and the latter form the subject of this last chapter. Catalytic uses have increased rapidly in recent years and are responsible for much of the current interest in the field. Although our understanding of these processes is patchy and rather inadequate, there are indications that a common mechanistic pattern may apply to many of the varied processes which are described below.

CARBONYLATION

This name is employed here to include all processes in which carbon monoxide is introduced into a molecule. It includes the reactions variously described as hydroformylation reactions and oxo-processes. Although iron and nickel carbonyls are active in many of these processes, cobalt carbonyl has been most widely used and most extensively studied. It catalyzes inter alia the hydroformylation of olefins according to

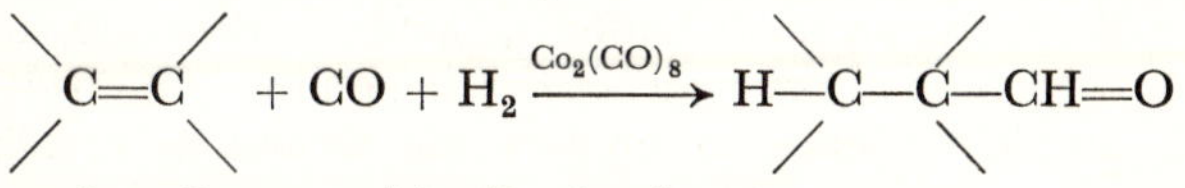

$$\ce{\underset{/}{\overset{\backslash}{C}}{=}\underset{\backslash}{\overset{/}{C}} + CO + H_2 ->[Co_2(CO)_8] H-\underset{/}{\overset{\backslash}{C}}-\underset{\backslash}{\overset{/}{C}}-CH{=}O}$$

a process first discovered by Roelen in 1937.

The sum of the available evidence suggests that the hydro-carbonyl formed according to

$$Co_2(CO_8) + H_2 \rightarrow 2HCo(CO)_4$$

is the active catalyst. The succeeding steps may be formulated as follows:

(a) $HCo(CO)_4 \rightleftharpoons HCo(CO)_3 + CO$

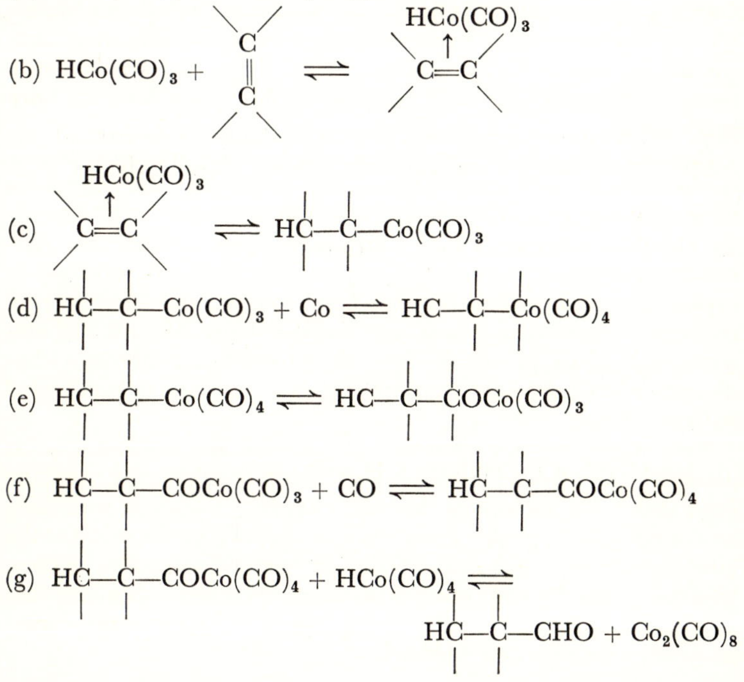

(b) $HCo(CO)_3 + \quad \ce{\underset{/\backslash}{\overset{\backslash/}{C}}{=}\!\!\underset{}{\overset{}{||}}\!\!\underset{}{\overset{}{C}}} \quad \rightleftharpoons \quad \ce{\overset{HCo(CO)_3}{\underset{/\quad\backslash}{\overset{\backslash\uparrow/}{C}{=}C}}}$

(c) $\ce{\overset{HCo(CO)_3}{\underset{/\quad\backslash}{\overset{\backslash\uparrow/}{C}{=}C}}} \rightleftharpoons HC{-}C{-}Co(CO)_3$

(d) $HC{-}C{-}Co(CO)_3 + Co \rightleftharpoons HC{-}C{-}Co(CO)_4$

(e) $HC{-}C{-}Co(CO)_4 \rightleftharpoons HC{-}C{-}COCo(CO)_3$

(f) $HC{-}C{-}COCo(CO)_3 + CO \rightleftharpoons HC{-}C{-}COCo(CO)_4$

(g) $HC{-}C{-}COCo(CO)_4 + HCo(CO)_4 \rightleftharpoons$
$$HC{-}C{-}CHO + Co_2(CO)_8$$

The process is commonly followed by reduction of the aldehyde by $HCo(CO)_4$, possibly by steps analogous to (a), (b), (c) and (g), to give the corresponding alcohol.

The above mechanism is by no means established in every detail, but is the most plausible scheme which has been proposed and which accords with all available evidence.

Only some of the salient features can be discussed here. Thus, step (a) accords with the observed retarding effect of high pressures of CO, which promote the reverse reaction. The formation of many stable π-olefin complexes (Chapter 5) lends credence to step (b). Whereas there is no direct evidence bearing on the isomerization (c) there is ample evidence to support the formation of alkyls as intermediates. As the stable tetracarbonyls, produced in step (d), they can be prepared by independent methods. Moreover when stabilized as allyl complexes, they are readily obtained from dienes and cobalt hydrocarbonyls:

$$HCo(CO)_4 \xrightarrow{-CO} HCo(CO)_3 \xrightarrow{CH_2=CH-CH=CH_2} HC{\begin{array}{c} CH_3 \\ \diagdown \\ CH \\ \diagup\diagup \\ \diagdown \\ CH_2 \end{array}}-Co(CO)_3$$

6-1

Steps (e), (f) and (g) represent reactions which can be carried out independently, but (f) and (g) could equally plausibly be replaced by

(h) $H-\overset{|}{\underset{|}{C}}-\overset{|}{\underset{|}{C}}-COCo(CO)_3 + HCo(CO)_4 \rightleftharpoons$

$$H\overset{|}{\underset{|}{C}}-\overset{|}{\underset{|}{C}}-CHO + Co_2(CO)_7$$

(i) $Co_2(CO)_7 + CO \rightleftharpoons Co_2(CO)_8$

or by

(j) $H-\overset{|}{\underset{|}{C}}-\overset{|}{\underset{|}{C}}-COCo(CO)_3 + H_2 \rightleftharpoons$

$$\left[H-\overset{|}{\underset{|}{C}}-\overset{|}{\underset{|}{C}}-COCoH_2(CO)_3 \right] \rightleftharpoons$$

$$H-\overset{|}{\underset{|}{C}}-\overset{|}{\underset{|}{C}}-CHO + HCo(CO)_3$$

The reaction in which the carbon monoxide becomes attached to the hydrocarbon chain, step (e), may be viewed as the key step in the whole sequence.

Taken with (f), it is a special case (i.e. $L = CO$) of the general process

$$RCo(CO)_4 + L \rightleftharpoons RCOCo(CO)_3L$$

This process was first studied in detail in the analogous manganese derivatives:

$$RMn(CO)_5 + L \rightleftharpoons RCOMn(CO)_4L$$

Here both alkyl and acyl derivatives are much more stable than in the cobalt case. They can be prepared from sodiopentacarbonyl-manganese and alkyl or acyl halides. When this is done and the acyl group is labelled with C^{14} it can be shown that none of the CO lost in the reverse reaction ($L = CO$) is derived from this acyl group. Hence the reaction must be pictured as an alkyl migration from the metal to bound CO or vice versa,

6-2

Reaction occurs similarly with other neutral donor ligands, e.g. phosphines and amines.

While the reactions in the cobalt and manganese series are closely similar, the kinetics reveal a significant mechanistic difference. The rate of the manganese reaction is proportional to the concentration of both alkylmetal carbonyl and ligand, L; in the cobalt case it is independent of the latter. This is the justification for writing two steps (e) and (f) for the reaction in the cobalt series corresponding to the above single bimolecular reaction of the manganese derivatives.

Another remarkable variation of this reaction occurs with sulphur dioxide:

$$RMn(CO)_5 + SO_2 \rightarrow RSO_2Mn(CO)_5$$

In this case addition of SO_2 must either involve direct insertion between the alkyl group and the metal atom or must be followed by migration of alkyl from metal or CO to sulphur.

Hydroformylations can not only be carried out catalytically at high temperature and pressure, but also stoicheiometrically using $Co_2(CO)_8$ and hydrogen (at 70–200 atm) or, preferably, using $HCo(CO)_4$ and carbon monoxide at atmospheric pressure. In the latter case it follows the course:

$$RCH{=}CHR + 2HCo(CO)_4 + CO \rightarrow RCH_2CHRCHO +$$
$$Co_2(CO)_8$$

This occurs at room temperature or below. By adding triphenylphosphine to a reaction of isobutene at 0°, Heck and Breslow succeeded in isolating the acylcobalt complex [cf. step. (f) above] as the triphenylphosphine derivative $Me_3C{\cdot}COCo(CO)_3PPh_3$. Its formation may be represented thus:

$$Me_2C{=}CH_2 + HCo(CO)_4 \rightarrow Me_3C{\cdot}Co(CO)_4$$
$$Me_3C{\cdot}Co(CO)_4 + PPh_3 \rightarrow Me_3C{\cdot}COCo(CO)_3PPh_3$$

Such acyl complexes are not only reducible to the aldehydes which normally result from the hydroformylation, but can also be converted very smoothly to the corresponding methyl esters with iodine and methanol.

In this particular example, such treatment gives exclusively $Me_3C{\cdot}CO_2Me$ and no $Me_2CHCH_2CO_2Me$, showing that, at the low reaction temperature only the more highly branched acyl complex is formed. This contrasts with the predominant formation of the less branched aldehyde under the usual conditions (110–160°) of hydroformylation:

e.g. $$Me_2C{=}CH_2 \rightarrow Me_2CH{\cdot}CH_2CHO + Me_3C{\cdot}CHO$$
$$\phantom{Me_2C{=}CH_2 \rightarrow} 96\% \phantom{Me_2CH{\cdot}CH_2CHO +} 4\%$$

A similar temperature effect was noted using methyl acrylate, but not with pentene-1. Other conditions, especially carbon monoxide pressure are known to be important in determining isomer ratios.

Since olefin isomerization is one of the common side reactions, the products may be derived from olefins differing from the starting material (see p. 170).

The other main side reaction is hydrogenation of both the original olefin and the aldehyde. The extent of hydrogenation depends greatly on hydrogen pressure. Formation of alkane cannot usually be avoided completely, and formation of alcohol can be made the principal result if desired. Unsaturated aldehydes undergo reduction to saturated aldehydes rather than hydroformylation and hence conjugated dienes also yield saturated monoaldehydes, by a combination of hydroformylation and reduction,

e.g. $CH_2{=}CH{-}CH{=}CH_2 + CO + H_2 \xrightarrow{Co_2(CO)_8}$

$$CH_3(CH_2)_3CHO + CH_3CH_2CH(CH_3)CHO$$

Dienes are also prone to form ketones as by-products. Thus 1,4-pentadiene reacts to give mainly methylcyclopentanone:

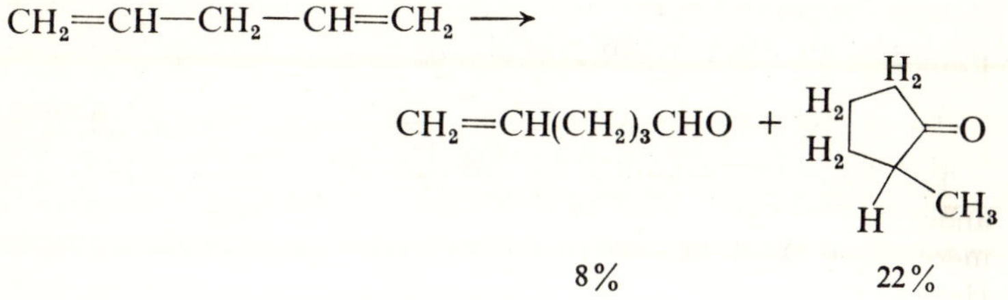

$$CH_2{=}CH{-}CH_2{-}CH{=}CH_2 \longrightarrow$$

$$CH_2{=}CH(CH_2)_3CHO +$$

8%   22%

6-3

Cyclization can be visualized either as proceeding via a cyclic cobalt complex (A) or a dicobalt complex (B). The formation

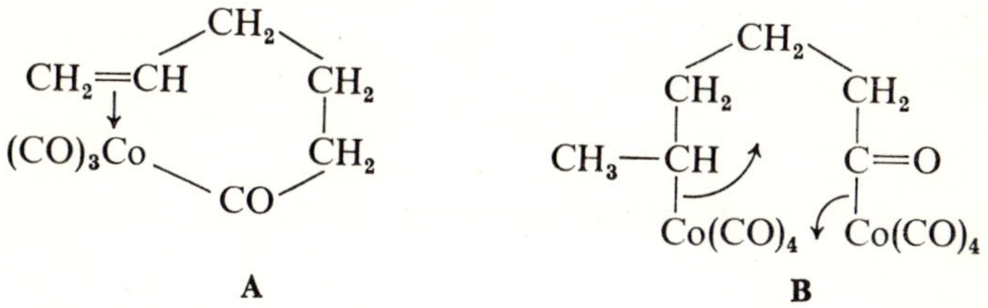

A   B

6-4

of ketones from mono-olefins is favoured by very low reaction temperatures.

Secondary and tertiary alcohols readily undergo hydroformylation presumably via the corresponding olefins. However, methanol and benzylic alcohols also react and this suggests that alkyl cobalt intermediates can be formed directly from these alcohols. Hydrogenolysis becomes a major side reaction,

e.g. $PhCH_2OH + H_2 + CO \xrightarrow{Co_2(CO)_8} PhCH_2CH_2OH + PhCH_3$

31%   63%

Although rhodium and iridium catalysts have been claimed to be effective at lower temperatures than cobalt, they have found little use. However, more efficient catalysts based on these metals are being developed. Thus $(Ph_3P)_3RhCl_3$ as well as being an efficient hydroformylation catalyst (cf. p. 168) will catalyze hydroformylation:

e.g. $C_4H_9CH{=}CH_2 + CO + H_2 \xrightarrow{66°/90\ atm}$

$$C_6H_{13}CHO + C_4H_9CH(CH_3)CHO$$
$$70\% \qquad\qquad\qquad 20\%$$

Equally interesting is the exploitation of the reversibility of such carbonylation reactions to provide an efficient method of decarbonylation of aldehydes, using $(Ph_3P)_2Ir(CO)Cl$ as catalyst.

The use of iron carbonyl in the presence of caustic alkali is another variation in which the function of the alkali is probably merely to assist reduction of $Fe(CO)_5$ to $HFe(CO)_4^-$ (see p. 87). Hence reaction can proceed in water without hydrogen according to

$$CH_2{=}CH_2 + 3CO + 2H_2O \xrightarrow[Fe(CO)_5]{NaOH} CH_3CH_2CH_2OH + 2CO_2$$

With other catalysts, carboxylation is the normal result of carbonylation reactions carried out in the presence of water. It may be formulated as involving hydrolytic cleavage of the acyl derivatives, e.g. of cobalt:

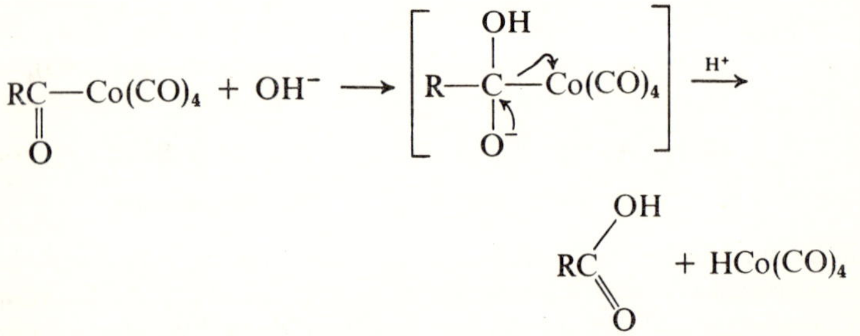

$$RC{-}Co(CO)_4 + OH^- \longrightarrow \left[R{-}\overset{OH}{\underset{O^-}{C}}{-}Co(CO)_4 \right] \xrightarrow{H^+}$$

$$RC\overset{OH}{\diagdown}{\diagup} + HCo(CO)_4$$

6-5

Thus it is analogous to the methanol cleavage of acylcobalt complexes mentioned above (p. 160) and the methoxide cleavage which has been employed to degrade various more stable acyl complexes

e.g. $RCOMn(CO)_5 + NaOMe \rightarrow NaMn(CO)_5 + RCOOMe$

Nickel carbonyl is the preferred catalyst for carboxylation reactions although palladium (e.g. as $[(Bu_3P)_2PdX]_2$) appears to be similarly effective. While it appears likely that acylnickel complexes are formed as unstable intermediates, no stable compounds of this type are known which could furnish an analogy.

Acids are used in most carboxylation systems and halides are generally beneficial; $NiBr_2$ is a better catalyst than $NiCl_2$ while NiI_2 leads to extensive side-reactions and NiF_2 is inactive. The catalytic reaction is carried out under conditions under which the active nickel halides are converted (or reconverted) to nickel carbonyl, so that the overall reaction follows the equation

$$\overset{\displaystyle \diagdown}{\underset{\displaystyle \diagup}{}} C = C \overset{\displaystyle \diagup}{\underset{\displaystyle \diagdown}{}} + CO + H_2O \xrightarrow{Ni(CO)_4} H\overset{|}{C} - \overset{|}{C} - COOH$$

In alcohol the ester rather than acid is formed, and in the presence of amines the corresponding amides result.

The carboxylation reaction, in contrast to hydroformylation, works equally well with acetylenes as with olefins. For both systems not only the above catalytic reaction, but also a stoicheiometric one occurring under mild conditions has been used:

$$4RC{\equiv}CR + Ni(CO)_4 + 2HCl + 4EtOH \rightarrow$$

$$NiCl_2 + 4RCH{=}CRCO_2Et + H_2$$

Terminal acetylenes give mainly the branched acids. Thus the elements of formic acid H——COOH may be thought of as adding according to Markownikoff's rule; but in general they add *cis-*

e.g. $PhC{\equiv}CH \longrightarrow CH_2{=}CPhCO_2H + PhCH{=}CHCO_2H$

$\qquad\qquad\qquad\qquad$ atropic acid $\qquad\qquad$ *trans*-cinnamic acid
$\qquad\qquad\qquad\qquad$ (48%) $\qquad\qquad\qquad\qquad$ (trace)

$$PhC{\equiv}CPh \longrightarrow \underset{H}{\overset{Ph}{\diagdown}} C = C \underset{CO_2H}{\overset{Ph}{\diagup}}$$

$\hfill$ **6-6**

Whereas the catalytic carboxylation of acetylenes generally works well at temperatures in the region of 150°, olefins require higher temperatures (170°–200°) though the conditions are still moderate compared to the purely acid-catalyzed reaction

e.g. $CH_2{=}CH_2 + CO + H_2O \xrightarrow[300°/250\ atm]{H_3PO_4} CH_3CH_2CO_2H.$

When the appropriate acid replaces water, formation of anhydride can be carried out efficiently:

e.g. $CH_2{=}CH_2 + CO + CH_3CH_2CO_2H \xrightarrow[230°]{Ni(OCOEt)_2}$

$(CH_3CH_2CO)_2O$ (80%)

Under anhydrous conditions, stoicheiometric reaction with palladium chloride has been used to form acid chlorides:

e.g. $C_2H_2 + CO + PdCl_2 \xrightarrow{C_6H_6}$

$ClCOCH{=}CH{-}CH{=}CHCOCl + ClCOCH{=}CHCOCl$

Alcohols react via dehydration to the olefin at 250–300° and even ethers react under similar conditions,

e.g.

$+ 2CO + H_2O \xrightarrow[250°]{Ni(CO)_4\,NiI_2}$

$HO_2C(CH_2)_4CO_2H + $

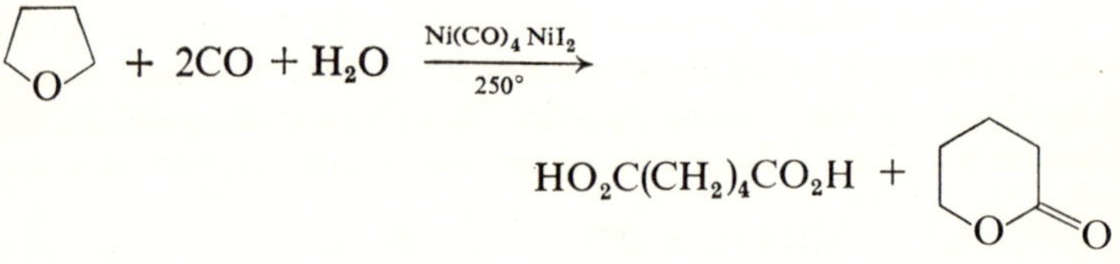

6-7

Aromatic halides react at 300° and high CO pressures (600 atm) to give acids in moderate yield:

$$ArCl + CO + H_2O \xrightarrow[\text{[or Fe(CO)}_5\text{ or Co}_2\text{(CO)}_8\text{]}]{Ni(CO)_4} ArCOOH$$

The anhydrides of these acids disproportionate to phthalic anhydrides under similar conditions:

e.g. $(C_6H_5CO)_2O \xrightarrow[325°/100\,atm]{Ni(CO)_4/CO} C_6H_6 + C_6H_4(CO)_2O$

Alkyl halides appear to have received less attention, but allyl chloride undergoes carboxylation smoothly according to

$CH_2{=}CH{-}CH_2Cl + CO + H_2O \xrightarrow{Ni(CO)_4} CH_2{=}CHCH_2CO_2H$

and a mixture of allyl chloride and acetylene has been shown to undergo the interesting addition:

$CH_2{=}CH - CH_2Cl + CH{\equiv}CH + CO + ROH \rightarrow$

$CH_2{=}CH{-}CH_2CH{=}CHCO_2R$

Other variants which have been studied include the reactions of α-haloacetylenes to give allenic acids in buffered solution or lactones under acid conditions:

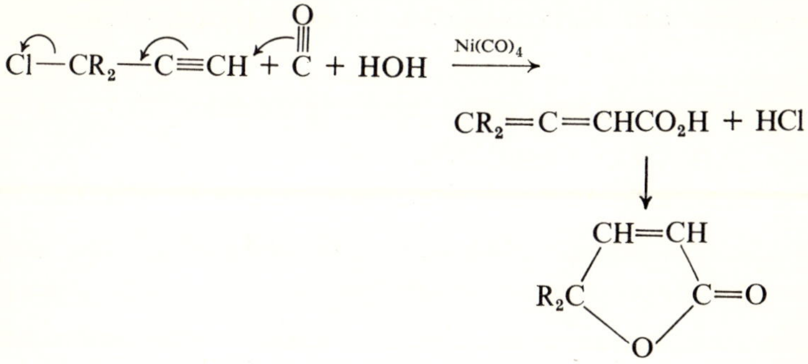

$$Cl-CR_2-C\equiv CH + C\!\!=\!\!O + HOH \xrightarrow{\;Ni(CO)_4\;}$$

$$CR_2\!\!=\!\!C\!\!=\!\!CHCO_2H + HCl$$

6-8

When propargyl bromide, replaces the chloride (R = H) in this reaction, the product is a keto-acid resulting from incorporation of two moles of this acetylene:

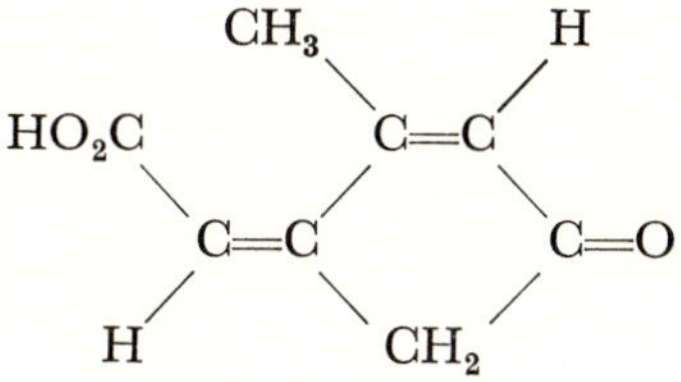

6-9

Ketones are the most prominent by-products. Thus ethylene gives diethyl ketone along with propionic acid and acetylenes give cyclopentenones, presumably by cyclization of the intermediate dienones:

e.g.

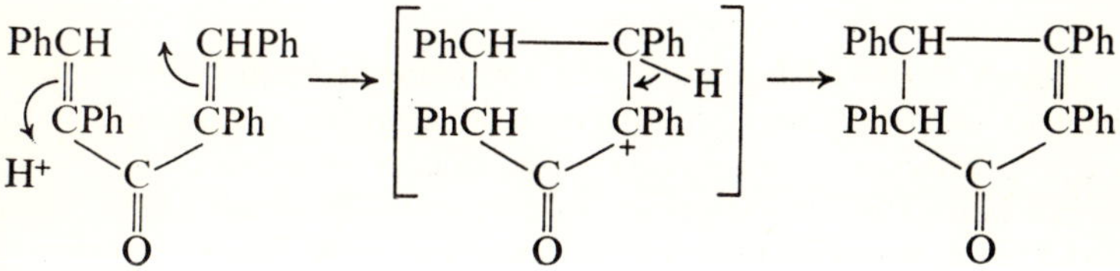

6-10

Ketones become particularly prominent with catalysts other than the usual nickel. The formation of cyclopentadienones and hydroquinones when iron carbonyls react with acetylenes can be linked directly with the presence of intermediate ferracyclopentadiene and quinone complexes respectively (cf. Chapter 5).

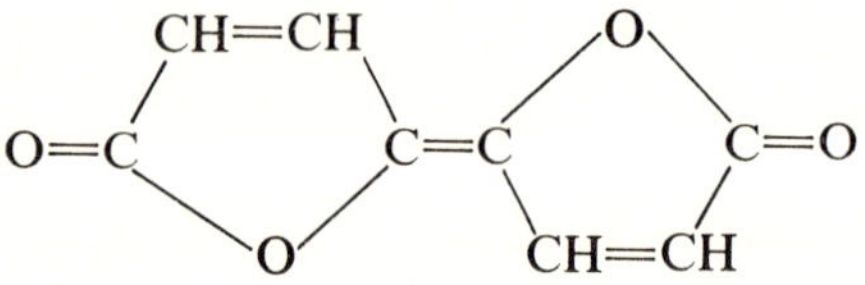

6-11

Similarly the cobalt-catalyzed formation of the dilactone (6-11) from acetylene:

$$2C_2H_2 + 4CO \xrightarrow{Co_2(CO)_8} C_8H_4O_4 \quad (70\%)$$

can be related to the isolable complexes "$Co_2(CO)_6(C_2H_2)$" and "$Co_2(CO)_9(C_2H_2)$" as intermediates:

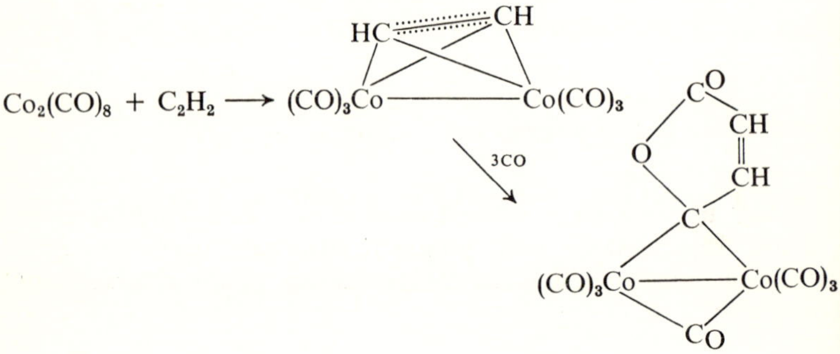

6-12

Cobalt carbonyl has also been the catalyst employed to effect various carbonyl insertion reactions in aromatic compounds with carbon-nitrogen or nitrogen-nitrogen double or triple bonds. The Schiff bases PhCH=NR react to give phthalimidines (A) in high yield, and ketazines, semicarbazones, etc. give related products. Azobenzene is converted to the 2-phenylindazolone (B) at 190° and further to the quinazoline derivative (C) at 230°, and benzonitrile to

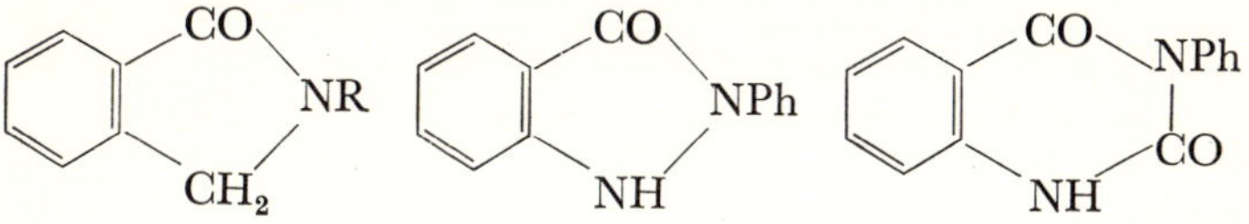

A   B   C   6-13

the benzylphthalimidine (A; $R = CH_2Ph$). The closely related conversion of hydrazines to ureas:

$$RNH \cdot NHR + CO \xrightarrow{\text{metal carbonyls}} RNHCONHR$$

occurs with iron, cobalt or nickel carbonyls and is itself a special case of the carbonylation of primary and secondary amines, which apparently most carbonyls can effect:

$$RNH_2 + CO \rightarrow RNHCHO + (RNH)_2CO$$

The reversibility of such systems is apparent from the formation of hydrazine when urea is heated with carbonyl-forming metals.

More generally, osmium, ruthenium and iridium salts in the presence of phosphines have been shown to abstract carbon monoxide or carbon monoxide and hydrogen from aldehydes or alcohols in reactions which must be considered reversals of the carbonylation (hydroformylation) processes.

e.g. $OsBr_4 + PPh_3 + CH_3CH_2OH \rightarrow OsHBr(CO)(PPh_3)_3$

$(NH_4)_2(IrCl_6) + PPh_3 + HOCH_2CH_2OH \xrightarrow{240°}$

$$Ir(CO)(PPh_3)_2Cl \quad (76\%)$$

Tracer experiments have confirmed that the carbonyl group in the resulting complex is derived from the $-CH_2OH$ group of the alcohol.

The reaction has preparative value for such monocarbonyl complexes. The square planar iridium complex $Ir(CO)(PPh_3)_2Cl$ is an extremely reactive complex which adds not only hydrogen chloride to give the octahedral $IrHCl_2(CO)(PPh_3)_2$, but forms adducts also with alkenes, alkyl and acyl halides, sulphur, oxygen and hydrogen, etc. The oxygen adduct is a useful oxygen transfer agent and with hydrogen we get good homogeneous hydrogenation systems.

HYDROGENATION

Hydrogen addition to the above iridium complex is formulated by Vaska as

$$\begin{array}{c} Cl \\ | \\ Ir \\ | \\ CO \end{array} + \begin{array}{c} H \\ \| \\ H \end{array} \rightleftharpoons \begin{array}{c} Cl \quad H \\ \diagdown \diagup \\ Ir \\ \diagup \diagdown \\ OC \quad H \end{array} \qquad \textbf{6-14}$$

with the two phosphine groups (not shown) perpendicular to the plane of the paper. The equilibrium favours the adduct at room temperature, so that the hydride may be isolated. This system catalyzes reduction of simple olefins, e.g. ethylene, only rather slowly at 60° whereas the pentacoordinate $IrH(CO)(PPh_3)_3$ causes rapid reduction of ethylene even at ambient temperature and pressure. The rhodium analogues of these two iridium complexes are somewhat less active catalysts, but $(Ph_3P)_3RhCl$ is highly active and has been shown to add hydrogen giving solutions with typical high field n.m.r. lines (18–28τ) which disappear rapidly on addition of an olefin. Os and Ru complexes have only been found to have weak activity under comparable conditions. The hydrocarbonyls of cobalt and iron, though requiring somewhat higher temperatures, are rather efficient homogeneous hydrogenation catalysts. With the cobalt complex olefinic groups are reduced under milder conditions than carbonyl groups, even when conjugated.

e.g. $CH_3CH{=}CHCHO \xrightarrow[125°]{Co_2(CO)_8/CO/H_2} CH_3CH_2CH_2CHO \xrightarrow{175°}$

$$CH_3CH_2CH_2CH_2OH$$

The mechanism given above (p. 157; steps (a)—(c) followed by steps analogous to (h) and (i) or (j) or (d) and (g) is applicable to the first step and if we accept the possibility of π-complex formation between the metal and aldehyde or ketone carbonyls:

$$\begin{array}{c} O \\ \| \\ Co{\leftarrow}{-}C \\ \diagup \diagdown \end{array}$$, an exactly analogous sequence can be written for their

reduction.

In contrast to the above hydrogenation, the double bonds in

furan are sufficiently stabilized to allow the following hydrogenations below 130°, without attack on the ring:

$$\text{(furan)}-COR \longrightarrow \text{(furan)}-CH_2R$$

$$\text{(furan)}-CH{=}CHCOCH_3 \longrightarrow \text{(furan)}-CH_2CH_2COCH_3$$

6-15

By working with preformed $HCo(CO_4)$ as a stoicheiometric reducing agent appreciable hydrogenation is possible at ambient temperature and pressure:

e.g.
$$PhC{=}CH_2 + 2HCo(CO)_4 \longrightarrow PhCH(CH_3)_2$$
$$\quad\ \ |$$
$$\quad\ \ CH_3$$

Iron hydrocarbonyl has been used similarly in:

$$C_2H_2 + 2HFe(CO)_4{}^- \rightarrow C_2H_4$$

$$CH_3COCH_3 + H_2Fe(CO)_4 \rightarrow CH_3CHOHCH_3$$

A significant advantage over heterogeneous catalytic hydrogenation methods lies in the absence of 'catalyst poisoning'. Thus thiophene derivatives may be reduced smoothly:

$$\text{(thiophene)}-COCH_3 \longrightarrow \text{(thiophene)}-CH_2CH_3 \longrightarrow \text{(thiophene)}-CH_2CH_3$$

6-16

Closely related to these carbonyl catalysts is the hydridocobalticyanide ion $[Co(CN)_5H]^{3-}$ formed, by hydrogen absorption, from potassium cyanocobaltate. This is not only an efficient homogeneous hydrogenation catalyst, but may have special relevance as a model for biological systems (cf. p. 46).

Organometallic complexes in the form of π-complexes of the olefin to be reduced are undoubtedly involved in the reported uses of solutions of platinum or ruthenium halides. Zeise salts are reduced directly by hydrogen to alkanes and stannous chloride has been shown to activate chloroplatinic acid as a catalyst under conditions where it promotes Zeise salt formation. Ruthenium(II) solutions though absorbing simple olefins, do not cause their reduction, but are effective for the reduction of, for example, maleic to succinic acid at 70°.

The use of various Ziegler-catalysts is of interest both for the high efficiency reported with some simple olefins, and for the additional correlation it provides between the different catalytic reactions discussed in this chapter. To provide soluble catalysts the transition metal complexes employed with the trialkylaluminium (usually tri-iso-butylaluminium) include the alkoxides of titanium and vanadium and the acetylacetonates of chromium, manganese and cobalt. As an example, may be quoted the quantitative conversion of 1-hexene to hexane in two hours at 30° using a 6:1 ratio of $Bu^i_3Al:Co(acac)_3$.

ISOMERIZATION OF OLEFINS

Most and possibly all catalysts discussed in this chapter are capable of catalyzing the isomerization of olefins. While of limited direct use, such isomerization is frequently important in determining the structure of the product of, for example, a hydroformylation reaction. Thus isomerization of normal alkenes is rapid compared to carbonylation and the nature of the product is therefore determined by the relative reactivity of the different isomers.

e.g. $CH_3CH_2CH{=}CH{-}CH_3 + CO + H_2 \xrightarrow[110°]{Co_2(CO)_8}$

$$CH_3CH_2CH_2CH_2CH_2CH_2OH + CH_3CH_2CH_2CHCH_2OH$$
$$\underset{}{\underset{CH_3}{|}}$$

$$70\% 28\%$$

Among mechanisms which have frequently been considered are the simple addition elimination sequences proceeding via alkyls:

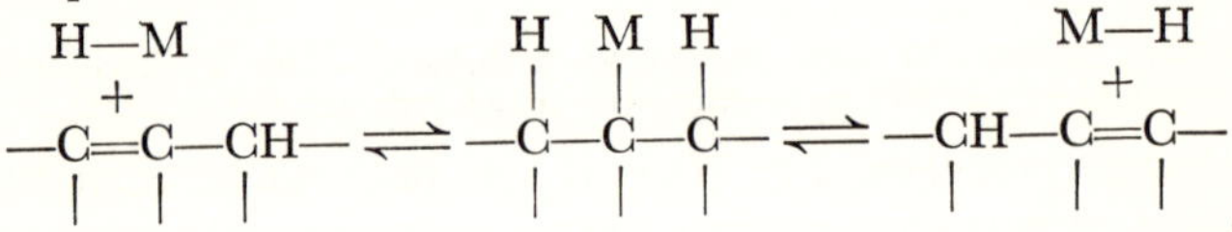

6-17

or via π-allyl complexes:

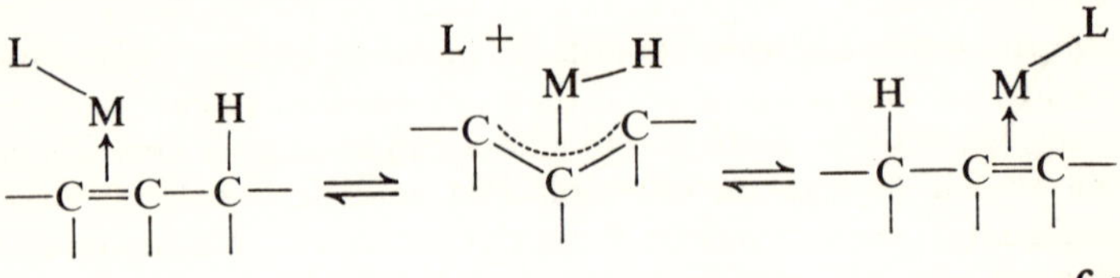

6-18

The actual mechanism may well vary with both the catalyst and the olefin. Thus the mechanism in 6-17, although not fully established, appears the most probable explanation with Ziegler type catalysts, since the addition and elimination steps themselves are clearly established and fundamental to the polymerization mechanism. For hydroformylation, however, neither of these pictures prove adequate since tracer experiments demand two concerted 1,2-migrations of hydrogen. Thus

$$R-CD_2-CH=CH_2 \xrightarrow{HCo(CO)_4} R-CD=CD-CH_3$$

without loss of D and

$$RCH_2-CH=CH_2 \xrightarrow{DCo(CO)_4} RCH=CH-CH_3$$

without deuterium incorporation. Similar though somewhat conflicting results are reported with $RhCl_3$ as catalyst, while palladium salts appear to cause isomerization by a 1,3-hydrogen migration.

Dienes in general isomerize to conjugated systems, e.g. with iron carbonyl:

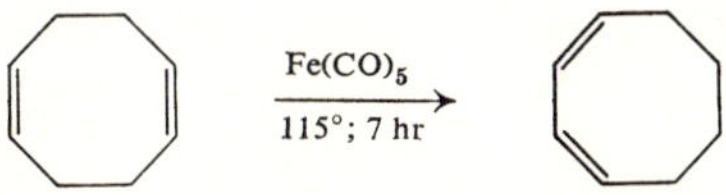

(94%)   6-19

OLEFIN OXIDATION

In the presence of water, olefins are oxidized by palladium chloride, ethylene giving acetaldehyde:

$$C_2H_4 + PdCl_2 + H_2O \rightarrow CH_3CHO + Pd + 2HCl$$

By coupling this reaction with the reoxidation of palladium by cupric chloride

$$Pd + 2CuCl_2 \rightarrow PdCl_2 + 2CuCl$$

and of cuprous chloride by oxygen

$$2CuCl + \tfrac{1}{2}O_2 + 2HCl \rightarrow 2CuCl_2 + H_2O$$

the overall process becomes the net, $PdCl_2$—$CuCl_2$ catalyzed, oxidation

$$C_2H_4 + \tfrac{1}{2}O_2 \rightarrow CH_3CHO$$

This is the basis of the technically important oxidation of ethylene to acetaldehyde and is equally applicable to other olefins, e.g. propylene $\rightarrow$ acetone and cyclohexene $\rightarrow$ cyclohexanone.

The reaction undoubtedly proceeds via an olefin-palladium complex, probably of the Zeise type, so that we may reformulate the first step as

$$[PdCl_4]^{2-} + C_2H_4 \rightarrow [PdCl_3C_2H_4]^- + Cl^-$$

$$[PdCl_3C_2H_4]^- + H_2O \rightarrow C_2H_4O + Pd + 3Cl^- + 2H^+$$

The hydrolysis step is postulated to proceed by simultaneous attack of hydroxide and migration of hydride:

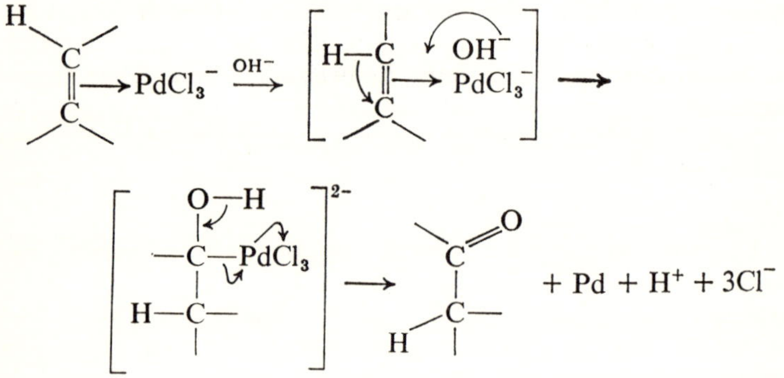

6-20

Such a mechanism is compatible both with the observed inhibition of the reaction by acids and the lack of incorporation of deuterium when the reaction is carried out in D_2O solution.

OLIGOMERIZATION OF OLEFINS AND ACETYLENES

A wide variety of self-condensations of olefins and acetylenes occur via their transition metal complexes and lead to either oligomers or polymers. This section deals with those cases where oligomers are the products of most interest. They concern conjugated dienes and acetylenes. Of the former, only butadiene has been studied in detail and its reactivity may well be exceptional rather than typical. It yields a variety of dimers and trimers, depending on the conditions used. The dimers include the open-chain 3-methyl-1,6-heptatriene formed with, for example, cobalt carbonyl plus triethylaluminium as catalyst:

$$2C_4H_6 \xrightarrow{\text{Co}_2(\text{CO})_8/\text{AlEt}_3}$$

$$CH_2\!\!=\!\!CH\!\!-\!\!CH\!\!=\!\!CH\!\!-\!\!\overset{\overset{\displaystyle CH_3}{\displaystyle |}}{CH}\!\!-\!\!CH\!\!=\!\!CH_2 \quad (90\%)$$

the 'Diels-Alder' dimer, vinylcyclohexene, observed with several types of catalyst and 1,5-cyclo-octadiene formed with various nickel catalysts.

e.g.

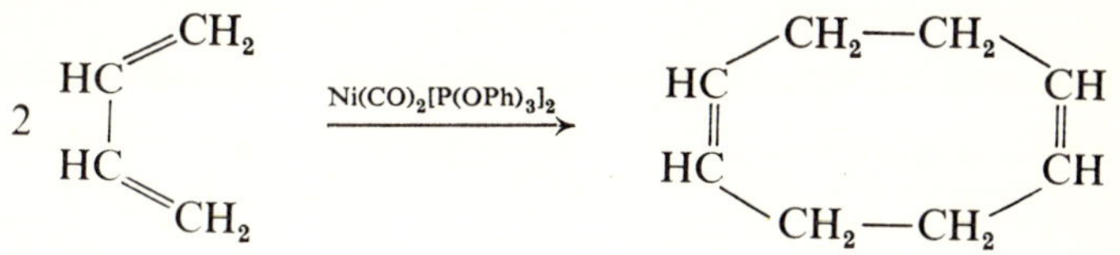

6-2

The influence of catalyst structure in the case of nickel complexes has been studied in some detail by Wilke. When all the groups attached to nickel can be displaced by butadiene, the reaction leads to trimers. But when nickel has one firmly held ligand, only dimers result. In the latter case, an intermediate complex (A) results and

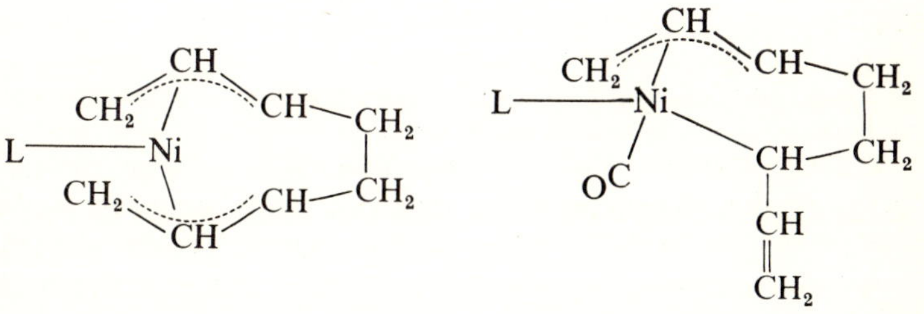

A

B

6-22

in some cases, e.g. L = (o-PhC$_6$H$_4$)$_3$P, this is isolable. Reduction of this intermediate with Et$_2$AlH gave n-octane, but warming with such ligands as PPh$_3$ led to cyclization and displacement of the ligand as 1,5-cyclooctadiene. Yet, at low temperature, carbon monoxide causes formation of vinylcyclohexene from the same intermediate and it is suggested that this occurs via a further intermediate of the type B. Simple warming of complex A apparently forms the 16-electron cyclo-octadiene (COD) complex L-Ni(COD) from which butadiene displaces the hydrocarbon ligand reforming A. Thus the reaction becomes catalytic. It is highly efficient giving nearly quantitative yields with a conversion of up to 1 kg of butadiene per gram of nickel per hour.

When the initial catalyst contains only readily replaceable groups, three moles of butadiene react to give the intermediate complex C. Thus cyclododecatrienenickel yields this product when

C   6-22

treated with butadiene at −40°C. Since warming causes cyclization of C to the cyclododecatriene complex, the reaction again becomes catalytic at higher temperature. The structure of the complex C follows from its reduction to n-dodecane and from x-ray crystallographic study of an analogous ruthenium complex. Its cyclization may be compared with the formation of diallyl from bis-allylnickel (cf. p. 49). In contrast to the behaviour of this nickel complex C, its palladium analogue loses the hydrocarbon ligand without cyclization, as 1,3,6,10-dodecatetraene.

Although all-*trans*-1,5,9-cyclododecatriene is the principal product (80%) of the nickel catalyzed reaction, lesser amounts of the *trans*-, *trans*-, *cis*- and the *trans*-, *cis*-, *cis*-isomers are also formed.

6-23

Several alternative and highly efficient catalysts containing titanium or chromium have been used. A catalyst obtained from $TiCl_4$ and Et_2AlCl in the ratio 1:5 gives almost exclusively the *trans-*, *trans-*, *cis-*isomer. One from CrO_2Cl_2 and $AlEt_3$ gives a 3:2 ratio of all-*trans* to *trans-*, *trans-*, *cis-* (but no *trans-*, *cis-*, *cis-*).

When mixtures of butadiene and other olefins or acetylenes are used with a nickel catalyst mixed products are formed. Thus when butadiene and ethylene react together they produce *trans-cis-*1,5-cyclodecadiene:

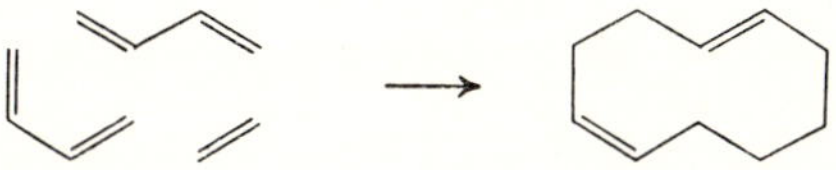

6-24

This product undergoes Cope rearrangement on heating; hence reactions conducted above 80° yield 1,2-divinyl-cyclohexane instead. When the reaction is carried out with a catalyst suitable for cyclo-octadiene synthesis, a mixture of the latter diene with the cyclo-decadiene is produced. However, cyclododecatriene formation is inhibited by ethylene so that with a catalyst lacking a strongly held ligand to block one coordination position, the decadiene becomes the main product, accompanied by some n-1,4,9-decatriene.

Cyclotrimerization of vinyl ethers (6-25) and mixed condensations

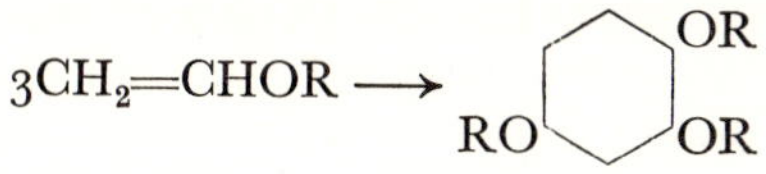
3CH₂=CHOR →
OR
RO
OR

6-25

of acetylenes with acrylates (6-26) were described by Reppe in

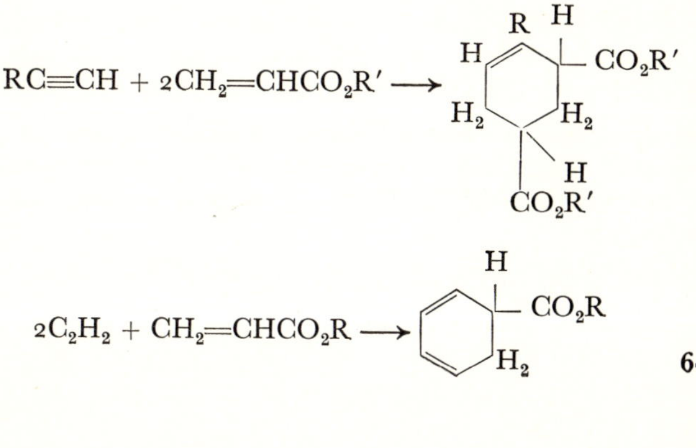
RC≡CH + 2CH₂=CHCO₂R′ →
R
H
H
CO₂R′
H₂
H₂
H
CO₂R′
2C₂H₂ + CH₂=CHCO₂R →
H
CO₂R
H₂

6-26

connection with his work on cyclotrimerization of acetylenes using phosphine-nickel complexes, e.g. $(Ph_3P)_2NiX_2$, $Ph_3PNi(CO)_3$, $(Ph_3P)_2Ni(CO)_2$.

With acetylenes alone, these catalysts yield benzene derivatives, terminal acetylenes giving chiefly the 1,2,4-trisubstituted com-

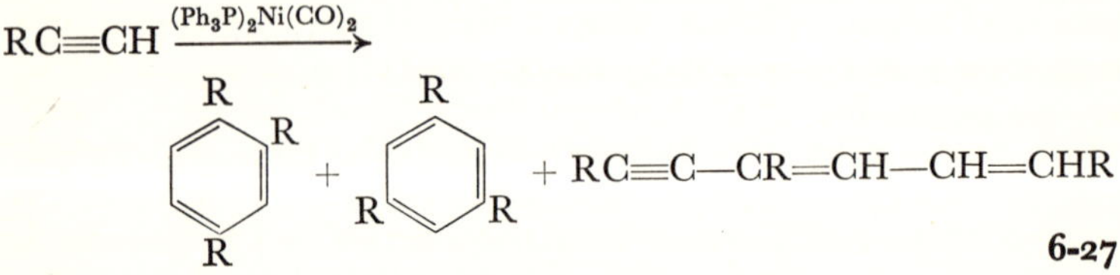
RC≡CH
(Ph3P)2Ni(CO)2
R
R
R
R
R
R
+
+ RC≡C—CR═CH—CH═CHR

6-27

pounds. These are accompanied by varying amounts of the 1,3,5-isomers and of linear trimers and polymers.

It may reasonably be assumed that here again, one phosphine ligand remains firmly bound to the nickel catalyst as a blocking group. Catalysts lacking such groups, notably nickel cyanide, nickel acetylacetonate, bis-acrylonitrilenickel and tetrakis(phosphorus trichloride)nickel lead to cyclooctatetraenes as at least major products:

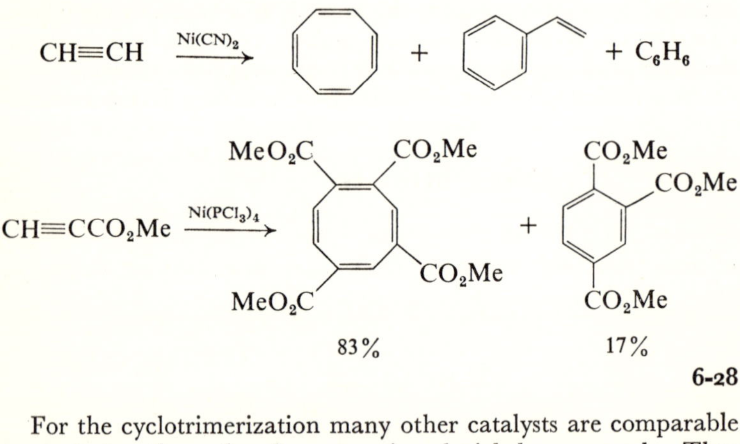
CH≡CH
Ni(CN)2
+
+ C6H6
MeO2C
CO2Me
CH≡CCO2Me
Ni(PCl3)4
CO2Me
MeO2C
+
CO2Me
CO2Me
CO2Me
83%
17%

6-28

For the cyclotrimerization many other catalysts are comparable to, or better than, the above-mentioned nickel compounds. Thus the dicarbonyl, $Ni(PPh_3)_2(CO)_2$, is a good catalyst for certain acetylenes,

e.g. $PhC{\equiv}CH \rightarrow$ 1,2,4-$C_6H_3Ph_3$ (70%)

$HC{\equiv}CCO_2Et \rightarrow$ 1,2,4-$C_6H_3(CO_2Et)_3$ (89%) + 1,3,5-$C_6H_3(CO_2Et)_3$ (6%)

but fails completely with many others, including most disubstituted acetylenes. It also leads to considerable formation of linear polymers rather than benzene derivatives: The yield of 1,2,4- + 1,3,5-$C_6H_3R_3$ from $RC\equiv CH$ drops from 65% for $R = CH_3$ to 5% for $R = C_5H_{11}$. Among other metal carbonyls, cobalt carbonyl, or its mercury derivative, $Hg[Co(CO)_4]_2$, were the best of a number tested. Thus, in refluxing dioxan, the mercury-cobalt complex transforms tolane to hexaphenylbenzene and phenylmethylacetylene to 1,2,4-trimethyl-3,5,6-triphenylbenzene, each in 90% yield. Molybdenum and nickel carbonyls are active at the same temperature, but iron carbonyl requires higher temperatures. The formation of some of the iron-acetylene complexes, mentioned in Chapter 5, must represent intermediate stages in this process. It is best understood in the case of cobalt where the first product formed is the complex $Co_2(CO)_6(RC_2R')$ with the structure A and this reacts with more of the same or a different acetylene to give complexes $Co_2(CO)_4(RC_2R')(R''C_2R''')_2$. The latter has been shown to have the structure B in the case where $R = R' = R'' = H$; $R''' = Bu^t$. This complex decomposes to 1,2-di-tert.-butylbenzene on treatment

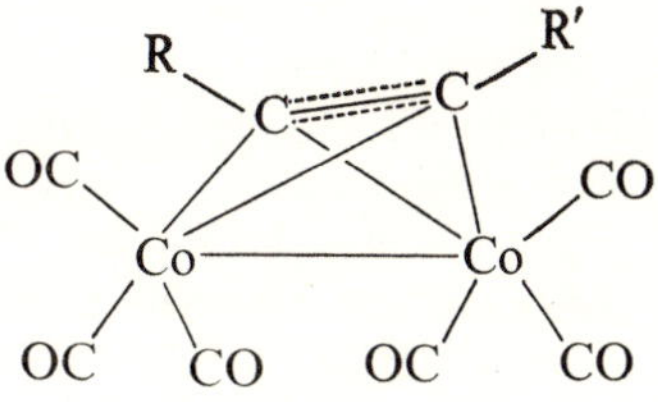

A

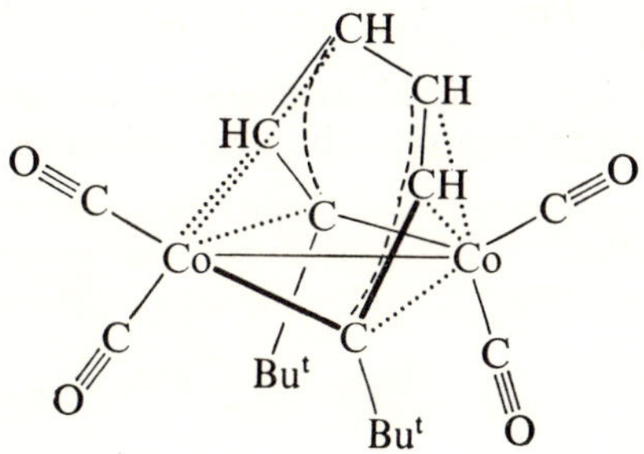

B   6-29

with bromine or on heating and a similar cyclization must take place
in the direct displacement of the 6-carbon bridge by more acetylene
when such reactions are carried out as catalytic processes.

Of a variety of heterogeneous catalysts which effect cyclotrimerization of acetylenes, the use of palladium-charcoal, e.g. to convert
dimethyl acetylenedicarboxylate to hexamethyl mellitate, could
involve similar intermediates to the homogeneous reactions. Other
catalysts include both homogeneous and heterogeneous Ziegler
catalysts. These are reported to lead to different orientation, as
well as better yields from alkylacetylenes,

e.g. $BuC{\equiv}CH \xrightarrow{\text{AlEt}_3/\text{TiCl}_4} 1,3,5\text{-}C_6H_3Bu_3$

and have been employed with diacetylenes,

e.g.

$$3HC{\equiv}C(CH_2)_4C{\equiv}CH \longrightarrow$$

6-30

If titanium alkyls are considered as the 'effective' catalysts in
such systems then this method is closely related to the use of nickel,
cobalt, manganese or chromium alkyls or aryls. With the three
latter metals, arene complexes are also formed. Thus both Ph_2Mn
and $(1,3,5\text{-}Me_3C_6H_3)_2Co$ convert 2-butyne to hexamethylbenzene
accompanied by its complexes $(C_6Me_6)_2M^+$ (M = Mn or Co).
The latter are important though minor constituents, but the more
stable chromium complexes may become the major or sole product,
so that the reaction ceases to be catalytic.

e.g. $CrO_2Cl_2 + AlEt_3 + MeC{\equiv}CMe \rightarrow (C_6Me_6)_2Cr^+$

An interesting feature of this reaction is the incorporation of
alkyl and aryl groups from the initial chromium complex. Thus

$$CrPh_3 \cdot 3THF + MeC{\equiv}CMe \longrightarrow$$

$$(C_6Me_6)_2Cr + C_6Me_6 +$$

6-31

with 20 moles of butyne per mole of triphenylchromium the yields of hexamethylbenzene and tetramethylnaphthalene are 55% and 38% respectively. Even more remarkable are the incorporation of the alkyl groups which must involve hydrogen transfer, probably to the metal atom:

$$Et_3Cr + PhC{\equiv}CPh \longrightarrow C_6Ph_6 + 1, 2, 3, 4\text{-}C_6H_2Ph_4$$

$$Me_3Cr + PhC{\equiv}CPh \longrightarrow C_6Ph_6 + \underset{Ph}{\overset{Ph}{\bigcirc}}H_2$$

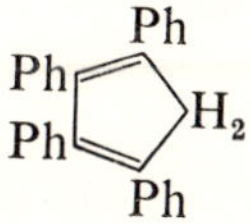

6-32

In contrast to the disubstituted acetylenes in the preceding examples, monoalkylacetylenes yield principally linear polymers under the same conditions.

POLYMERIZATION OF OLEFINS

The low temperature olefin polymerization discovered by Ziegler and extended by Natta is the main use of organometallic catalysis in industry. In this section it is intended only to give brief consideration to those features of the basic chemistry of this process which are concerned directly with the organometallic catalyst. It is not possible to discuss here the minor catalyst variations which allow this process to be controlled to give polymers with particular stereochemical structure and properties.

In the absence of transition metal salts, aluminium alkyls are useful for the oligomerization of ethylene and other simple olefins. The process depends on the insertion reaction

(i) $\qquad R_3Al + CH_2{=}CH_2 \rightarrow R_2AlCH_2CH_2R$

which can continue indefinitely and in random fashion

$$R_2AlCH_2CH_2R + CH_2{=}CH_2 \begin{array}{c} \nearrow RAl(CH_2CH_2R)_2 \\ \\ \searrow R_2AlCH_2CH_2CH_2CH_2R \end{array}$$

so that the distribution of chain length from a given amount of ethylene can be calculated statistically. To become useful this process must be coupled with the displacement reaction

(ii) $R_2AlCH_2CH_2R + CH_2{=}CH_2 \rightarrow$
$$R_2AlCH_2CH_3 + CH_2{=}CHR$$

Although this may occur as a direct displacement with certain catalysts, it is normally a two step process involving olefin elimination:

(iii) $R_2AlCH_2CH_2R \rightarrow R_2AlH + CH_2{=}CHR$

and hydride to olefin addition:

(iv) $R_2AlH + CH_2{=}CH_2 \rightarrow R_2AlCH_2CH_3.$

Step (iii) is always slow relative to both (i) and (iv), provided the alkyl chain is unbranched. If elimination (iii) is assisted by branching at the β carbon, the rates become comparable. Hence the reaction of triethylaluminium with propylene proceeds chiefly by the steps: [in this and subsequent equations 'al' is written for simplicity to represent $\frac{1}{3}Al$]

$$CH_3CH_2al + \underset{\underset{\displaystyle CH_3}{|}}{CH{=}CH_2} \longrightarrow CH_3CH_2\underset{\underset{\displaystyle CH_3}{|}}{CH}{-}CH_2{-}al$$

$$CH_3CH_2\underset{\underset{\displaystyle CH_3}{|}}{CH}{-}CH_2{-}al + CH_3CH{=}CH_2 \longrightarrow$$

$$CH_3CH_2CH_2{-}al + CH_3CH_2\underset{\underset{\displaystyle CH_3}{|}}{C}{=}CH_2$$

6-33

The process is important for the copolymerization of ethylene and propylene, but to avoid formation of n-propylaluminium groups which would then react further to give 2-methylpentane-1

$$Pr{-}al + \underset{\underset{\displaystyle CH_3}{|}}{CH{=}CH_2} \longrightarrow Pr\underset{\underset{\displaystyle CH_3}{|}}{CH}{-}CH_2al \xrightarrow{C_3H_6}$$

$$Pr{-}al + CH_3CH_2CH_2\underset{\underset{\displaystyle CH_3}{|}}{C}{=}CH_2$$

it is necessary to use only sufficient propylene for very incomplete reaction in the first step and to follow this by high-temperature displacement with ethylene:

$$CH_3CH_2-\underset{\underset{CH_3}{|}}{CH}-CH_2-al + CH_2{=}CH_2 \longrightarrow$$

$$CH_3CH_2al + CH_3CH_2\underset{\underset{CH_3}{|}}{C}{=}CH_2$$

In this way and with suitable recycling procedures isopentene can be obtained in up to ~90% yield with only ~10% of the higher homologue. The isopentene is dehydrogenated to isoprene for polymerization to rubber and the 2-methylpentene-1 fraction can also be converted to isoprene by a cracking process:

$$CH_3CH_2CH_2\underset{\underset{CH_3}{|}}{C}{=}CH_2 \longrightarrow CH_4 + CH_2{=}CH-\underset{\underset{CH_3}{|}}{C}{=}CH_2$$

The olefin insertion and addition reactions (i) and (iv) have parallels with alkali metal derivatives (see Chapter 2) and also with metal carbonyl derivatives. In the case of cobalt, the additions to butadiene,

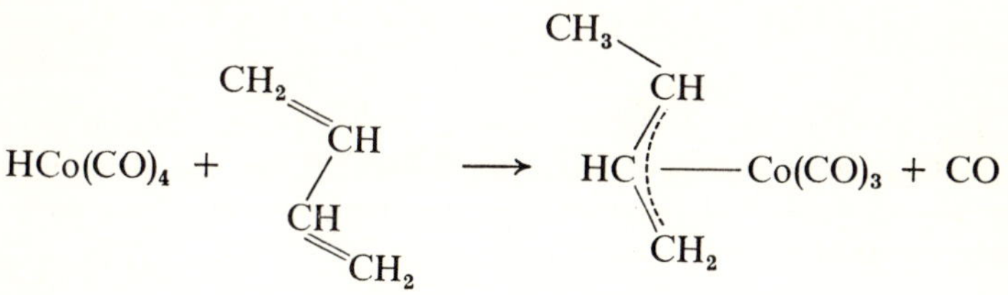

and

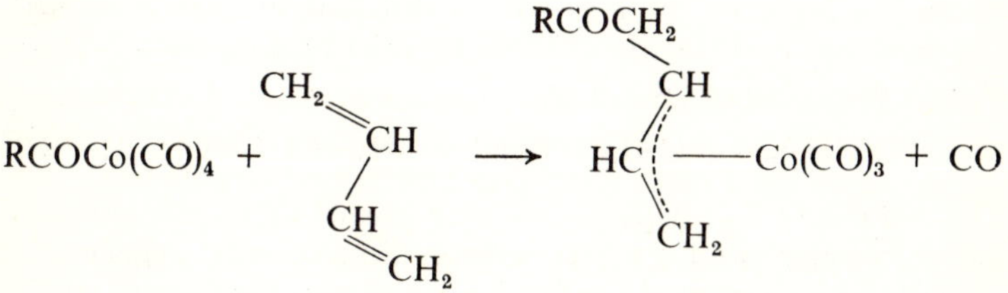

6-34

present the closest analogy. In both cases the product is a stable π-allyl complex and hence does not undergo further insertion.

With π-allyl nickel bromide the insertion of acetylene and carbon monoxide according to

$$(C_3H_5NiBr)_2 + CO + CH\equiv CH \xrightarrow[0°]{\text{ether}}$$

$$Ni(CO)_4 + CH_2{=}CH{-}CH_2CH{=}CHCOBr$$

has been demonstrated. While insertion of mono-olefins into alkyl and acyl cobalt and nickel complexes in the same fashion is probably possible, it must be slow compared to insertion of carbon monoxide and to all other steps of the carbonylation sequences.

In the aluminium and titanium alkyls insertion must be rapid to account for the success of the Ziegler-Natta polymerizations. As postulated for the cobalt hydrocarbonyl addition (p. 157), the olefin may first form a complex with the metal by donation of its π-electrons into a vacant orbital of the metal. In the case of aluminium this must be the vacant p-orbital. Migration of the alkyl group as depicted then completes the process:

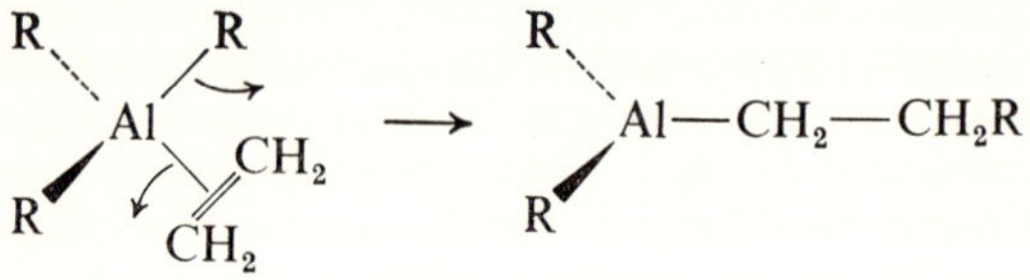

6-35

The chief value of this process is probably the formation of C_{12}—C_{20} olefins and alcohols from ethylene. In a typical sequence the aluminium alkyl is recycled at the butyl- level. This with 2 equivalents of ethylene reacts by

$$Bu\text{-}al + 2CH_2{=}CH_2 \rightarrow H(CH_2)_nal$$

where n is an even number with a distribution from 4 to $\sim$18. Displacement is efficiently effected by brief heating with 1-butene at high temperature ($\sim$300°):

$$H(CH_2)_nal + C_4H_8 \rightleftharpoons Bu\text{-}al + CH_2{=}CH(CH_2)_{n-2}H$$

The useful (say C_{12}—C_{18}) olefins are removed by fractionation and the remainder used in the reverse displacement, regenerating butene and a mixture of alkyls with n now ranging from C_4 to C_{10}. This mixture is further condensed with ethylene and by continuous recycling the ultimate product is a 94% yield of C_{12}—C_{18} olefins with the remainder as higher alkenes. Only ethylene is used up, all other materials being regenerated in the process. If the alcohols are desired, they can either be obtained via epoxidation of the alkenes, or directly from the appropriate aluminium alkyls by autoxidation. In the latter case the aluminium alkyls are of course used up and fresh triethylaluminium must be prepared in stoicheio-metric amounts.

Whereas trialkyl aluminiums readily undergo the insertion reaction, dialkylaluminium halides are quite inactive. However the rapid exchange

$$R_2AlCl + R_3'Al \rightleftharpoons RR'AlCl + RR_2'Al$$

confers full activity on a mixture of the chloride with a little trialkyl and allows the reaction to be controlled by alternate addition of aluminium chloride (to convert R_3Al to R_2AlCl) or aluminium trialkyl, thus stopping and starting the insertion process at will.

In the presence of transition metal salts, including compounds of Cr, V, and Zr, but most commonly and effectively Ti, the insertion reaction is not only greatly accelerated, but dialkyl aluminium chloride becomes active without any free trialkyl. Although reaction conditions vary, combinations of titanium compounds with many other alkyls are also effective. Indeed the balance of evidence strongly suggests that the rapid chain growth in these systems occurs on the transition metal rather than on aluminium. The precise degree of activity of the catalysts and their selectivity depend on the exact method of preparation and can be modified by many addends. Both tri- and tetravalent titanium catalysts may be active under various conditions. Thus although trimethylalumin-ium can cause stepwise replacement of all four chlorines from $TiCl_4$ by methyl at low temperature, it is known that under the conditions employed in preparing the catalysts, triethylaluminium causes rapid and probably complete reduction to $TiCl_3$ if not beyond. Un-doubtedly further reaction leads to alkyls of Ti^{III} and the com-monly used solid catalysts must be regarded as essentially composed of a complex mixture of alkyl-titanium(III)- and -aluminium chlorides. The metal atoms in such a solid are probably held together by chloride bridges. One suggested mechanism involves pentacoordinate titanium atoms on such a solid; these must carry at least one alkyl group and would react by first forming a μ-bond to ethylene followed by migration of the alkyl group. Thus the process is analogous to that envisaged above for the insertion reaction on aluminium.

In such a scheme the aluminium alkyl is ascribed the triple role of reducing and alkylating the titanium compound and of controlling the composition of the final catalyst. It may further take part in chain transfer processes, but not to any significant extent in the polymer growth reaction itself.

In several attempts to throw light on the details of the mechanism, soluble catalyst systems have been preferred. While obviously facilitating, for example, the study of reaction kinetics, and although some of these catalysts are highly active, it cannot be assumed that all the details of the mechanism remain the same. In at least one such system—$(C_5H_5)_2TiCl_2 + Et_3Al$—it has been shown that the presence of some tetravalent titanium (secured by admission of small amounts of air) is essential. Nevertheless, the main species in these solutions are again Ti^{III} compounds as shown by the strong paramagnetism. Several mixed complexes have been isolated from these solutions. Two such compounds have the structures shown, but the exact relationship of such isolable complexes to the active catalysts present in solution remains obscure.

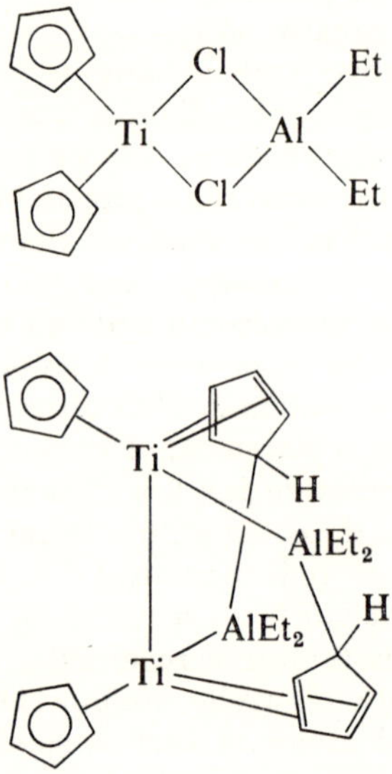

6-36

Apart from their use in the formation of linear polyethylene and isotactic polypropylene at or near atmospheric pressure, catalysts based on $TiCl_4$—Et_3Al or $TiCl_4$—Et_2AlCl are used for the polymerization of isoprene to a rubber which is almost indistinguishable from natural rubber and of butadiene to various synthetic rubbers. The sensitivity of the process to catalyst structure is well illustrated in the latter case by the observation that whereas a 1:4·5 ratio of $TiCl_4$ to Et_2AlCl converts butadiene chiefly to its cyclic trimer (cf. above), a 1·05:1 ratio of these components leads to 1,4-*trans*-polybutadiene of high molecular weight. Relatively small further modifications of the catalyst allow the alternative production of the 1,4-*cis*- or even the 1,2-polymer. The same polymers are obtained with various other catalysts of the alkyl-transition metal complex type. Thus diallylcobalt iodide is reported to yield 1,4-*cis*-polybutadiene while triallylchromium gives the 1,2-polymer. The latter catalyst is also applicable for the formation of linear polyethylene.

Bibliography

General Texts

COATES, G. E. (1960) *Organometallic Compounds*. Methuen, London.

EISCH, J. and GILMAN, H. (1960) Organometallic Compounds. In *Advances in Inorganic and Radiochemistry* edited by Emeleus and Sharpe, Vol. II. Academic Press, New York and London.

KAUFMANN, H. C. (1961). *Handbook of Organometallic Compounds*. Van Nostrand, London.

KING, R. B. (1965) *Organometallic Syntheses*, Vol. I. Academic Press, New York and London.

KRAUSE, E. and VON GROSSE, A. (1937) *Chemie der Metallorganischen Verbindungen*. Borntraeger, Berlin.

Reviews of Groups of Compounds

Carbonyls

ABEL, E. W. (1963) The Metal Carbonyls, *Q. Rev. chem. Soc.* **17**, 133.

ANDERSON, J. S. (1947) Chemistry of the Metal Carbonyls, *Q. Rev. chem. Soc.* **1**, 331.

BYELOZERSKI, N. A. (1958) *Metal Carbonyls*. Gosudarst. Nauch.—Tekh Izdatel. Lit. Chernoi i Tsvetnoi Met. Moscow.

CHATT, J., PAUSON, P. L. and VENANZI, L. M. (1960) Metal Carbonyls and Related Compounds. In *Organometallic Chemistry* edited by Zeiss. Reinhold, New York.

HIEBER, W., BECK, W. and BROWN, G. (1960) Anionic Carbon Monoxide Complexes, *Angew. Chem.* **72**, 795.

HIEBER, W., BECK, W. and ZEITLER, G. (1961) Neuere Anschauungen über Reaktionsweisen der Metallcarbonyle, insbesondere des Mangancarbonyls, *Angew. Chem.* **73**, 364.

KING, R. B. (1964) Reactions of Alkali Metal Derivatives of Metal Carbonyls and Related Compounds. In *Advances in Organometallic Chemistry* edited by Stone and West, Vol. II. Academic Press, New York and London.

Isocyanides

MALATESTA, L. (1959) Isocyanide Complexes of Metals. In *Progress in Inorganic Chemistry* edited by Cotton, Vol. I. Interscience, London.

Alkyls and hydrides

CHATT, J. (1962) Hydrido and Related Organo-complexes of Transition Metals, *Proc. chem. Soc.* 318.

COATES. G. E. and GLOCKLING, F. (1960) Transition Metal Alkyls. In *Organometallic Chemistry* edited by Zeiss. Reinhold, New York.

GREEN, M. L. H. (1960) Hydride Complexes of Transition Metals, *Angew. Chem.* **72,** 719.

KAESZ, H. D. and STONE, F. G. A. (1960) Vinylmetallics. In *Organometallic Chemistry* edited by Zeiss. Reinhold, New York.

SEYFERTH, D. (1962). Vinyl Compounds of Metals. In *Progress in Inorganic Chemistry* edited by Cotton, Vol. III. Interscience, London.

TREICHEL, P. M. and STONE, F. G. A. (1964) Fluorocarbon Derivatives of Metals. In *Advances in Organometallic Chemistry* edited by Stone and West, Vol. I. Academic Press, New York and London.

Olefin and Allyl complexes

BENNETT, M. A. (1962) Olefin and Acetylene Complexes of Transition Metals, *Chem. Rev.* **62,** 611.

CAIS, M. (1964) Alkene Complexes of Some Transition Metals. In *The Chemistry of the Alkenes* edited by Patai. Wiley Interscience, New York and London.

FISCHER, E. O. and WERNER, H. (1963) *Metall-π-Komplexe mit di- und oligo-olefinischen Liganden.* Verlag Chemie, Weinheim.

GREEN, M. L. H. and NAGY, P. L. I. (1964) Allyl Metal Complexes. In *Advances in Organometallic Chemistry* edited by Stone and West, Vol. I. Academic Press, New York and London.

GUY, R. G. and SHAW, B. L. (1962) Olefin, Acetylene and π-Allylic Complexes of Transition Metals. In *Advances in Inorganic and Radiochemistry* edited by Emeleus and Sharpe, Vol. IV. Academic Press, New York and London.

PETTIT, R. and EMERSON, G. F. (1964) Diene-Iron Carbonyl Complexes and Related Species. In *Advances in Organometallic Chemistry* edited by Stone and West, Vol. I. Academic Press, New York and London.

Cyclopentadienyl and arene complexes

BIRMINGHAM, J. M. (1964) Synthesis of Cyclopentadienyl Metal Compounds. In *Advances in Organometallic Chemistry* edited by Stone and West, Vol. II. Academic Press, New York and London.

FISCHER, E. O. and FRITZ, H. P. (1959) Compounds of Aromatic Ring Systems and Metals. In *Advances in Inorganic and Radiochemistry* edited by Emeleus and Sharpe, Vol. I. Academic Press, New York and London.

NESMEYANOV, A. N. and PEREVALOVA, E. G. (1958) Cyclopentadiene Compounds of Metals, *Usp. Khim.* **27**, 3.

PAUSON, P. L. (1959) Compounds Derived from Cyclopentadiene. In *Non-Benzenoid Aromatic Compounds* edited by Ginsburg. Interscience, London.
—(1960) Cyclopentadienyl Metal Compounds. In *Organometallic Chemistry* edited by Zeiss. Reinhold, New York.

PLESSKE, K. (1962) Ring Substitution and Secondary Reactions of Aromatic Metal π-Complexes, *Angew. Chem.* **74**, 301, 347; international edition (1962), **1**, 312, 394.

ROSENBLUM, M. (1965) *Chemistry of the Iron Group Metallocenes*, Part I. John Wiley, New York and London.

WILKINSON, G. and COTTON, F. A. (1959) Cyclopentadienyl and Arene Metal Compounds. In *Progress in Inorganic Chemistry*, edited by Cotton, Vol. I. Interscience, London.

ZEISS, H. (1960) Arene Complexes of the Transition Metals. In *Organometallic Chemistry* edited by Zeiss. Reinhold, New York.

Physical Properties and Theory

BOER, E. DE (1964) Electronic Structure of Alkali Metal Adducts of Aromatic Hydrocarbons. In *Advances in Organometallic Chemistry* edited by Stone and West, Vol. II. Academic Press, New York and London.

FRITZ, H. P. (1964) Infrared and Raman Spectral Studies of π-Complexes Formed between Metals and C_nH_n Rings. In *Advances in Organometallic Chemistry* edited by Stone and West, Vol. I. Academic Press, New York and London.

RICHARDSON, J. W. (1960) Carbon-Metal Bonding. In *Organometallic Chemistry* edited by Zeiss. Reinhold, New York.

SKINNER, H. A. (1964) The Strength of Metal-to-Carbon Bonds. In *Advances in Organometallic Chemistry* edited by Stone and West, Vol. II. Academic Press, New York and London.

Single Metals

BRAUDE, E. A. (1955) Organic Compounds of Lithium. In *Progress in Organic Chemistry* edited by Cook, Vol. 3. Butterworth, London.

FELD, R. and CROWE, P. L. (1965) *The Organic Chemistry of Titanium*. Butterworth, London.

FUSON, R. C. (1964) Conjugate Addition of Grignard Reagents to Aromatic Systems. In *Advances in Organometallic Chemistry* edited by Stone and West, Vol. I. Academic Press, New York and London.

GILMAN, H. (1954) The Metalation Reaction with Organolithium Compounds. In *Organic Reactions* edited by Adams, Vol. VIII. John Wiley, New York and London.

JONES, R. G. and GILMAN, H. (1951) The Halogen-Metal Interconversion Reaction With Organolithium Compounds. In *Organic Reactions* edited by Adams, Vol. VI. John Wiley, New York and London.

KHARASCH, M. S. and REINMUTH, O. (1954) *Grignard Reactions of Non-Metallic Substances.* Prentice-Hall, New Jersey and London.

KUIVILA, H. G. (1964) Reactions of Organotin Hydrides with Organic Compounds. In *Advances in Organometallic Chemistry* edited by Stone and West, Vol. I. Academic Press, New York and London.

SCHRAUZER, G. N. (1964) Some Advances in the Organometallic Chemistry of Nickel. In *Advances in Organometallic Chemistry* edited by Stone and West, Vol. II. Academic Press, New York and London.

SHIRLEY, D. A. (1954) The Synthesis of Ketones from Acid Halides and Organometallic Compounds of Mg, Zn and Cd. In *Organic Reactions* edited by Adams, Vol. VIII. John Wiley, New York and London.

SHRINER, R. L. (1942) The Reformatsky Reaction. In *Organic Reactions* edited by Adams, Vol. I. John Wiley, New York and London.

ZIEGLER, K. (1960) Organo-Aluminium Compounds. In *Organometallic Chemistry* edited by Zeiss. Reinhold, New York.

Catalysis

BIRD, C. W. (1962) Synthesis of Organic Compounds by Direct Carbonylation Reactions Using Metal Carbonyls, *Chem. Rev.* **62,** 283.

ORCHIN, M. and WENDER, I. (1957) Reactions of Carbon Monoxide. In *Catalysis* edited by Emmett, Vol. V. Reinhold, New York.

SMIDT, J., HAFNER, W., JIRA, R., SIEBER, R., SEDLMEIER, J. and SABEL, A. (1962) The Oxidation of Olefins with Palladium Chloride Catalysts, *Angew. Chem.* **74,** 93; international edition (1962) **1,** 80.

WENDER, I., STERNBERG, H. W. and ORCHIN, M. (1957) The Oxo Reaction. In *Catalysis* edited by Emmett, Vol. V. Reinhold, New York.

WILKE, G. (1963) Cyclooligomerization of Butadiene and Transition Metal π-Complexes, *Angew. Chem.* **75,** 10; international edition (1963) **2,** 105.

Index